STATISTICAL METHODS IN
RESEARCH AND PRODUCTION

A

STATISTICAL METHODS
IN
RESEARCH AND PRODUCTION
WITH SPECIAL REFERENCE TO THE CHEMICAL INDUSTRY

EDITED BY

OWEN L. DAVIES, M.Sc., Ph.D.

AUTHORS

GEORGE E. P. BOX, B.E.M., B.Sc., Ph.D.

WILFRED R. COUSINS, B.A., B.Sc.

OWEN L. DAVIES, M.Sc., Ph.D.

FRANCIS R. HIMSWORTH, B.Sc., Ph.D.

HAROLD KENNEY, M.A., M.I.Mech.E.

MAURICE MILBOURN, A.R.C.S., B.Sc., F.Inst.P.

WILLIAM SPENDLEY, B.Sc.

WILFRED L. STEVENS, B.A., B.Sc.

PUBLISHED FOR

IMPERIAL CHEMICAL INDUSTRIES LIMITED

BY

OLIVER AND BOYD

LONDON: 39A WELBECK STREET, W.1
EDINBURGH: TWEEDDALE COURT

1961

A*

First published	-	-	-	-	1947
Second edition (revised)		-		-	1949
Second edition (revised) (reprinted)					1954
Third edition (revised and enlarged)					1957
Third edition (reprinted with corrections)		-	-	-	1958, 1961

Printed in Great Britain at THE KYNOCH PRESS, *Birmingham*

AUTHORS' PREFACE

In scientific and industrial work the correct interpretation of data is of profound importance, since unless right conclusions are drawn the acquisition of numerical results has little or no value. Statistical methods, which have played such a notable part in agronomic and biological research, provide also an indispensable tool for solving many of the problems which are encountered in the chemical industry, not only in relation to research and production but also in relation to such problems as sickness, accidents and age-distribution of workers. This has been recognised by Imperial Chemical Industries Ltd. for many years, and the use of such methods has been continuously encouraged. As part of this policy of encouragement a team of authors was invited to write a handbook which would not only serve to give wider publicity to statistical methods within the Company's own organisation and emphasise the economies to be achieved from their intelligent use, but would also help new staff to acquire a working knowledge of the subject. The authors were allowed to draw freely on information in the Company's possession, so that the examples would represent genuine problems which had been met in actual practice.

It was represented to the authors that, since problems of a similar type to those discussed in this handbook were common to many branches of industry, it would be helpful to British industry to publish the handbook and make it available to a wider public. After careful consideration the authors accepted this suggestion, and the first edition of this handbook was published in 1947. A sequel dealing with the planning of experiments, written by a similarly constituted team, was first published in 1954 entitled *The Design and Analysis of Industrial Experiments.**

Advances in theoretical statistical methods and their application to industrial research since the publication of the first edition, together with the additional experience gained within the industry, have now necessitated a complete revision of the handbook, and every opportunity has been taken in this third edition to bring the subject up to date. This has involved the addition of much new matter and the inclusion of many new examples.

Chapters 2, 3, 9 (formerly Chapter 7) and 10 (formerly Chapter 9) are substantially the same as in earlier editions, but all other chapters have been completely rewritten. In Chapter 4 (and in later chapters) emphasis is now placed on confidence limits rather than on tests of significance, because for most purposes the former contain all the information contained in the latter and have proved to be of greater practical value. Important additions to

* *The Design and Analysis of Industrial Experiments*, edited by Owen L. Davies. Oliver and Boyd (Edinburgh and London, 1956).

v

Chapter 4 are methods for calculating the confidence limits of an estimate of a standard deviation and of the ratio of two standard deviations.

Chapter 5 is completely new: it embodies recent ideas on the economics of experimentation and shows how guidance may be obtained on the amount of routine testing or the number of comparative experiments which can be economically justified.

Chapter 6 (formerly Chapter 5), dealing with the Analysis of Variance, has been considerably modified, and extended to include calculation of confidence limits for the estimated variances.

The chapter in earlier editions on the relationships between variables (Chapter 6) has now been separated into two chapters, 7 and 8. Chapter 7 considers linear relationships between two variables; a clear distinction is made between functional and regression relationships, and it is shown that the former are usually the more important in industrial research. Further additional matter in this chapter is the Analysis of Covariance, which is considered from the point of view of simple regression methods. This approach has distinct advantages over the more formal one usually adopted.

Chapter 8 considers multiple and curvilinear relationships in detail, with particular reference to difficulties of interpretation to which relationships between several variables are usually subject.

The chapter on sampling (now Chapter 11) has been completely rewritten in order to give more emphasis to sampling inspection procedures, their costs and their reliabilities.

Experience with earlier editions has indicated that a glossary is not required, intelligent use of the index being sufficient for the purpose, and the space formerly taken up by the glossary has now been used to better advantage.

Acknowledgments are due to members of I.C.I. staff and others who have supplied data and commented on the drafts, and to the Biometrika Trust, the British Standards Institution, and the publishers of this volume for permission to use copyright matter.

★   ★   ★   ★   ★

Sections, tables in the text, formulae, figures and references are numbered on the decimal system, but no attempt is made to keep these various systems of numbers in alignment, e.g. Table 7·3 falls in § **7·7** and Formula (7·6) in § **7·5**. Sections are numbered in bold type, formula numbers in italics, and other numbers in roman type.

References to literature are enclosed in square brackets: thus [1·3] means "Refer to Sir Ronald A. Fisher's *Design of Experiments*." An exception is made in referring to the second handbook, which for brevity is quoted as "Design and Analysis."

In addition to tables in the text, sixteen general tables of functions have been inserted at the end of the volume and numbered A, B, . . . , H.

CONTENTS

Prior distribution and costs known: A testing scheme ... Outline
of method ... Prior distribution ... Power curve ... Distribution
of outgoing quality ... Economics of the scheme ... Calculation
of an optimal scheme. *Prior distribution unknown:* Planning of
plant trials. *Prior distribution and costs unknown:* Planning a
laboratory experiment ... Procedure from point of view of significance testing ... Single- and double-sided tests ... Comparison of
two means ... Number of observations to compare standard
deviations.

Additive property of variances ... Types of classification. *Separation and estimation of variances:* Analysis of variance of hierarchic
data ... Estimation of analytical and sampling error variances and
their confidence limits ... Test of significance ... Hierarchic
classification with three sources of variation ... Precision of
sampling and testing schemes ... General hierarchic classification
... Unequal numbers of observations in groups ... Cross-classifi-
cations ... General two-way classification ... Interaction. *Comparison of means:* Multiple confidence limits and Tukey's test ...
Further applications of analysis of variance ... Different numbers
of observations in the cells.

APPENDICES. 6A. Combination of results from several samples
... 6B. Analysis of hierarchic data ... 6C. Confidence
limits of the components of variance ... 6D. Comparison
of several variance estimates ... 6E. Analysis of variance of
two-way cross-classification ... 6F. Estimation of missing
values in a two-way cross-classification ... 6G. Comparisons
of the efficiencies of designs based on approximately the
same number of analyses.

Functional relationship ... Regression ... *Linear regression:*
Estimation of regression lines ... Variation about the regression
... Standard error of the regression coefficient ... Standard error
of the regression estimate ... Standard error of a prediction ...
Difference between two regression coefficients ... Conditions for
valid estimation of the regression equations ... Effect of errors of
measurement. *Linear functional relationships:* One variable with
negligible error ... Standard error of estimate. Both variables
subject to error ... Standard errors of the constants ... Errors in x
and y unknown ... Controlled and uncontrolled experiments ...

Parallel line assays ... Estimation of ratio of strengths ... Confidence limits ... *Allowance for concomitant variation: Correlation:* The Normal surface ... Correlation coefficient ... Comparison of correlation coefficients and confidence limits.

APPENDICES. 7A. To fit a straight line to data by the method of least squares ... 7B. Standard error of regression coefficient ... 7C. Calculation of correlation coefficient and regression equation from grouped data ... 7D. Fieller's theorem ... 7E. Fitting a linear functional relation when both variables are subject to error.

Multiple regression equations: Separation of effects ... Total and partial regression coefficients ... Method of least squares ... Solution of equations and standard errors ... Orthogonality ... Prediction ... Confidence regions for simultaneous estimates ... Omission of a variable ... Regression on many variables ... Analysis of variance for multiple regressions ... Use of significance tests ... Regression analysis of plant records ... *Curvilinear regression:* Fitting of simple and multiple regression ... Tests of significance and precision ... Extrapolation ... Orthogonal polynomials. *Allowance for concomitant variation (Analysis of Covariance):* Comparison of regressions "within groups" ... *Regressions and functional relationships ... Correlation.*

APPENDICES. 8A. Fitting of multiple and curvilinear regressions by the method of least squares ... 8B. Solution of the least squares equations ... 8C. Calculations for Example 8·2: Efficiency of a water-gas plant.

Binomial distribution ... Mean and variance ... Precision of the estimate of a proportion ... Poisson distribution ... χ^2 distribution ... Single classification, equal and unequal expectations ... *Contingency tables:* $2 \times k$ contingency table ... Three dimensional contingency table ... 2×2 contingency table ... Continuity correction ... General considerations.

General purposes ... Types of variation ... Analysis of data ... Process control ... Sampling ... Construction ... Estimation of Universe average and Universe standard deviation ... Drawing limit lines ... Plotting the points ... Interpretation ... Level of control ... Compliance with specifications ... Value of control charts and advantages of a state of statistical control.

APPENDIX. 10A. Use of control charts.

Universal Decimal Classification   .. $\begin{cases} 658.5{:}519.2 \\ 66{:}519.2 \end{cases}$

CHAPTER 1

INTRODUCTION

Object of Handbook

1·1 The object of this handbook is to bring together under one cover those methods of statistical analysis which are most likely to be of use in the Chemical Industry. Most of these methods are available in the literature, but the applications described are often somewhat different from those encountered in chemical research and manufacture. A considerable fund of experience in the application of such methods in the Chemical Industry is available to the authors, and it is thought that an account of these methods, written from this point of view, would be of use to those engaged in Research and Process work.

Nature of Statistical Methods

1·2 The science of Statistics may be defined as the study of chance variations, and statistical methods are applicable wherever such variations have a large effect on the phenomena being studied—a situation frequently encountered throughout science and industry. Most measurements, for instance, are subject to an experimental error, and the behaviour of most industrial plants is subject to variations due to a multiplicity of causes whose effects it would be impossible to trace out separately. In fact, the conditions obtaining in many experiments on industrial plants are such that the individual results are subject to chance variations comparable in size to the effects being studied, and it is necessary to examine a large body of data covering a considerable period of time in order to draw any worth-while conclusions.

From their very nature statistical methods, like other mathematical devices, cannot reveal anything that is not already implicit in the data. In simple cases the experimenter's judgment should usually lead him to the same conclusions as would be arrived at by the application of statistical methods, and the latter would merely serve to test these conclusions free from any preconceived notions on the part of the observer. As the complexity of the data increases, however, it becomes more and more difficult to arrive at a reliable conclusion by the unaided judgment, and some form of statistical treatment becomes essential if correct inferences are to be drawn from the data.

Every experimenter should have at the very least an elementary knowledge of statistical methods, so that he may be able to apply the simpler methods for himself, to follow the reasoning used in more complex studies carried out by others, and to know when he should seek help. For these purposes no more than an elementary knowledge of mathematics is required.

1·21 One question of importance in many statistical problems is: "What are the limits of error of some quantity calculated from the data, taking into account the chance variations to which these are known to be subject?" A simple form of this question might, for instance, arise in the following way. We know from past experience the average value and usual variability of the quality of a certain product; a group of experimental batches by a new process gives a product of a slightly higher quality than the normal average; because of chance variations, however, the true value of the difference may be either greater or less than that actually found, and we wish to establish limits on either side of the experimental value, within which we may reasonably expect the true value to lie. Such limits are known as Confidence Limits, and the range between them is known as a Confidence Interval. The more widely we space the limits the greater will be the probability that they will include the true value; there is thus for each pair of limits a corresponding probability, known as the Confidence Coefficient. In a simple case, such as that of comparing a single experimental batch with the normal run of a product, the experimenter could, by inspection of the figures, obtain a fair idea of the width of the confidence interval without recourse to formal mathematical methods, and this might well suffice for his needs. When, however, the values to be compared are averages or other figures derived by calculation from the original data it is less easy to form a mental assessment of the confidence interval, and statistical treatment is indicated.

If the confidence interval obtained does not include zero, we may say with the appropriate degree of confidence that a real difference exists. Such a difference is often termed Significant to indicate that the apparent effect is unlikely to have arisen purely by chance. This specialised use of the word "significant" should be noted; in statistical discussions the word always has this restricted meaning and bears no relationship to the practical importance of the result. If the difference is found not to be significant, this is no proof that a true difference does not exist: the true value may lie anywhere in the confidence interval. If the information required is merely whether or not a result is significant, it is possible, without actually calculating the confidence limits, to carry out a test which will show directly whether the confidence interval for a given level of probability includes zero; such tests are known as Tests of Significance. When we carry out a test of significance we run the risk of two kinds of error; the first is the risk of asserting that a true difference exists when in fact it does not, and the second is the risk of asserting that there is no difference when in fact the true difference is large enough to be of practical importance. The risks of both these kinds of error should always be considered; they are usually referred to in statistical literature as "Errors of the First and Second Kinds" (Chap. 5).

It will in general be found that in research work, where the object is usually to obtain information rather than to make clear-cut decisions, confidence limits are more useful than tests of significance; where, however, clear-cut decisions are required, as in testing and inspection, a test of significance based on a consideration of the errors of the first and second kind is usually preferable.

In many cases the two quantities to be compared have first to be derived from the data. Suppose the question to be answered was: "Are the experimental batches more (or less) variable than usual, and is this difference greater than might reasonably be attributed to chance?" Then we should require first a quantity which measured the variability of a set of figures, and second a knowledge of what the chance variations of this quantity were likely to be. The quantity generally used for this purpose is the standard deviation (Chap. 3) (or its square, the variance), and mathematicians have produced sets of tables showing the chance variations to be expected in this quantity under various conditions.

1·22 A further elaboration of the type of problem treated in the last section arises when data are subject to variations arising from a number of separate causes. Thus variations in the analysis of a product might be caused partly by the raw material, partly by the method of manufacture, and partly by errors in testing. A technique known as Analysis of Variance allows us to separate these different causes of variation and to determine their magnitudes (Chap. 6).

Another type of problem is that of regression and correlation (Chap. 7). Here we are concerned with several pairs of figures, such as for example a process temperature and the quality of the final product. The question to be answered in such a case would be, in terms of the example: "How is the average value of the quality related to the temperature?" This type of relationship can be represented by a regression equation which shows how the average value of one quantity changes as the value of some other quantity is changed. The constants of such equations are known as Regression Coefficients, and confidence limits can be calculated to show their reliability, or tests of significance applied to them to indicate the plausibility of the hypothesis that there is no real relationship. In regression problems a number of different situations can arise, depending on the purpose for which the regression equation is required and on the nature of the association between the variables, particularly if a definite functional relationship can be assumed to exist between them; these problems will be discussed fully in Chapter 7. In Chapter 8 consideration is given to cases where the regression equation defines a curve rather than a straight line and also to cases where there are more than two variables.

1·23 Sometimes the quantities involved in a problem, instead of being continuous variables, are frequencies. Such cases arise for example in considering the occurrence of defective articles, in particle counts, and in many similar problems. Unless the numbers involved are large, wide random fluctuations in frequency are inevitable; these fluctuations follow laws different from those applicable to continuous variables. The commonest of these laws are the Binomial Distribution and the Poisson Distribution, which are discussed in Chapter 9.

1·24 In industry most decisions depend ultimately on questions of cost and profit. Where the necessary data are available it is possible to combine statistical probabilities with economic considerations. Let us say, for example, that a works manager wishes to know how much testing should be carried out on a certain raw material, and that he knows the errors of sampling and testing, the variability of the material, the cost of testing, and the economic consequencies of accepting poor material and of rejecting good material. On the basis of these it is possible to calculate the expected profits and losses associated, in the long run, with any given level of testing, and from this he can find the most profitable level to employ (Chap. 5). Provided the requisite information is available, much more complex problems than this can be treated in a similar way.

1·25 Another type of problem which lends itself to statistical treatment is that involved in sampling and in drawing up specifications (Chap. 11). These two activities are associated, since any consideration of a specification must, almost inevitably, involve consideration of the method by which the material is to be sampled in order to ascertain whether it complies with the specification. Ideally, the specification adopted should be the one which gives the maximum net profit; frequently, however, the necessary information to calculate this is not available, and less refined methods of treatment have therefore to be employed.

1·26 Quality Control is the name commonly given to a graphical method of revealing abnormalities in sets of figures, such as the measurements of parts from repetitive operations, or tests from the operation of a continuous plant (Chap. 10). This method has had great success in the light engineering industry; its application in the chemical industry has proved of value particularly in problems such as the filling of containers and the manufacture of synthetic fibres. Further applications will undoubtedly arise in the course of time, but it seems unlikely that quality control will be as important in the manufacture of bulk chemicals as it is in repetitive engineering operations.

Planning of experiments

1·3 Apart from its use in the extraction of information from experiments already carried out, statistics plays a very important part in the correct planning of series of experiments so as to obtain the maximum of information from a given number of experiments; careful planning can often effect major economies in the amount of experimental work which has to be done. This very important subject of the planning of experiments has not been included in the present handbook, as it forms the subject matter of a second volume which has recently been issued, entitled *The Design and Analysis of Industrial Experiments* [1·1]. This second volume is referred to at various places in the present work; the contraction "*Design and Analysis*" is used to denote it.

ADVICE FOR FURTHER READING

[1·1] DAVIES, O. L. (editor). *The Design and Analysis of Industrial Experiments.* Oliver and Boyd (London and Edinburgh, 1956) for Imperial Chemical Industries Ltd.

[1·2] FISHER, R. A. *Statistical Methods for Research Workers* (twelfth edition). Oliver and Boyd (Edinburgh and London, 1954).

[1·3] FISHER, R. A. *The Design of Experiments* (sixth edition). Oliver and Boyd (Edinburgh and London, 1951).

[1·4] KENDALL, M. G. *The Advanced Theory of Statistics*, Vol. I (fifth edition) and Vol. II (third edition). Charles Griffin (London, 1951 and 1952).

[1·5] TIPPETT, L. H. C. *The Methods of Statistics* (fourth edition). Williams and Norgate (London, 1952).

[1·6] DARRELL HUFF. *How to Lie with Statistics.* Gollancz (London, 1954).

[1·7] JOHNSON, N. L., and TETLEY, H. *Statistics: An Intermediate Text Book* (two volumes). Cambridge University Press (1949).

CHAPTER 2

FREQUENCY DISTRIBUTIONS

STATISTICAL methods are concerned with the study of variation. The nature of the variation in a body of data is shown by a frequency distribution. To describe numerically the principal features of a distribution a measure of location, such as the arithmetic mean, and a measure of spread, such as the standard deviation, are used. A particularly important theoretical distribution is the Normal distribution. Ways of transforming data to achieve approximate normality are described.

Frequency table

2·1 The first step in examining a body of data is to assemble them in a form such that the main features can be readily appreciated, particularly the degree of spread and the manner in which the results are distributed over the range, for example whether they are distributed uniformly or tend to be concentrated round a central value. The results written down in order of occurrence may vary erratically, and with a large number it is difficult to derive any general conclusions. The simplest method of arranging the data is to divide the whole range of variation into a number of groups, count the number of observations

Table 2·1

PERCENTAGE CARBON IN A MIXED POWDER

Range of Values of % Carbon	Number of Results	Proportion of Results
4·10–4·19	1	0·006
4·20–4·29	2	0·011
4·30–4·39	7	0·039
4·40–4·49	20	0·112
4·50–4·59	24	0·135
4·60–4·69	31	0·174
4·70–4·79	38	0·214
4·80–4·89	24	0·135
4·90–4·99	21	0·118
5·00–5·09	7	0·039
5·10–5·19	3	0·017
Total	178	1·000

falling in each group, and write these in the form of a table. As an illustration, Table 2·1 shows the results of 178 measurements of the carbon content of a mixed powder fed to a plant over a period of one month. The total range was from about 4·1% to 5·2%, and this range was divided into the groups 4·10–4·19%, 4·20–4·29%, etc. The table gives the numbers of results falling into each group.

A table of this kind, which shows the frequency of occurrence of the different values, is known as a Frequency Table. The distribution of the results is known as a Frequency Distribution.

It is clear from the table that:

  (i) The results cluster round a central value of about 4·7%.
 (ii) They are spread roughly symmetrically round the central value.
(iii) Small divergences from the central value are found more frequently than large divergences.

Ambiguity may arise in classifying some observations if the end values of the groups are not clearly defined. This is considered in detail in Appendix 2B.

Graphical representation

2·11 The above characteristics of the frequency distribution are shown even more clearly if the results are plotted as in Figure 2·1. In this diagram the horizontal axis is divided into segments corresponding to the ranges of the

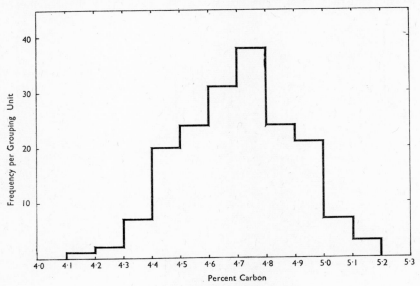

Fig. 2·1. Histogram

groups. On each segment a rectangle is constructed whose area is proportional to the frequency in the group. In the present example, since the range is the same for all groups, the heights of the rectangles are also proportional to the frequencies. It is usually better to make the groups of equal width; but in some cases unequal groups are more suitable, and the *area* must then be made proportional to the frequency.

This diagram is known as a Histogram and is usually the best form for plotting a frequency distribution, especially if, as in this case, the variable is continuous. When a set of results is available in grouped form only, the observations within any group are assumed to be uniformly distributed over the group.

Frequency curve

2·12 It is reasonable to suppose, and it is found in practice, that if the number of observations were very much larger and if the groups were made much narrower, the irregular step-form of Figure 2·1 would change to a smoother shape with smaller steps, and eventually to a smooth curve. This smooth curve may be regarded as defining the true underlying distribution; with a small number of results only an approximation to the curve is possible, since unless the groups are reasonably wide the group frequency will on the average be very small and often zero. The smoothed curve is known as a Frequency Curve. Figure 2·2 is a curve which could reasonably be assumed to represent the data of Table 2·1. If verticals are drawn at the extremes of

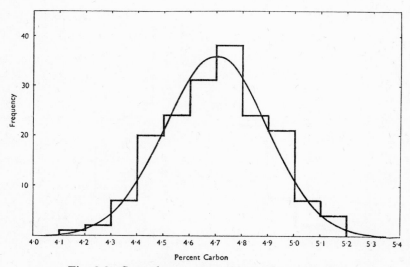

Fig. 2·2. Smooth curve superimposed on histogram

each group, the areas enclosed between the verticals, the curve and the base-
line are approximately equal to the frequencies of Table 2·1. The larger the
number of observations the more nearly will the areas under the curve
approximate to the actual frequencies. For small numbers of observations
the divergences can be relatively large.

A histogram or frequency curve expressed in terms of proportional frequencies instead of actual frequencies is usually a more useful representation
of the distribution. The curve may then be referred to as the Probability
Distribution, because the probability of the occurrence of a given observation
is defined as the proportional frequency with which it occurs in a large number
of observations. The area enclosed by verticals at x_1 and x_2 gives the probability that an observation will have a value between x_1 and x_2, and this
probability, multiplied by the total number of observations made, is the
expected number of observations for the range x_1 to x_2 in a sample of that
size. Figure 2·3 is a curve (based on a theoretical distribution function) which
could reasonably be assumed to represent the probability distribution of
Table 2·1. Verticals have been drawn at the group limits and the histogram
of Figure 2·1 superimposed in terms of proportional frequencies, i.e. actual
frequencies divided by 178. Table 2·2 shows the frequencies derived from
the probability curve, together with those observed; there is good agreement.
The probability is highest for values of x near 4·7, and is very low for values
greater than 5·0 or less than 4·4. The greater the number of observations,
if the group widths are suitably chosen, the nearer will the relative frequencies approach the corresponding probabilities.

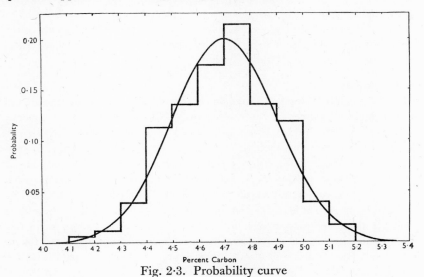

Fig. 2·3. Probability curve

Table 2·2

CALCULATED AND OBSERVED FREQUENCIES

(Based on Table 2·1)

Range of Values	Observed Frequency	Calculated Frequency	Difference (calc.-obs.)
4·10–4·19	1	1	0
4·20–4·29	2	5	3
4·30–4·39	7	9	2
4·40–4·49	20	17	− 3
4·50–4·59	24	25	1
4·60–4·69	31	32	1
4·70–4·79	38	32	− 6
4·80–4·89	24	25	1
4·90–4·99	21	17	− 4
5·00–5·09	7	9	2
5·10–5·19	3	5	2
5·20–5·29	0	1	1
Total ..	178	178	0

The differences between the calculated and observed frequencies are small, and the observations agree reasonably well with the assumption that their basic probability distribution has the mathematical form used in calculating the frequencies given in Table 2·2. This, however, does not prove that the actual distribution has in fact this form; other mathematical forms could be suggested that would give agreement at least as good as that shown in the table. Previous experience may, however, suggest that one particular type of distribution is more likely than another.

Probability density

2·13 The height of a given rectangle in a histogram is such that the area of the rectangle is proportional to the frequency. The ordinate of a frequency curve has a similar interpretation as follows. Let x_1 and x_2 $(x_2 > x_1)$ be two values of the continuous variable x. If F_1 is the relative frequency, or probability, for all values of x up to x_1, and F_2 is the relative frequency for all values up to x_2, then $F_2 - F_1$ is the relative frequency of all values between x_1 and x_2. If x_1 and x_2 represent the extremities of a group, the area of the corresponding rectangle in the histogram is proportional to $F_2 - F_1$, and its height is therefore proportional to $(F_2 - F_1)/(x_2 - x_1)$. In the frequency curve, which represents the relative frequency distribution expected for an indefinitely large number of observations, if $(x_2 - x_1)$ is very small it can be represented by dx, and $(F_2 - F_1)$ by dF. In the limit, as $(x_2 - x_1)$ approaches zero, dF/dx represents the height, i.e. the ordinate of the curve at the point x, and is known as the Probability Density.

2·14 Usually the only direct information available is the set of observed results, and the problem is then to deduce the probability distribution or at least a good approximation to it. Only if a very large number of results are available can this be done; but, if a reasonable assumption about the general shape of the curve can be made, either on the basis of past experience or from general knowledge of similar situations, it may be possible to deduce the probability distribution with fair confidence. This is, in fact, a main feature of statistical methods. An assumption is made about the general form of the probability distribution, and from the observations estimates are made of the constants required to define this distribution quantitatively. It is then possible to deduce the probabilities of future events: for example, the probability that an observation will exceed a certain value; the probability that the average of a number of observations will be within given limits; the probability that the averages of two sets of observations will differ by a given amount or more; and so on.

Universe

2·15 The hypothetical set of all possible observations of the type which is being investigated is known as the Universe (or Population) of values. Any finite set of these observations can be regarded as a sample drawn from this Universe. As the sample size increases, its properties resemble more and more closely those of the Universe, provided that the sample values may be considered as randomly selected from the Universe (see § **2·61**).

The Universe is best represented by its probability or frequency distribution [§ **2·12**], and when the variable is continuous the distribution can be represented by a smooth curve. A continuous variable can take any value within the range covered: examples are weights, dimensions, concentrations. When the variable can only take certain specific values, for example, counts of dust particles, numbers of defective items, numbers of days absent from work, the distribution cannot then be represented exactly by a continuous curve. It can, however, be represented graphically by means of vertical lines; a line is drawn for each of the possible values of the variable, its length being proportional to the probability of occurrence of the given value. This is known as a Discrete Distribution; the more important types of discrete distributions are considered in Chapter 9.

Measures of central tendency and spread

2·2 The curve of Figure 2·2 and the histogram of Figure 2·1 have three obvious characteristics:

(i) There is a certain value (about 4·7% carbon) which represents the "centre" of the distribution, and serves to locate it.

(ii) The values are spread round this central value, extending over a range of about $\pm$ 0·5%.

(iii) The spread is not uniform, most values being close to the central value. This reflects the shape of the curve.

We might, therefore, characterise the distribution by means of three criteria:

(a) The central value (4·7% approximately).

(b) A quantity expressing the degree of spread.

(c) The "shape" of the curve, i.e. the general form of the distribution.

These may or may not be sufficient to define the distribution curve completely, but as will be shown below, they very often are sufficient. The equation of the curve may be written:

$$y = f(x;\ a, b)$$

where a and b are constants, measuring the central value and the degree of spread respectively, and the function f defines the shape.

Arithmetic mean

2·21 The commonest measure of location, or central value, is the arithmetic mean (commonly abbreviated to "mean" or "average"). It is simply the sum of all the observations divided by their number:

$$\text{Arithmetic Mean} = \bar{x} = \Sigma x/N \quad \ldots\ldots\ldots\ldots\ldots(2\cdot1)$$

It is the most useful of such measures, but others which are better in special cases are described in §§**3·23–3·26**. With a symmetrical distribution, such as that shown in Figure 2·2, the mean is the point at which the curve reaches a maximum. The mean of the data in Table 2·1 is 4·70%.

A distinction must be drawn between the mean of a set of observed values and the mean of the underlying probability distribution or Universe. The observed mean should be regarded as an estimate of the true value which becomes better as the number of observations on which it is based is increased. This statement is intuitively felt to be true, and is in fact true except in unusual and unimportant circumstances.

The symbol used for the Universe mean is μ; $\bar{x}$ becomes a better estimate of μ as N increases, and approaches μ as N approaches infinity.* This is expressed symbolically by

$$\bar{x} \rightarrow \mu \quad \text{as} \quad N \rightarrow \infty$$

---

* In the limit $\mu = \Sigma_x p_x x$, where p_x is the proportion of observations having the given value of x; when the distribution is continuous, p_x becomes $dp_x = f(x)\,dx$ where $f(x)$ is the ordinate of the frequency or probability distribution at the value x. The summation sign has then to be replaced by the integral sign, and we have

$$\mu = \int_{-\infty}^{+\infty} f(x)\,x\,dx.$$

Standard deviation

2·22 The most useful measure of the spread is the Standard Deviation, which for a sample of N observations $x_1, x_2, \ldots, x_N$ is given by the expression

$$\text{Standard deviation} = s = \sqrt{\left\{ \sum_{i=1}^{N} (x_i - \bar{x})^2/(N-1) \right\}} \quad \ldots\ldots(2\cdot2)$$

where $\bar{x}$ is the mean of the sample. In special cases other measures are preferable or more convenient; these are considered later.

The standard deviation is seen to be the root mean square deviation from the mean, except that the divisor is $(N-1)$ and not N. If the Universe mean, μ, were known and the deviations were taken from it instead of from the sample mean $\bar{x}$, the divisor would be N.

Without going into detail at this stage it may be said that most of the observations are likely to be within the range $(\bar{x} - 2s)$ to $(\bar{x} + 2s)$, and practically all within the range $\bar{x} \pm 3s$.

For the data of Table 2·1, $s = 0\cdot197\%$. The range $\bar{x} \pm 2s$ is equal to $4\cdot70\% \pm 0\cdot39\%$, i.e. $4\cdot31\%$ to $5\cdot09\%$; only six of the observations lie outside these limits.

We must distinguish between the true, or Universe, value of the standard deviation and that calculated from a set of observations, which is an *estimate* of the Universe value. The symbol used for the Universe standard deviation is σ; s becomes a better estimate of σ as N increases, and σ may be defined as the value of Expression (2·2) in the limit as N tends to infinity.* This is expressed by

$$\sigma = \lim_{N \to \infty} \sqrt{\left\{ \sum_{i=1}^{N} (x_i - \bar{x})^2/(N-1) \right\}} \quad \ldots\ldots\ldots(2\cdot3)$$

or, briefly, $s \to \sigma$.

Form of distribution

2·3 The "shape" of the distribution is obviously a more elusive concept than mean or standard deviation, and it cannot be calculated from the observed data. The data may, however, give some idea of the probable shape. For example, from Table 2·1 or Figure 2·1 we can deduce that the distribution has a central peak and falls off roughly symmetrically on both sides. We must, however, on the basis of past experience or auxiliary information make some assumption about the actual form of the distribution, provided it is in reasonable accord with the observations. A number of types

---

* In the limit $\sigma = \sqrt{\left\{ \sum_x p_x(x - \mu)^2 \right\}}$; for a continuous distribution

$$\sigma = \sqrt{\left\{ \int_{-\infty}^{+\infty} f(x)(x - \mu)^2 \, dx \right\}}.$$

p_x and the expressions for μ are defined in the previous footnote.

of distribution have been fully studied, because they, or at least close approximations to them, frequently arise in practice, and it is usual to assume that an actual distribution takes one or other of these standard forms. In this chapter only the most important of the distributions is discussed, the so-called Normal distribution; others are mentioned in Chapter 9.

2·31 It is clear that two distributions of different form, i.e. giving frequency curves of quite different shape, could have the same values of the mean and standard deviation. Table 2·3 shows two distributions, each of which has a mean of zero and a standard deviation of about 2·9.

Table 2·3
DISTRIBUTIONS WITH THE SAME MEAN AND STANDARD DEVIATION

Central Values of the Groups	Number of Observations	
	I	II
− 8·5	3	o
− 7·5	5	o
− 6·5	11	o
− 5·5	23	o
− 4·5	40	100
− 3·5	67	100
− 2·5	93	100
− 1·5	121	100
− 0·5	137	100
0·5	137	100
1·5	121	100
2·5	93	100
3·5	67	100
4·5	40	100
5·5	23	o
6·5	11	o
7·5	5	o
8·5	3	o
Total ..	1,000	1,000

All the groups are of equal width and are depicted by their central values. In distribution I the frequency is a maximum at the two middle groups, tailing off on both sides to nearly zero at ± 9. In distribution II the frequency is constant over the range − 5 to + 5, and is zero outside these limits. Clearly, if the distribution under consideration might be either I or II, the mean and standard deviation would give an incomplete description. Usually, however, something will be known about the type of distribution. In many cases, for example, the errors of chemical analysis or variation in plant output, the distribution is more likely to resemble I than II, i.e. small divergences are more frequent than large divergences. It is then reasonable to assume that the "shape" of the distribution is like that of distribution I, and with this assumption a knowledge of only the mean and standard deviation gives a good picture of the distribution.

The Normal distribution

2·4 The most commonly used of the theoretical distributions is the Normal or Gaussian distribution, which gives a bell-shaped probability curve; examples of this distribution have already been given in Tables 2·2 and 2·3.

Many of the distributions found in observational and experimental work are roughly of the Normal type, but the uses of the Normal distribution are by no means limited to data which are exactly, or very nearly, Normal. It is of the utmost importance in theoretical and applied statistics, but not, as is sometimes supposed, because data naturally occur in this form.

2·41 If data are Normally distributed, the probability that x will assume a value between x_1 and $(x_1 + dx)$ is given by:

$$dP = \frac{1}{\sigma\sqrt{(2\pi)}} \exp\{-(x_1 - \mu)^2/2\sigma^2\} \, dx \ldots\ldots\ldots(2\cdot4)$$

where μ is the Universe mean, σ is the Universe standard deviation, exp ( ) denotes the exponential function, i.e. $\exp(x) = e^x$.

The integral of $(2\cdot4)$ over all values of x is equal to unity, i.e. dP is the relative frequency or probability corresponding to the range x_1 to $(x_1 + dx)$.

The value of $y = dP/dx$ is a maximum when $x = \mu$, and falls off symmetrically on both sides, as in Figure 2·3, which is a Normal curve with mean 4·70% and standard deviation 0·197%. Measurements encountered in practice are usually distributed in approximately this form. This does not mean, however, that the distribution is in fact Normal; distributions whose properties are different from those of the Normal appear similar to it when plotted as frequency curves, and even more so when the cumulative frequencies are plotted (see Appendix 2A).

2·42 Equation $(2\cdot4)$ appears complicated, and it is by no means clear at first sight why such an equation should be assumed to represent the distribution of observed quantities. It can, however, be deduced from quite reasonable assumptions, and it has certain properties which make it of very wide applicability. The most important of these is as follows. Suppose we have a number of observations of some quantity having any probability distribution whatever (with certain exceptions which are of no practical importance); if

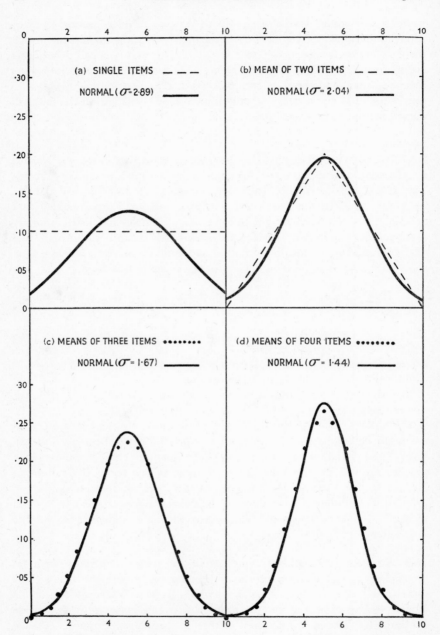

Fig. 2·4. Distribution of means of samples from a rectangular distribution compared with the Normal distribution we take the averages of pairs of observations and plot the probability distribution of these averages it will be found to resemble the Normal form more closely than does the original distribution. Repeating this process with averages of three, four, etc., the distribution approaches more and more closely to the Normal form. This is not simply a superficial resemblance; it can be proved that with almost any original distribution the distribution of sample averages tends rapidly to the Normal form as the sample size increases.

Figures 2·4(b), (c) and (d) show the distributions of the averages of samples of two, three, and four observations, from the original distribution of Figure 2·4(a). The dotted line in Figure 2·4(a) represents the rectangular distribution, so named from the shape of the diagram, all values between the given limits being equally probable. From an original distribution which is very far from Normal, averages of even three or four observations are distributed quite close to the Normal form, as is evident from the Normal curves superimposed. In Figures 2·4(c) and (d) the curves are too close to draw separately; the dots shown are for the mean of three or four observations from the rectangular distribution, the curve being that of the corresponding Normal distribution. Even the "triangular" distribution for means of two is quite close to the Normal curve, except near the extremes or "tails" of the curve.

Similar results are found with other distributions which are far from Normal. Since distributions encountered in practice are usually much closer to Normality it is safe to assume that the means of small samples, even of two, are distributed in nearly the Normal form. In many statistical problems we are concerned not with single observations but with means, and it is then safe to assume that the distribution of the means is approximately Normal.

Most of the common statistical tests are based on the assumption that the data are Normally distributed, an assumption which cannot usually be verified, but since in most cases the quantities required are averages, the tests are of general applicability. There are some exceptions, which will be pointed out as they arise.

Standard measure

2·43 Equation (2·4) involves two parameters, μ and σ, which must be determined before the frequencies can be calculated. It can be simplified by writing it in terms of the deviation of x from μ, using σ as the unit of measurement. This is done by making the substitution:

$$u = (x - \mu)/\sigma \quad \dots\dots\dots\dots\dots\dots\dots\dots(2·5)$$

when (2·4) becomes

$$dP = \frac{1}{\sqrt{2\pi}} \exp(-u^2/2)\, du \dots\dots\dots\dots\dots\dots(2·6)$$

This simple form is known as the Standardised Form of the Normal equation, and the variable expressed in the form (2·5) is said to be in Standard

c

Measure. The equation now contains no adjustable constants, and if the value of u is known, $dP/du = y$ is determined uniquely.

Equation (2·6) gives the probability of occurrence of observations for which u lies between the values u and $u + du$. It can be integrated to give the total number of observations having u less than a given value, and hence the number greater than a given value, or between two given values. The integration cannot be performed explicity, but the definite integral has been tabulated for a wide range of values of u.

Normal frequency: Numerical values

2·44 If the variable x is known to be Normally distributed, with mean μ and standard deviation σ, the probability of occurrence of a value of x lying between two given values x_1 and x_2 is the integral of the right-hand side of Equation (2·6) between the corresponding values of u given by (2·5). Using u as the variable, the following are some typical values of the probability that u will lie within the range $\pm u_1$, i.e. that x will not deviate from the mean value by more than u_1 times the standard deviation:

Table 2·4
PROBABILITY THAT $|u|$ WILL NOT EXCEED A GIVEN VALUE

u_1	P
0·5	0·383
1	0·683
1·5	0·866
2	0·955
2·5	0·988
3	0·9973
4	0·9999

A full set of values can be derived from Table A at the end of the volume.

It is clear that a Normally distributed variable will seldom give a value of $|u|$ greater than 3, and a value greater than 4 will be very rare, occurring only once in about 10,000 observations. It is usual to consider that if an isolated value of $|u|$ greater than 2 is obtained there is some doubt whether it represents an observation from a Normal Universe with the given mean and standard deviation. The odds against finding such a value in a single trial are about 19 to 1. If, however, a series of observations is made, it must not be assumed that if the largest value of u is slightly greater than 2 it does not belong to the same Universe as the others. On the average, a set of 20 observations will give one value of u greater than 2, and even in a smaller set, say 10, it is quite likely that one or two observations will give u greater than 2. It is true to say that the odds against any particular value of u exceeding 2 are approximately 19 to 1, but the odds against the largest in a set of, say, 10 are very much smaller. The probability that at least one value of u out of a set of 10 will exceed 2 is about 0·40, and for a set of 20, about 0·64.

Similarly, if an isolated observation, or one out of a small set, gives u greater than 3, this may be taken as a strong indication that it does not belong to the given Normal Universe, while a value of 4 or more could be taken as definite evidence.

If the Universe is only approximately Normal, care must be taken not to use the probabilities of Table 2·4 as precise measures.

The Normal curve is symmetrical about $u = 0$, and thus the area under the curve to the right of u_1 is equal to the area to the left of $- u_1$; that is, the probability of occurrence of a value greater than u_1 is the same as the probability of occurrence of a value less than $- u_1$. Let each of these probabilities be a. Then it is sufficient to tabulate the values of a corresponding to positive values u only. The entry in Table A for a given value u_1 of u is the probability, a, of obtaining a value of u greater than or equal to u_1. This is also the probability that u will be less than $- u_1$. The probability that u will lie outside the range $- u_1$ to $+ u_1$, i.e. that $|u| > u_1$, is thus $2a$.

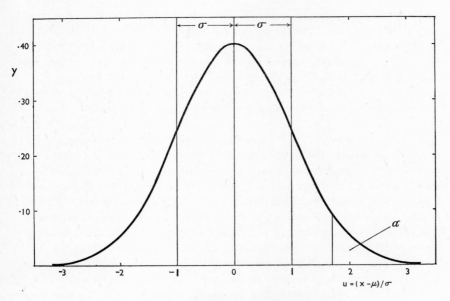

Fig. 2·5. Normal probability curve

Universe and sample

2·5 A set of data obtained under uniform conditions may be regarded as a sample from some Universe. If the exact form of the Universe is known it is possible to calculate the probability that a random sample drawn from it will possess certain properties, for example that the mean of the sample will be within given limits, or that its standard deviation will not exceed a given value. Suppose that the Universe is Normal, with mean μ and standard deviation σ; it will be shown later that the mean of a random sample of n is also Normally distributed with mean μ and standard deviation $\sigma/\sqrt{n}$. If $\mu = 100$ and $\sigma = 5$, then for samples of four the standard deviation of the mean is $5/\sqrt{4} = 2·5$, and practically all samples will have mean values in the range $100 \pm 3 \times 2·5$, i.e. between 92·5 and 107·5.

2·51 Problems of this kind may arise in dealing with an established process where the mean and standard deviation of the Universe are accurately known. But a commoner situation, especially in experimental work, is that when only a small body of data is available it is necessary to argue in the reverse direction, i.e. to deduce the properties of the Universe from those of the sample. It is easy to calculate certain properties of the sample such as the mean and standard deviation, and these can be used as estimates, though perhaps uncertain estimates, of the corresponding properties of the Universe. For example, it is futile to attempt to "prove" that a Universe is Normal unless some hundreds of results are available; to apply tests for Normality to a sample of ten or twenty results may be misleading. It is necessary to assume, usually from knowledge of the same or a similar type of situation, the probable form of the Universe. Very often the assumption is that the Universe is Normal, and while this may not be strictly true it may often be justified in that it leads to valid conclusions for the reasons given in § **2·42**. In special cases some other more likely assumption may of course be made.

2·52 A distinction must be made between problems which depend on a precise knowledge of the form of the Universe and those which require only an approximate knowledge. Suppose, for example, we want to know how many observations out of a total of 10,000 will exceed the mean value by more than three times the standard deviation. For a Normal Universe the probable number is 13, but for Universes of different form, even if they superficially resemble the Normal, the answer may be very different. The distribution of means of samples of three from a rectangular Universe appears much like the Normal (see Figure 2·4(c)); but the range is finite, and it can be shown that it is impossible for the mean of three results to differ from the Universe mean by more than three times the standard deviation. If, for example, the Universe covers the range 0 to 1, then the mean is 0·5 and the standard deviation can be shown to be $1/\sqrt{12}$.* For samples of three the mean is again 0·5 and the standard deviation $1/\sqrt{(3 \times 12)} = \frac{1}{6}$ [§ **3·51**]. The range covered by the mean ± 3 times the standard deviation is thus $\frac{1}{2} \pm 3(\frac{1}{6}) = 0$ to 1. No result, and hence no mean, can lie outside this range.

On the other hand, many statistical tests, such as those described in Chapters 4 and 5, are not seriously affected, even if the Universe is far from Normal; procedures such as the Analysis of Variance (see Chapter 6) and the associated statistical tests, although derived on the assumption that the results come from Normal distributions, remain valid. In such cases, therefore, it is safe to assume Normality. If, on the other hand, it is known that the distribution is of some other type, this information should preferably be used.

Samples and sampling fluctuations
2·6 Since the parameters of a Universe of observations, for example its mean and standard deviation, can never be exactly known, we are compelled to estimate these parameters from data which are a finite set of observations forming part of the Universe of all possible observations. Any such set of observations is referred to as a sample taken from the Universe. It is necessary, however, to define the sample and show how it is obtained before its properties can be used as estimates of the properties of the Universe.

2·61 A Random Sample is defined as a set of observations drawn from a Universe in such a way that every possible observation has an equal chance of being drawn at every trial; in other words, the probability that any observation will have a given value, or will lie within a given range of values, is proportional to the relative frequency with which that value occurs in the Universe. In random values from a Normal Universe, for example, values of x near the mean will occur more frequently than those far from the mean.

The properties of individual small samples may deviate more or less widely from those of the Universe. These variations in the properties of small samples, due only to chance causes, are known as Random Sampling Fluctuation or Variations, the word "random" being frequently omitted. Statistics is largely a study of these fluctuations. The statistical method consists essentially of calculating, from a knowledge of the properties of the Universe, the probable effects of random sampling on the properties of the sample and comparing the results of this calculation with the observations

---

* The square of the standard deviation is:

$$\int_0^1 (x - \tfrac{1}{2})^2 \, dx = \int_0^1 (x^2 + \tfrac{1}{4} - x) \, dx$$
$$= \left[x^3/3 + x/4 - x^2/2 \right]_0^1 = (\tfrac{1}{3} + \tfrac{1}{4} - \tfrac{1}{2}) - 0$$
$$= \tfrac{1}{12}$$

made. This concept of sampling fluctuations is therefore of great importance; it is the basis of most statistical theory and will occur frequently in this handbook. It should be recognised that all measurements (with some trivial exceptions) are subject to some uncertainty, and this being the case, repeated observations or samples will not in general be identical but will vary about the expected value.

When the term "sampling variations" or "sampling fluctuations" occurs, therefore, it refers to the variation between repeated observations of the same quantity, or between the statistics derived from repeated samples drawn from one Universe by a process of random sampling. If it can be assumed that sampling is random, the observations may be used to estimate the properties of the Universe; but if the sampling is not random a bias may be introduced, and the properties of the Universe so estimated may show systematic deviations from the true properties. No amount of repetition will eliminate this bias.

In some cases, such as a number of trials of a chemical experiment, it is not practicable to carry out the trials in a strictly random order, and it must be assumed that the results are a random set drawn from a Universe of all possible experiments under the same conditions. This does not absolve the experimenter from arranging his conditions so that, as far as can be foreseen, no bias is introduced. The existence of an unknown bias can be serious and lead to wrong conclusions.

Transformation of the variable
2·62 Occasionally it will be found that a distribution departs so far from Normality that it would not be safe to apply the common statistical tests, and it would be a great advantage if, by a simple transformation of the variable, an approximately Normal distribution could be obtained. For example, if the weights of a collection of spheres were given and found not to be Normal, a natural transformation would be to use the cube root of the weight, in the hope that the diameters were Normally distributed. A distribution in which the standard deviation is more than 30% of the mean is usually skew, but this skewness may often be removed by using the logarithm of the observation. The distribution of $\log x$ will not necessarily be Normal, but will in such cases be much closer to the Normal form, and may be close enough to justify the assumption of Normality. A few other typical transformations which may be employed to Normalise a skew distribution are the square, square root and reciprocal of the variable.

If there is some theoretical reason for assuming any particular relationship between the standard deviation and the mean, a suitable transformation is easily obtained. It may be worth while spending some time on the problem, since if an approximately Normal distribution can be obtained the statistical analysis and conclusions can be made more precise.

Appendix 2A

FREQUENCY DIAGRAMS

2A·1 In § 2·11 the diagram known as the Histogram is described. While it is usually the best method of representing frequency data graphically this is not always so, and two other types of diagram are described in this appendix.

Frequency polygon

2A·2 If the variable is not continuous but can assume only certain values, for example if it can only be a positive integer, as with numbers of failures, accidents, etc., the histogram is clearly inappropriate, since it represents the data in each group as equally distributed over the range. The appropriate method of plotting such data is simply to erect lines proportional to the frequencies. It is usual, however, to plot the frequencies as points and join the points by straight lines, thus forming, with the x-axis, a polygon, called the Frequency Polygon. This diagram is sometimes used for continuous variables also; if several diagrams are to be superimposed for comparison, histograms give a confused picture and polygons are preferable. Figure 2A·1 shows the data of Table 2·1 and Figure 2·1 plotted as a frequency polygon. Note that the abscissae are the mid-points of the groups. The Normal curve is also shown, and is seen to fit reasonably well.

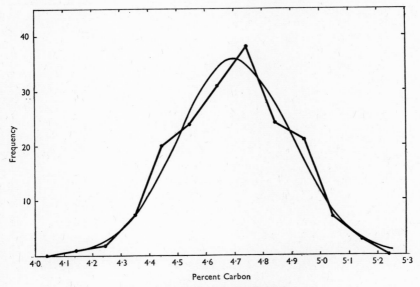

Fig. 2A·1. Frequency polygon

Table 2A·1
CUMULATIVE FREQUENCIES BASED ON TABLE 2·1

Range of Values of % Carbon	Group Frequency	Cumulative Frequency	Cumulative Proportional Frequency
4·10–4·19	1	1	0·006
4·20–4·29	2	3	0·017
4·30–4·39	7	10	0·056
4·40–4·49	20	30	0·169
4·50–4·59	24	54	0·303
4·60–4·69	31	85	0·478
4·70–4·79	38	123	0·691
4·80–4·89	24	147	0·826
4·90–4·99	21	168	0·944
5·00–5·09	7	175	0·983
5·10–5·19	3	178	1·000
Total	178	—	—

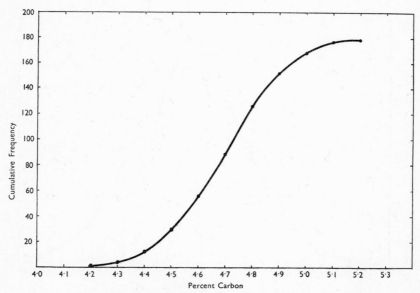

Fig. 2A·2. Cumulative frequency distribution: ogive

Cumulative distribution or ogive

2A·3 In the histogram or frequency polygon we plot the numbers of results falling within certain subdivisions of the total range, i.e. the group frequencies. In some cases we may be interested, not in the frequencies in the various groups, but rather in the proportions of results falling above or below given values; we then plot the cumulative frequencies. Table 2A·1 shows the cumulative frequencies for the data of Table 2·1; they are obtained by summing the group frequencies up to the group in question.

We see immediately that, for example, 94% of the results are less than 5·00% carbon.

If these figures are plotted we get a Cumulative Frequency Curve, or Ogive, as in Figure 2A·2. The S-shape is characteristic of most ogives, and arises whenever the frequency has a maximum value well inside the range of the variable. The ogive gives very little idea of the actual form of the distribution; all frequency curves with a maximum near the middle give ogives of much the same shape. It is sometimes used to test whether data are Normally distributed by comparing it visually with the ogive of a Normal distribution. This procedure is not, however, recommended.

APPENDIX 2B

NOTES ON GROUPING

CARE must be taken in forming frequency tables that the groups are clearly and unambiguously defined. If a series of groups is given as:

$$0\text{–}10,\ 10\text{–}20,\ 20\text{–}30,\ \ldots \quad\ldots\ldots\ldots\ldots\ldots\ldots(a)$$

it is not clear in which group the exact values 10, 20, . . . are to be placed. The difficulty may be avoided in a number of ways. A value 10 may, for example, be assigned one-half to group 0–10 and one-half to group 10–20. Where possible, however, the group limits should be arranged so that this is unnecessary. If the observations to be classified in the above groups are restricted to whole numbers, the group limits may be modified to:

$$0\text{–}9,\ 10\text{–}19,\ 20\text{–}29,\ \ldots \quad\ldots\ldots\ldots\ldots\ldots\ldots(b)$$

There is then no ambiguity. If they are recorded to the nearest 0·1, the groups would be:

$$0\text{–}9\text{·}9,\ 10\text{–}19\text{·}9,\ 20\text{–}29\text{·}9,\ \ldots \quad\ldots\ldots\ldots\ldots\ldots(c)$$

Another method is to define the groups as:

$$0\text{–}\ \ ,\ 10\text{–}\ \ ,\ 20\text{–}\ \ ,\ \ldots \quad\ldots\ldots\ldots\ldots\ldots\ldots(d)$$

meaning "equal to or greater than 0 but less than 10," etc. In methods (b), (c) and (d) there is no doubt about placing any observation.

It is also important to find the correct central value of each group, i.e. the average of the extreme observations which could fall in the group. In method (a) the central values are 5, 15, 25, . . ., but in method (b) the central values are 4·5, 14·5, 24·5, ... In (b) the group 10–19 includes all values between 9·5 and 19·5 (whose average is 14·5), on the assumption that the variable is continuous but is measured to the nearest whole number. Similarly in method (c) the group 10–19·9 includes all values between 9·95 and 19·95, giving a central value of 14·95. Method (d) is similar to (b) and (c), but the group limits will depend on the degree of accuracy of recording each result. If the results are recorded to the nearest 0·1, then (d) would be identical with (c). In methods (b), (c) and (d) the central value calculated in this way is the same as the average of the group limits. In Table 2·1 the method used is similar to (b) or (c) above.

It is important to state clearly how the grouping is done, and the groups can then be specified by their limits or central values as desired. Without a clear statement there may be ambiguity if only the central values, say, are quoted. With these precautions there is usually little to choose between the methods.

CHAPTER 3

AVERAGES AND MEASURES OF DISPERSION

WHEN a number of repeat measurements are made these may be regarded as a sample of the results from the Universe of results which might have been obtained. From such a sample of observations we can calculate the sample mean and sample standard deviation, which are estimates of the Universe or true values. The calculation and properties of these estimates are described and measures of their reliability known as "standard errors" are introduced.

Introduction

3·1 When a set of data has been assembled, consisting, say, of a number of observations of some quantity, it is necessary to condense the data into such a form that at least the main features of the assembly are made clear. If two or more similar sets of data are to be compared, such condensation is even more necessary. The condensation may be done in a qualitative way by grouping the data and forming a frequency table or diagram as shown in Chapter 2, but for most purposes it is necessary to have quantitative measures which adequately represent the data and so far as possible represent the Universe from which the observations were drawn. In this chapter the more important of these measures are described and their computation and applications illustrated. A measure of this kind is referred to as a Statistic.

3·11 The use made of these statistics will be made clear in the chapters that follow. As well as providing a concise summary of the information contained in a collection of data, they are essential for the purpose of deciding whether two sets of data show real differences, as distinct from differences which could be ascribed to sampling fluctuations; whether two variables are correlated with each other; and a wide variety of similar questions. They establish the accuracy of any function derived from the data, i.e. they fix the limits within which the true value will lie, the observed values differing from the true value because of sampling fluctuations [§ **2·61**].

3·12 The statistics most commonly used to represent the properties of a distribution fall into the following categories:
- (*a*) Measures of Location, or Central Value, giving the location of some central or typical value. An example is the arithmetic mean.
- (*b*) Measures of Dispersion, showing the degree of spread of the data round the central value. An example is the standard deviation.

(c)   Measures of Skewness. Skewness means lack of symmetry, and measures of skewness show the extent to which the distribution departs from symmetry.

(d)   Measures of Kurtosis. Kurtosis may be defined as "peakedness," and a measure of kurtosis serves to differentiate between a flat distribution curve, and a sharply peaked curve.

Other less important measures may be used to bring out other properties of the distribution, but the above four types will suffice for most industrial or research applications.

Measures of location

3·2   There are three main types of measure:

(a)   The means—arithmetic, geometric, harmonic.

(b)   The median.

(c)   The mode.

All have their uses, but the arithmetic mean is by far the most important. In special cases the others have advantages.

Arithmetic mean

3·21   The arithmetic mean has been introduced in § 2·21; it is defined as

$$\bar{x} = \Sigma x/N \quad \ldots \ldots \ldots \ldots \ldots \ldots \ldots \ldots (3\cdot1)$$

This gives the arithmetic mean of a sample of N observations. If the sample is a random one from a Normal distribution, $\bar{x}$ is also the best available estimate of the Universe mean, μ. As N increases, $\bar{x}$ becomes a more and more precise estimate of μ. The arithmetic mean is widely used as a measure of the location of a set of data, but while it is probably the most useful of all statistics, other properties of the data are of nearly equal importance.

Computation of arithmetic mean

3·22   The computation of the arithmetic mean is straightforward, but if N is large it is profitable to use various aids to computation which reduce labour and also the chance of errors. These are as follows.

(a)   If the observations consist of several figures, they can usually be converted to smaller numbers of one or two significant figures (positive or negative) by subtracting from each a constant quantity and restoring this at the end of the computation. These small numbers are easier to handle. If the constant subtracted is x_0, then:

$$\bar{x} = \Sigma x/N = x_0 + \Sigma(x - x_0)/N \quad \ldots \ldots \ldots \ldots (3\cdot11)$$

(b)   If the numbers all end in one or more zeros or are decimal fractions (pure or mixed), they may be divided or multiplied by a power of 10. If they are vulgar fractions and have a convenient common denominator, they are best expressed in terms of this denominator as unit. This frequently happens with British units of length, weight, etc., and computation is simplified by using, say, $\frac{1}{4}$ lb. or $\frac{1}{16}$ in. as unit. If the data are multiplied by h, so that the new variate is $x' = hx$, then:

$$\bar{x} = \frac{\Sigma x}{N} = \frac{1}{h} \frac{\Sigma x'}{N} \dots\dots\dots\dots\dots\dots(3\cdot12)$$

(c) When N is very large, a long summation can be avoided by grouping the data [§ **2·1**]. The loss of accuracy is small if the grouping is suitably carried out. The procedure is to sort the data in groups of suitable size and treat each group as though all the observations in it had the value of the centre of the group. If the number of groups is not too small, the loss of accuracy due to this assumption will be negligible compared with other uncertainties. It is convenient to use between ten and twenty groups: with less than ten the loss of accuracy may become appreciable, and with more than twenty the increased accuracy does not compensate for the extra labour. If the N observations are divided into k groups containing $f_1, f_2, \ldots, f_k$ observations respectively, and with central values $x_1, x_2, \ldots, x_k$, then:

$$\bar{x} = \sum_{i=1}^{k} f_i x_i / N \dots\dots\dots\dots\dots\dots(3\cdot13)$$

Devices (a), (b) and (c) may, of course, be used in combination. Appendix 3A illustrates the computation of the arithmetic mean using all three.

If a number of samples are available, for each of which the arithmetic mean has already been calculated, the grand mean can be found as follows.

Let the samples contain $n_1, n_2, \ldots, n_k$ observations, with sample means $\bar{x}_1, \bar{x}_2, \ldots, \bar{x}_k$. Then the grand mean is:

$$\bar{x} = (n_1 \bar{x}_1 + n_2 \bar{x}_2 + \ldots + n_k \bar{x}_k)/N$$
$$= \sum_{i=1}^{k} n_i \bar{x}_i / N \dots\dots\dots\dots\dots\dots\dots(3\cdot14)$$

where $N = n_1 + n_2 + \ldots + n_k$.

If the samples are all of equal size, this reduces to:

$$\bar{x} = \frac{1}{k} \sum_{i=1}^{k} \bar{x}_i \dots\dots\dots\dots\dots\dots(3\cdot15)$$

i.e. the grand mean is the mean of the sample means.

Geometric mean

3·23 The Geometric Mean is defined as:

$$g = (x_1 x_2 \ldots x_N)^{1/N} \dots\dots\dots\dots\dots\dots(3\cdot2)$$

i.e. the Nth root of the product of the N observations. For calculation it is better to use:

$$\log g = \frac{1}{N} \sum_{i=1}^{N} \log x_i \dots\dots\dots\dots\dots\dots(3\cdot21)$$

Harmonic mean

3·24   The Harmonic Mean is defined by the relation

$$\frac{1}{H} = \frac{1}{N} \Sigma \frac{1}{x} \quad \dots \dots \dots \dots \dots \dots \dots \dots (3 \cdot 3)$$

The use of the geometric or harmonic mean amounts to a transformation of the variable to log x or $1/x$ respectively, and the calculation of the arithmetic mean of the new variable [§ **2·62**]. For example, if the variable covers a very wide range, such as the percentage impurity in a chemical, usually about 0·1% but with occasional values up to 1% or more, it may be advantageous to use log x instead of x to get a more symmetrical and more nearly Normal distribution. The arithmetic mean of log x is the logarithm of the geometric mean of x, so that the average used is equivalent to using the geometric mean as the average value of x.

Median

3·25   If the data are arranged in order of magnitude, the median is the central member of the series, i.e. there are equal numbers of observations greater than and less than the median. If N is odd, this definition is complete. If N is even it is ambiguous, and in this case it is usual to take the arithmetic mean of the two central values as the median.

The median of the Universe can be estimated from the cumulative curve or Ogive; it is the value of x at which the curve intersects the 50% frequency line. This method should be used for data presented in grouped form. For a symmetrical distribution the median is identical with the arithmetic mean, but for a skew distribution it is not.

An application of the median, though not always under that name, is the use of the half-life of a radioactive element as a measure of its activity. The half-life is the time at which half the atoms present have disintegrated; it is therefore the median value of the time at which individual atoms disintegrate. The time for complete disintegration is infinite, since the distribution is exponential. As it is impossible to measure the lives of all the atoms, the median has the practical advantage that the distribution is expressed thereby in terms of only half the atoms—those which disintegrate first. Actually, for elements with a long half-life even this is impossible, but since the nature of the distribution is known to be the same for all radioactive elements it is sufficient to measure the time required for only a small fraction of the atoms to disintegrate. The median or half-life is also used as a measure of the toxicity of insecticides. If a batch of insects is exposed to the test material they do not all die at the same time, and a proportion may survive completely. The median life is the time taken for half of them to die; it is a measure of the toxicity of the material—low values mean high toxicity.

For non-Normal distributions which are sharply peaked, the median may be a more reliable measure of location than the mean, and is then preferred. For an example of this use of the median in mechanical testing see [3·2].

Mode

3·26   The Mode is the value of the variable which occurs most frequently, i.e. for which the frequency is a maximum. A more precise definition is the value of x at which the frequency is greater than for neighbouring values of x on either side; the frequency curve shows a maximum in the usual sense. More than one mode is possible. In most applications concerned with experimental investigations, however, distributions with more than one mode are rare. The presence of two or more modes usually means that the data are not homogeneous, i.e. that two or more distinct distributions have been combined. Data from two or more machines set at different average values, for example, will, if the averages differ sufficiently, give a multimodal distribution.

It will seldom be necessary to find the mode exactly. If an approximate result is required it is sufficient to plot a frequency diagram, draw a smooth curve, and note the point of maximum frequency. Large samples are necessary to carry out this procedure: small samples give irregular diagrams through which it is difficult to draw a smooth curve.

Measures of dispersion

3·3   The Measures of Dispersion discussed below are the Range, Variance, Standard Deviation, Coefficient of Variation, and the Mean Deviation. The variance and standard deviation, which are in substance equivalent, are of great importance, both theoretically and practically. The coefficient of variation is closely allied to the standard deviation. The range is important in special circumstances. The mean deviation is seldom used.

Variance

3·31   The Variance of a Universe is the mean squared deviation of the items from the Universe mean and is denoted by σ^2 [§ **2·41**]. The symbols V and s^2 are used for the variance deduced from sample data. Owing to its convenience, the symbol V is often used to denote also the Universe variance, particularly when it relates to the variance of a function of the observations as in § **3·72**.

In a sample of N, drawn from a Universe of mean μ, the variance of the Universe is estimated by:

$$V = \frac{\Sigma(x - \mu)^2}{N} \dots\dots\dots\dots\dots\dots\dots(3\cdot4)$$

In general μ is not known, and an estimate, $\bar{x}$, based on the sample must be used. It can be shown that the sum of the squared deviations from the arithmetic mean is less than that from any other value, i.e.

$$\Sigma(x - a)^2 \text{ is a minimum when } a = \bar{x} \dots\dots\dots\dots(3\cdot41)$$

Thus $\Sigma(x - \bar{x})^2$ is less than $\Sigma(x - \mu)^2$, so that if $\bar{x}$ is substituted for μ in (3·4) the variance is underestimated. It can be shown that this bias is removed by using $(N - 1)$ in place of N as the divisor, i.e.

$$V = \frac{\Sigma(x - \bar{x})^2}{N - 1} \quad \dots\dots\dots\dots\dots\dots(3·42)$$

This gives the best estimate of the Universe variance from the data available. (For proof see Appendix 3F.)

Degrees of freedom

3·311 The divisor $(N - 1)$ represents the number of Degrees of Freedom of the estimate of variance, i.e. the number of independent comparisons that can be made among N observations. If there are N observations, $x_1, x_2, \dots,$ x_N, there are $(N - 1)$ independent comparisons such as $(x_1 - x_2)$, as can readily be verified for a small value of N. The comparisons used in Equation (3·42) are $(x_1 - \bar{x})$, etc. Only $(N - 1)$ of these are independent, since $\bar{x}$ is calculated from the observations, and if $\bar{x}$ and $(N - 1)$ of the values of x are given, the other is determined. The variance measures the spread of the data, or the extent to which they differ among themselves. If they are all identical, there are no differences and the estimate of variance is zero; if they differ only slightly from each other, the variance is small; if they differ widely from each other, the variance is large.

If only a few results are available, the estimate of the variance, as of the mean, is of low precision. For the mean, the precision depends on the number of results used in calculating it, but for the variance the precision depends on the number of independent differences in the data from which the variance is calculated directly or indirectly.

Suppose that measurements are made of a certain quantity, the true mean and variance being unknown. It is assumed that there is no bias, i.e. no systematic error in the measurement, differences between repeats being due to random sampling variations. If one measurement is made and gives a result of, say, 91, then we have an estimate of the true, or mean, figure, but have clearly no information as to the accuracy of the measurement. We have:

$$\bar{x} = 91$$
$$V = \Sigma(x - \bar{x})^2/(N - 1) = 0/0$$

This is indeterminate, as it should be. If we had divided by N, the variance would have been 0, which is clearly false.

If a second measurement is made, say 101, we get not only a new and better estimate of the mean, but also one comparison or difference on which to base an estimate of variance, i.e. $(x_1 - x_2) = 10$. Note that the separate differences of each of the observations from the mean are not independent, since the mean was calculated from the data; if $\bar{x} = 96$, $x_1 = 91$, then x_2 must be 101. The estimate is therefore said to have one degree of freedom.

If a third measurement is made and gives a result 90, we have:
$$\bar{x} = \tfrac{1}{3}(91 + 101 + 90) = 94$$
$$V = (3^2 + 7^2 + 4^2)/2 = 74/2 = 37$$
$$s = \sqrt{V} = \sqrt{37} = 6\cdot1$$

With three observations there are only two independent comparisons, since if two are given, say $(x_2 - x_1)$ and $(x_2 - x_3)$, the third is known, i.e. $(x_1 - x_3)$ $= (x_2 - x_3) - (x_2 - x_1)$. As before, if the mean and two results are known, the third result is determined. There are therefore only two degrees of freedom.

If the true mean is known beforehand the case is different, since every observation then provides a comparison—its difference from the true mean—to that the number of degrees of freedom is equal to the number of observasions. This will, however, rarely occur.

The extension to any number of results is obvious. The same reasoning can be applied to the case, discussed in Chapter 7, of the spread of results round a straight line (the regression line) instead of round a point (the mean). At least two results are necessary to give the position of the line, and with only two, no estimate of the spread of the results round the line can be made. Two constants are required to define the line; two degrees of freedom are thus "used up," and the number of degrees of freedom of the estimate of the variance about the line is $(N - 2)$. This can be generalised to the fitting of data to any type of equation: the degrees of freedom are always the number of observations less the number of constants calculated from the data and used to determine the equation.

The idea of degrees of freedom is of fundamental importance in statistical analysis, and its meaning should be firmly grasped. In estimating the variance from a large number of observations no great error is made if N is used instead of $N - 1$, but in the techniques used in later chapters estimates based on small numbers of degrees of freedom are widely used, and it is important to use the correct divisor.

Standard deviation

3·32 The variance is of great importance in many applications of statistics, but since it is not a linear function of the variable its numerical implication is not easily appreciated. Its square root, however, has the same dimensions as the variable, and is therefore a more easily appreciated measure of dispersion. The square root of the variance is known as the Standard Deviation; it is, apart from the arithmetic mean, the most familiar of all statistics. After experience with its use a good idea of the "spread" of the distribution can be obtained from the value of the standard deviation. The symbol for the Universe standard deviation is σ, and that for the estimate from a sample is s.

D

Coefficient of variation

3·33 The Coefficient of Variation is the standard deviation expressed as a percentage of the arithmetic mean, i.e.

$$v = 100\sigma/\mu \quad \dots\dots\dots\dots\dots\dots\dots(3\cdot5)$$

Its main use is to illustrate the degree of spread in terms of the mean. It can, for example, be used to show whether the percentage error of a testing machine is a constant fraction of the load being measured—i.e. whether σ varies with μ—or whether the variability of the output of a plant increases if the mean output is raised. It is helpful, especially to the non-technical reader, in comparing groups with widely differing means, and should usually be quoted. The coefficient of variation is, however, meaningless in cases where the origin of measurement is not uniquely fixed. For example, consider a set of temperature measurements varying by a few degrees, with a standard deviation of (say) 2° C. and a mean of 20° C. The coefficient of variation will have no meaning in this case, since the origin of measurement is arbitrary. The only unique origin is 0° K., and the coefficient of variation is then small and may be misleading. Care must be taken, therefore, to avoid the coefficient of variation in cases of this nature. Statistically, the standard deviation and coefficient of variation are equivalent, and the choice between them will be made on technical grounds.

Computation of variance and standard deviation

3·34 Equation $(3\cdot42)$ as it stands is not the most convenient form for computing the variance; the mean $\bar{x}$ will in general contain more significant figures than the variates, and $(x - \bar{x})$ may be a cumbersome number. The computation can be simplified by the use of the identity*:

$$\Sigma(x - \bar{x})^2 = \Sigma x^2 - S^2/N \quad \dots\dots\dots\dots\dots(3\cdot6)$$

where $S = \Sigma x$.

Thus

$$V = \frac{\Sigma x^2 - S^2/N}{N - 1} \quad \dots\dots\dots\dots\dots(3\cdot61)$$

The arithmetic is lightened, especially as S will already have been computed to find $\bar{x}$.

The use of the devices (a), (b) and (c) given in § **3·22** for computing the arithmetic mean can be used with even greater effect in computing the variance. When device (a)—subtracting a constant from each observation—is used, no correction need be applied to the variance, which is clearly the same whatever arbitrary origin is taken, since it measures the variation about

---

* This identity is easily proved:
$$\begin{aligned}
\Sigma(x - \bar{x})^2 &= \Sigma(x^2 + \bar{x}^2 - 2x\bar{x}) \\
&= \Sigma x^2 + N\bar{x}^2 - 2\bar{x}\Sigma x \\
&= \Sigma x^2 - N\bar{x}^2, \text{ since } \Sigma x = N\bar{x} \\
&= \Sigma x^2 - S^2/N
\end{aligned}$$

the arithmetic mean. If device (b)—multiplying each variate by h—is used, then if the result of the calculation is V' it is corrected by dividing by h^2, i.e. $V = V'/h^2$. The standard deviation is similarly corrected by dividing by h. If device (c)—grouping—is adopted, V is given by:

$$V = \frac{\Sigma fx^2 - S^2/N}{N - 1} \quad \dots\dots\dots\dots\dots(3\cdot62)$$

where $S = \Sigma fx$. In other words, the group frequencies are multiplied by x^2 and the products are summed and corrected for the mean by subtracting S^2/N.

Examples of the computation of V, s and v are given in Appendices 3B and 3C.

Combination of variances

3·341 Suppose a number of samples are available and it is required to estimate the variance and standard deviation from all samples, assuming that the sample variances differ only because of sampling fluctuations, but allowing for the possibility that the sample means may be different—i.e. the samples are assumed to be drawn from Universes with the same variance but different means. For example, when concrete is being made in batches, the mean strengths of the batches vary because of inevitable variations in the composition of the concrete, and in addition the strengths of test cubes made from one batch vary because of sampling and testing errors. To estimate the extent of sampling and testing errors, two or more cubes from each batch are tested, and the variance is deduced from the variation among them. A single batch would give an unreliable estimate unless many cubes were tested, and it is necessary to combine the results from many batches whose mean strengths vary. The procedure is to calculate for each sample the sum of squared deviations from the sample mean—this is commonly referred to as the sum of squares—add these for all samples and divide by $(N - k)$, where N is the total number of observations and k the number of samples. $N - k$ is seen to be the sum of the numbers of degrees of freedom of all the samples.

$$V = \frac{\Sigma(x_1 - \bar{x}_1)^2 + \Sigma(x_2 - \bar{x}_2)^2 + \dots + \Sigma(x_k - \bar{x}_k)^2}{N - k} \quad \dots(3\cdot63)$$

where the suffixes refer to the different samples and the summation is carried out over the observations of each sample.

The divisor $(N - k)$ represents the degrees of freedom of the estimate, one degree being used up for each sample mean. In this formula the difference between N and $(N - k)$ will be much more important than that between N and $(N - 1)$ in Equation ($3\cdot61$) unless N is large compared with k.

If the sample variances are given, an alternative formula may be used.

$$V = \frac{V_1(n_1 - 1) + V_2(n_2 - 1) + \dots + V_k(n_k - 1)}{N - k} \quad \dots(3\cdot64)$$

since $V_1 = \Sigma(x_1 - \bar{x}_1)^2/(n_1 - 1)$, $V_2 = \Sigma(x_2 - \bar{x}_2)^2/(n_2 - 1)$, etc., n_1, n_2, etc., being the numbers of observations in the first, second, etc., samples.

If all the samples are of equal size ($n_1 = n_2$, etc.), then:

$$V = (V_1 + V_2 + \ldots + V_k)/k \quad \ldots\ldots\ldots\ldots (3\cdot65)$$

i.e. the overall variance is the mean of the sample variances. Expression (3·64) is a weighted mean, each variance being weighted by its degrees of freedom. The estimate of the standard deviation from the sample data is given by $\sqrt{V}$, and not by the mean of the sample standard deviations. An example of the computation is given in Appendix 3D.

If each sample contains only two measurements, Equation (3·65) can be simplified to

$$V = \Sigma w^2/2k$$

where w is the range, or difference, of the two results.*

Range

3·35 The Range is the simplest of all measures of dispersion. It is simply the difference between the highest and lowest values of the variable in a sample. It is therefore very easy to calculate, and this makes its use attractive if it supplies sufficiently reliable information. The range of a large sample obviously conveys little information, since it says very little about the inter-mediate observations, but for small samples it has been found that the range conveys a large proportion of the information contained in a sample and can be used with confidence as a measure of dispersion. In the limiting case of a sample of two, the range divided by $\sqrt{2}$ is equal to the standard deviation. As the sample size increases, the range contains relatively less and less in-formation and becomes a less efficient measure of dispersion.

The formula (3·63) for calculating the variance from a number of samples gives the best estimate of the variance. A simpler, but less precise, estimate of the standard deviation is found from the mean range instead of the mean square for samples of equal size. The formula is [3·1]:

$$s = \bar{w}/d_n \quad \ldots\ldots\ldots\ldots\ldots\ldots (3\cdot66)$$

where $\bar{w}$ is the mean range and d_n is a constant, depending on the size of the sample. The factors d_n are given in Table G·1.† In general, the larger the sample the less efficient is the estimate obtained from the mean range. The loss in efficiency becomes serious for large samples, and the range method

$$* \; V = (x_1 - \bar{x})^2 + (x_2 - \bar{x})^2$$

$$= \left(x_1 - \frac{x_1 + x_2}{2}\right)^2 + \left(x_2 - \frac{x_1 + x_2}{2}\right)^2$$

$$= \left(\frac{x_1 - x_2}{2}\right)^2 + \left(\frac{x_2 - x_1}{2}\right)^2 = w^2/2$$

† It is interesting to note that, for $n = 3$ to 12, d_n is very nearly equal to $\sqrt{n}$ (within less than 5%).

should not be used for samples of more than 12. The range method is best suited for samples of six items or less. With samples of six, about six sample ranges are sufficient to give a good estimate of the standard deviation. An example is given in Appendix 3D, where the standard deviation within samples is calculated in the ordinary way and also from the mean range of 17 samples of five observations. The agreement is very good and the saving in labour considerable. The best-known application of the range is in control chart work, where it is widely used instead of the standard deviation (Chap. 10).

An important application is in estimating the standard deviation of a chemical analysis from a series of duplicate tests. These tests must be independent and also true duplicates; if only part of the analysis, say the final stage, is repeated, the difference between the tests corresponds to only a part, and perhaps a small part, of the real analytical error.

Mean deviation

3·36 The Mean Deviation is defined as the arithmetic mean of the deviations from the mean, all taken with the positive sign:

$$\text{M.D.} = \frac{\Sigma |x - \bar{x}|}{N} \quad \dots \dots \dots \dots \dots (3\cdot 67)$$

where $|x - \bar{x}|$ is the absolute value of $x - \bar{x}$. The mean deviation finds applications where the distribution has long "tails," i.e. where outlying results are rather frequent. It is less affected by outlying results than is the standard deviation. The squares of a few large deviations tend to outweigh those of the more numerous small deviations; in the mean deviation, which does not involve squaring, the effect of a few large values is not so great. Otherwise the mean deviation is of little practical use, and unless there are good reasons for using it the standard deviation is preferable. Apparent ease of calculation should not be considered a good reason for using the mean deviation.

Measures of skewness

3·4 A distribution will not in general be completely symmetrical; the frequency may fall away more rapidly on one side of the maximum than on the other. If this is so the distribution is said to be skew, and it may be desirable to have some numerical measure of the extent of the skewness. Such measures are used mainly in descriptive statistics; in experimental work, if a distribution is found to be skew, it is better to seek a transformation of the variable which will yield a nearly symmetrical distribution and carry out the necessary calculations in terms of the new variable [see § 2·62]. Measures of skewness need not be discussed here. It may be noted that in a symmetrical distribution mean, median and mode coincide; in a skew distribution the median lies between the mean and the mode.

Measures of kurtosis

3·41 Kurtosis, denoted by β_2, is based on the fourth power of the deviations from the mean. The mean of the fourth powers of these deviations is called the fourth moment, m_4:

$$m_4 = \Sigma(x - \mu)^4/N \dotfill (3·7)$$

and $$\beta_2 = m_4/\sigma^4 \dotfill (3·71)$$

β_2 is therefore a standardised measure, obtained by dividing m_4 by the fourth power of the standard deviation. It is thus independent of the unit of measurement, like the standardised deviation u [§ **2·43**].

β_2 is essentially positive. For a Normal distribution it is equal to 3. If the distribution is more sharply peaked than the Normal, i.e. if it has long "tails," β_2 is greater than 3; if it is flatter than the Normal, β_2 is less than 3. Unless a large body of data is available there is little point in calculating β_2, since it is greatly affected by one or two outlying results.

Standard error of the arithmetic mean

3·5 The extent to which a single observation may depart from its true value is measured by the standard deviation. For example, the probability that any particular observation differs from the true value by more than twice the standard deviation is about 0·05. The mean of a number of observations is in general a more reliable estimate of the true value than a single observation, and this implies that the standard deviation of the mean is smaller than that of individual observations. If a number of samples, each containing N observations, are taken, the means will be distributed about the true mean with a certain standard deviation, which is less than that of the original data. The standard deviation of the mean (or of any other statistic) is usually known as its Standard Error. The larger the number in the sample, the more precise is the estimate of the mean, i.e. the smaller is the Standard Error of the Mean. Two important, and very general, properties of the standard error of the mean are as follows.

3·51 It can be shown, independently of any assumption about the form of the parent Universe, that the standard error of the mean of n observations is equal to $\sigma/\sqrt{n}$, where σ is the standard deviation of the parent Universe; the proof is given in § **3·71** below. This shows how the reliability of the mean is related to the sample size. The standard error is then inversely proportional to the square root of n. If for example we increase n by four times, we halve the standard error of the mean.

3·52 The second important result is that, whatever the nature of the parent Universe, the distribution of the sample mean tends rapidly to the Normal form as the sample size increases. In most cases of practical importance the parent Universe is roughly Normal in form (i.e. with one maximum, tailing off smoothly on both sides and not highly skew), and in these cases, for even small samples, say four or more, it may be assumed for all practical purposes that the mean is distributed Normally with a standard error of $\sigma/\sqrt{n}$. [See also § 2·42.]

Standard error of the variance and standard deviation

3·6 It can be shown that sample estimates V of the Universe variance σ^2 have, if the parent distribution is Normal, a standard error $\sigma^2\sqrt{(2/\phi)}$, where ϕ is the number of degrees of freedom. This result is of less importance than that for the standard error of the mean, since (*a*) it assumes that the parent Universe is Normal, and (*b*) even when the parent Universe is Normal the distribution of the variance is far from Normal except for large samples—say greater than 100. The standard deviations of samples from a Normal Universe are distributed with standard error $\sigma/\sqrt{(2\phi)}$, but again the distribution of s is not Normal even when the parent Universe is Normal except for large samples—say greater than about 30—and the result is not of great utility. These standard errors give a rough guide to the precision of the estimates V and s, but cannot be used as exact measures in the way that the standard error of the mean can be used. Methods for comparing the estimates V or s with standard values or with other estimates are given in Chapters 4 and 5.

Covariance

3·7 Suppose two quantities, x_1 and x_2, are measured, and used to calculate a third quantity, X, which is found from x_1 and x_2 by the formula $X = ax_1 \pm bx_2$. Knowing the standard errors of x_1 and x_2 we wish to calculate that of X. Assume that we have available a large number of observations of x_1 and x_2 and hence of X. Let μ, μ_1 and μ_2 be the true mean values of X, x_1 and x_2; then

$$\mu = a\mu_1 \pm b\mu_2$$

Denote by δx the deviation of an observation from its mean. Then:

$$\delta X = a\delta x_1 \pm b\delta x_2$$

and
$$(\delta X)^2 = a^2(\delta x_1)^2 + b^2(\delta x_2)^2 \pm 2ab\delta x_1\delta x_2$$

The mean value of $(\delta x_1)^2$ over all observations is the variance of x_1, $V(x_1)$, and similarly for $V(x_2)$ and $V(X)$. Thus:

$$V(X) = a^2V(x_1) + b^2V(x_2) \pm 2ab \text{ cov }(x_1x_2) \quad \ldots\ldots\ldots(3\cdot8)$$

where cov (x_1x_2) is the Covariance of x_1 and x_2 and is defined as $\Sigma\delta x_1\delta x_2/N = \Sigma(x_1 - \mu_1)(x_2 - \mu_2)/N$. It is analogous to a variance, but instead of the square of one variable it contains the product of two variables. The estimate of the covariance from a sample, the true means being unknown, is given by $(\Sigma x_1 x_2 - N\bar{x}_1\bar{x}_2)/(N - 1)$. As with the variance, the divisor is $(N - 1)$, since the mean must be estimated from the data.

The covariance is a measure of the degree of correlation between the variables x_1 and x_2. This subject is treated in Chapters 7 and 8. The familiar correlation coefficient r is in fact given by

$$r = \text{cov}\,(x_1 x_2)/s_1 s_2$$

i.e. r is the covariance expressed in standard measure by dividing by the standard deviations of x_1 and x_2. If the variables are independent of each other, that is if the fact that x_1 varies in a certain direction has no influence on the variation in x_2, the covariance is zero.

If x_1 and x_2 in Formula $(3\cdot8)$ are independent observations, e.g. independent analyses, then the errors in the measurements of x_1 and x_2 will be independent. The error variance of X will then be:

$$V(X) = a^2 V(x_1) + b^2 V(x_2)$$

The following is an example. The rate of consumption of material in passing through a plant is estimated from measurements of the rate at which it enters, x_1, less the rate at which it leaves, x_2. The rate of consumption is $X = x_1 - x_2$. Both x_1 and x_2 will vary with time, and they are also subject to errors of measurement. These errors are independent, so that the error variance of X is given by $V(x_1) + V(x_2) = V_1 + V_2$, and its standard error by $\sqrt{(V_1 + V_2)}$. Note that this statement refers only to the errors in x_1, x_2 and X. There will also be some real variation in x_1 and x_2, which will be reflected in corresponding variations in X. In order to relate the *total* variance of X to the *total* variances of x_1 and x_2 we have then to take into account the covariance of x_1 and x_2 and use Formula $(3\cdot8)$.

Standard error of a linear function of the variables

3·71   When the quantities x_1, $x_2 \ldots$, vary independently and

$$X = a_1 x_1 \pm a_2 x_2 \pm a_3 x_3 \pm \ldots \pm a_n x_n$$

then $$V(X) = a_1{}^2 V(x_1) + a_2{}^2 V(x_2) + \ldots + a_n{}^2 V(x_n) \quad \ldots\ldots(3\cdot81)$$

Note that the variance of X is the sum of the variances of x_1, etc. (with the appropriate multipliers), whether the coefficients in the expression for X are positive or negative.

An interesting particular case arises if X is equal to the mean of a random sample $x_1, \ldots, x_n$ drawn from a Universe with standard deviation σ. Then

$$X = (x_1 + x_2 + \ldots + x_n)/n$$

Since x_1, x_2, $\ldots$ are observations of the same quantity x,

$$V(x_1) = V(x_2) = \ldots = V(x).$$

Also $$a_1 = a_2 = \ldots = 1/n$$

$$\therefore\, V(X) = V(\bar{x}) = \left(\frac{1}{n}\right)^2 V(x) + \left(\frac{1}{n}\right)^2 V(x) + \ldots$$

$$= V(x)/n$$

and $$S.E.(\bar{x}) = \sigma/\sqrt{n}, \text{ as given in expression in § 3·51.}$$

Standard error of a general function of the variables

3·72   If $X = f(x_1, x_2, \ldots, x_n)$, where f is any function, then approximately

$$V(X) = \left(\frac{\partial X}{\partial x_1}\right)^2 V(x_1) + \left(\frac{\partial X}{\partial x_2}\right)^2 V(x_2) + \cdots$$

$$+ \frac{\partial X}{\partial x_1} \cdot \frac{\partial X}{\partial x_2} \operatorname{cov}(x_1 x_2) + \frac{\partial X}{\partial x_1} \cdot \frac{\partial X}{\partial x_3} \operatorname{cov}(x_1 x_3) + \cdots$$

$$+ \text{ terms involving higher differentials} \ldots\ldots\ldots(3\cdot82)$$

The terms involving higher differentials can be ignored if the extent of the variation is so small that they are negligible compared with the terms involving only first differentials.   The terms involving covariances vanish if the covariances are zero, i.e. if x_1, x_2, etc., are mutually independent.   If these two conditions are fulfilled, Formula $(3\cdot82)$ reduces to the first line.   This form is exact for linear functions of mutually independent variables; for other functions of mutually independent variables it is sufficiently close if the standard deviations are small.   A working rule is that the standard deviation of any variable must not be large in comparison with its mean value, say not greater than 20% of the mean.   The general formula is useful in cases where, say, the efficiency of a chemical reaction is calculated by a more or less complex formula from the original data.   An example is given in Appendix 3E.

REFERENCES

[3·1] DAVIES, O. L., and PEARSON, E. S. "Methods of Estimating from Samples the Population Standard Deviation," *Journal of the Royal Statistical Society Supplement*, **1** (1934), 76–93.

[3·2] BUIST, J. M., and DAVIES, O. L. "Methods of Averaging Physical Test Results. Use of Median," *Rubber Journal*, **CXII** (1947), 447–54.

APPENDIX 3A

COMPUTATION OF THE ARITHMETIC MEAN

The following is an example of the computation of the arithmetic mean of a large number of observations—large enough, that is, to make grouping worth while.   The data consist of ninety-five successive measurements of the efficiency of oxidation of ammonia on one unit of a nitric acid plant, i.e. the percentage of the ammonia converted to nitric oxide.

The figures range from 90·1% to 98·4%. They are first grouped into 17 groups, each 0·5 unit wide. The group limits and central values are shown in Table 3A·1. For each observation a mark is made in Col. 5 in the appropriate group, and these marks are summed to give the group frequencies in Col. 6.

Table 3A·1

EFFICIENCY OF OXIDATION IN ONE UNIT OF NITRIC ACID PLANT

(1)	(2)	(3)	(4)	(5)	(6)	(7)
Group No.	Group Limits	Group Mid-point y	x	Diagram	Group Frequency f	fx
	%	%				
1	90·0–90·4	90·2	− 7	′	1	− 7
2	90·5–90·9	90·7	− 6	′ ′ ′ ′	4	− 24
3	91·0–91·4	91·2	− 5	′ ′ ′	3	− 15
4	91·5–91·9	91·7	− 4	′ ′ ′	3	− 12
5	92·0–92·4	92·2	− 3	′ ′ ′ ′ ′ ′ ′ ′ ′	9	− 27
6	92·5–92·9	92·7	− 2	′ ′ ′ ′ ′ ′ ′	7	− 14
7	93·0–93·4	93·2	− 1	′ ′ ′ ′ ′ ′ ′ ′ ′	9	− 9
8	93·5–93·9	93·7	0	′ ′ ′ ′ ′ ′ ′ ′ ′ ′ ′ ′ ′ ′ ′ ′	16	− 108
9	94·0–94·4	94·2	1	′ ′ ′ ′ ′ ′ ′ ′ ′	9	9
10	94·5–94·9	94·7	2	′ ′ ′ ′ ′	5	10
11	95·0–95·4	95·2	3	′ ′ ′ ′ ′	5	15
12	95·5–95·9	95·7	4	′ ′ ′ ′ ′ ′	6	24
13	96·0–96·4	96·2	5	′ ′ ′ ′ ′	5	25
14	96·5–96·9	96·7	6	′ ′ ′ ′ ′	5	30
15	97·0–97·4	97·2	7	′ ′ ′ ′ ′	5	35
16	97·5–97·9	97·7	8	′ ′	2	16
17	98·0–98·4	98·2	9	′	1	9
				Total ..	95	+ 173 − 108 + 65

$$\bar{x} = + 65/95 = 0·68 \text{ working unit}$$
$$\therefore \bar{y} = 93·7 + 0·68/2$$
$$= 93·7 + 0·34$$
$$= 94·04\%$$

Note. Devices (a) and (b) [§ **3·22**] are applied automatically by entering x in Col. 4, calling a group near the middle $x = 0$ and the remainder as shown.* It will be seen that the constant subtracted is $93·7 = x_0$, and the

* For machine calculation it is better to avoid negative values of x. The first group would then be labelled $x = 0$, and the remainder accordingly.

multiplier h is 2, i.e. $x = 2(y - 93\cdot7)$. Col. 7 is then formed by multiplying x by f. Col. 6 is summed to check the total frequency, and Col. 7 summed to give Σfx, from which $\bar{x}$ is calculated. The remainder of the working is shown below Table 3A·1.

In practice, Cols. 1 and 3 would not be included.

The true arithmetic mean, found by summing the ninety-five original numbers, is 94·06%. The loss of accuracy by grouping is thus very small.

APPENDIX 3B

COMPUTATION OF VARIANCE: UNGROUPED DATA

In this example thirteen analyses for percentage of carbon in a mixed powder were obtained in a trial intended to judge the precision of the analytical method.

Table 3B·1

ANALYSIS OF CARBON CONTENT OF A MIXED POWDER

% Carbon $= A$	$100(A - 4\cdot50)$ $= x$	x^2	A	x	x^2
4·42	− 8	64	4·64	14	196
4·47	− 3	9	4·29	− 21	441
4·70	20	400	4·52	2	4
4·72	22	484	4·57	7	49
4·53	3	9	4·58	8	64
4·55	5	25	4·66	16	256
4·60	10	100			
			Total ..	+ 75	2,101

Working Units

Sum $(S) = +75$

$$\bar{x} = +\frac{75}{13} = +5\cdot8$$

$$\Sigma x^2 = 2{,}101$$

$$\frac{S^2}{13} = \frac{75^2}{13} = \underline{432\cdot7}$$

$$\Sigma(x - \bar{x})^2 = 1{,}668\cdot3$$

$$V(x) = \frac{1{,}668\cdot3}{12} = 139\cdot0$$

$$S.D.(x) = \sqrt{139} = 11\cdot8$$

Converted to Original Units

$$\bar{A} = 4\cdot500 + \frac{5\cdot8}{100} = 4\cdot558\%$$

$$V(A) = \frac{139\cdot0}{100^2} = 0\cdot0139$$

$$S.D.(A) = \frac{11\cdot8}{100} = 0\cdot118\%$$

$$= \sqrt{0\cdot0139}$$

$$v = \frac{0\cdot118 \times 100}{4\cdot558} = 2\cdot59\%$$

Inspection showed that the average was about 4·5%, and this quantity was subtracted from each result. The results (see Table 3B·1) were given to 0·01; each remainder, after subtracting 4·50, was multiplied by 100, giving a series of two-figure integers ranging from -21 to $+22$. If $A = \%$ carbon, and x the variable formed as above, $x = 100(A - 4\cdot50)$. The computation of the mean, variance, standard deviation, and coefficient of variation is shown below Table 3B·1.

APPENDIX 3C

COMPUTATION OF VARIANCE: GROUPED DATA

To illustrate this computation, the data of Appendix 3A are used. Table 3C·1 repeats the necessary figures from Table 3A·1, with an additional column for fx^2.

Table 3C·1

(Based on Table 3A·1)

x	f	fx	fx^2	x	f	fx	fx^2
-7	1	-7	49	1	9	9	9
-6	4	-24	144	2	5	10	20
-5	3	-15	75	3	5	15	45
-4	3	-12	48	4	6	24	96
-3	9	-27	81	5	5	25	125
-2	7	-14	28	6	5	30	180
-1	9	-9	9	7	5	35	245
0	16	0	0	8	2	16	128
				9	1	9	81
		-108	434				
Total Frequency $= 95$						$+173$	929
						-108	434
				Total		$+65$	1,363

The subsequent stages of the computations are given on the next page. The $S.D.(y)$, calculated from the ninety-five individual observations (as in App. 3B), is 1·89, so that the error due to grouping is negligible for the standard deviation as for the arithmetic mean. Note that the standard error of the mean is $1\cdot87/\sqrt{95} = 0\cdot19$, which is ten times the difference between the true mean and the "grouped" mean. The error due to grouping is thus negligible compared to the sampling error.

Working Units

$$S = +65$$

$$\bar{x} = +\frac{65}{95} = +0.68$$

$$\Sigma f x^2 \qquad = 1{,}363$$

$$S^2/n = \frac{65^2}{95} \qquad = \quad 44\cdot5$$

$$\therefore \Sigma f(x - \bar{x})^2 \quad = \overline{1{,}318\cdot5}$$

$$\therefore V(x) = \frac{1{,}318\cdot5}{94} = 14\cdot03$$

$$S.D.(x) = \sqrt{14\cdot03} = \ 3\cdot75$$

Converted to Original Units

$$\bar{y} = 93\cdot7 + \frac{0\cdot68}{2} = 94\cdot04\%$$

$$V(y) = \frac{14\cdot03}{2^2} \qquad = 3\cdot51$$

$$S.D.(y) = \frac{3\cdot75}{2} \qquad = 1\cdot87\%$$

$$= \sqrt{3\cdot51}$$

Appendix 3D

COMPUTATION OF VARIANCE FROM A NUMBER OF SAMPLES

3D·1 The data, given in Table 3D·1, are figures for the efficiency of ammonia oxidation, similar to those in Appendix 3A, but in the present example the data are in samples of five, each sample representing tests on five burners

Table 3D·1

EFFICIENCY OF AMMONIA OXIDATION

Sample No.	$x = $ (Efficiency $-$ 90) $\times$ 10				
1	29	18	62	1	13
2	9	21	20	32	23
3	20	24	35	20	32
4	30	− 5	30	82	48
5	13	36	34	13	41
6	31	34	74	3	47
7	6	29	60	26	76
8	27	79	74	27	33
9	− 10	16	18	7	42
10	33	16	5	2	− 3
11	12	27	20	46	13
12	34	− 4	7	28	− 12
13	47	− 15	15	36	28
14	57	45	57	62	20
15	50	30	27	40	33
16	27	22	39	63	48
17	34	10	14	− 30	42

in a unit, done on one day. The seventeen samples were taken in five consecutive weeks. We wish to estimate the variance within samples, i.e. within the sets of five tests done at one time, but allowing for any change in the mean from day to day.

For each sample the sum S and Σx^2, which is termed the Crude Sum of Squares, are formed. The quantity $S^2/5$ is subtracted from Σx^2 to give $\Sigma(x - \bar{x})^2$. This is done in tabular form in Table 3D·2.

Note that the figures in Table 3D·2 are arranged in groups of two, to assist in summation. Thus 1 51 29 would normally be written 15,129. Any convenient grouping can be used: groups of two are used in Barlow's *Tables of Squares* [T·3]. (See references at end of volume.) One advantage is that the placing of the decimal in taking the square root is simplified.

Table 3D·2

(Based on Table 3D·1)

(1)	(2)	(3)	(4)	(5)	(6) = (5) − (4)	(7) = (6)/4
Sample No.	S	S^2	$S^2/5$	Σx^2	$\Sigma(x-\bar{x})^2$	Sample Variance
1	1 23	1 51 29	30 26	51 79	21 53	5 38
2	1 05	1 10 25	22 05	24 75	2 70	68
3	1 31	1 71 61	34 32	36 25	1 93	48
4	1 85	3 42 25	68 45	1 08 53	40 08	10 02
5	1 37	1 87 69	37 54	44 71	7 17	1 79
6	1 89	3 57 21	71 44	98 11	26 67	6 67
7	1 97	3 88 09	77 62	1 09 29	31 67	7 92
8	2 40	5 76 00	1 15 20	1 42 64	27 44	6 86
9	73	53 29	10 66	24 93	14 27	3 57
10	53	28 09	5 62	13 83	8 21	2 05
11	1 18	1 39 24	27 85	35 58	7 73	1 93
12	53	28 09	5 62	21 49	15 87	3 97
13	1 11	1 23 21	24 64	47 39	22 75	5 69
14	2 41	5 80 81	1 16 16	1 27 67	11 51	2 88
15	1 80	3 24 00	64 80	68 18	3 38	85
16	1 99	3 96 01	79 20	90 07	10 87	2 72
17	70	49 00	9 80	41 16	31 36	7 84
Total..	24 05	—	8 01 23	10 86 37	2 85 14	71 30

The variance within samples can be found from the total of either Col. 6 or Col. 7, since the samples are of equal size.

The degrees of freedom for each sample are $n - 1 = 4$, and the degrees of freedom for the variance within all seventeen samples are:

$$N - k = 85 - 17 = 68$$

From Col. 6: $V = \dfrac{28{,}514}{85 - 17} = \dfrac{28{,}514}{68} = 419 \cdot 3$

From Col. 7: $V = 7{,}130/17 = 419 \cdot 3$

$s = \sqrt{419 \cdot 3} = 20 \cdot 5$

From Col. 2: $\bar{x} = 2{,}405/85 = 28 \cdot 3$

Converting to original units:

$$\bar{y} = 90 \cdot 00 + 28 \cdot 3/10 \qquad = 92 \cdot 83\%$$
$$V = 419 \cdot 3/10^2 \qquad\qquad = 4 \cdot 193$$
$$s = 20 \cdot 5/10 \qquad\qquad = 2 \cdot 05\% \; (= \sqrt{4 \cdot 193})$$
$$v = (2 \cdot 05)(100)/92 \cdot 83 \quad = 2 \cdot 21\%$$

If a calculating machine is available, much of the above working need not be written down. Usually the separate sample variances will be of interest, however, and the separate items in Col. 6 are required. If a machine is not used, the working for each sample is done on a separate sheet. The working for Sample 1 is as follows:

x	x^2		
29	841		
18	324		
62	3,844		
1	1		
13	169		
Total 123	5,179	$= \Sigma x^2$	(Enter Col. 5.)
$(123)^2/5 =$	3,026	$= S^2/5$	(Enter Col. 4.)
	2,153	$= \Sigma(x - \bar{x})^2$	(Enter Col. 6.)
$2{,}153/4 =$	538	$= V$	(Enter Col. 7.)
Sample mean $= 123/5$		$= 24 \cdot 6$ in working units	
Sample $S.D. = \sqrt{538}$		$= 23 \cdot 2$ in working units	

In original units, mean $= 92 \cdot 46\%$ and standard deviation $= 2 \cdot 32\%$ actual. A similar calculation, or such of it as is required, is carried out for each sample.

If the sample variances are required, and the samples are all of equal size, only Cols. 2 and 7 need be totalled. If the sample sizes vary, the total of Col. 6 is required to estimate V. Cols. 4 and 5 need not be totalled, but they provide a check on Col. 6, since (Total 5) − (Total 4) = (Total 6).

Estimation of standard deviation from the mean range

3D·2 We can also estimate the standard deviation from the mean value of the range, since the sample size (5) is small enough and the number of samples (17) large enough. The details of the calculation are as follows:

Sample No.	Range (w)
1	61
2	23
3	15
4	87
5	28
6	71
7	70
8	52
9	52
10	36
11	34
12	46
13	62
14	42
15	23
16	41
17	72
Total..	815

The mean range $\bar{w} = 815/17 = 47 \cdot 9$

From Table G·1, the conversion factor for samples of 5 is 2·326.

$$\therefore s = 47 \cdot 9/2 \cdot 326 = 20 \cdot 6$$

This is in excellent agreement with the standard deviation found from the sum of squares, and is obtained with much less trouble. Note, however, that all the samples must be of equal size.

APPENDIX 3E

STANDARD ERROR OF A FUNCTION OF VARIABLES

In estimating the efficiency of an ammonia oxidation (nitric acid) plant converter the following formula is used:

$$Y = \frac{N(100 - 1 \cdot 25A)}{A} = \frac{100N}{A} - 1 \cdot 25N$$

where $A = \%$ NH_3 in inlet gas

$N = \%$ NO in exit gas

$Y = \%$ of the NH_3 converted to NO = "oxidation efficiency"

Let $V(A)$ = variance of NH_3 analysis (experimental error)

$V(N)$ = variance of NO analysis (experimental error)

$V(Y)$ = variance of efficiency determination (experimental error)

$$\frac{\partial Y}{\partial A} = -\frac{100N}{A^2}; \quad \frac{\partial Y}{\partial N} = \frac{100}{A} - 1.25$$

∴ From Formula (3·82):

$$V(Y) = \frac{10^4 N^2}{A^4} V(A) + \left(\frac{100}{A} - 1.25\right)^2 V(N)$$

For this equation to be valid it is necessary that the errors in A and N from which $V(A)$ and $V(N)$ are calculated should be independent of each other. It would not be valid, for example, to take a number of separate efficiency determinations and use the set of values of A and N to calculate $V(A)$ and $V(N)$. As A increases, N increases (on average), so that the changes in A and N are highly correlated, and far from independent. If, however, we take two or more samples of inlet gas simultaneously (or at any rate in so short a time that the percentage of NH_3 does not vary appreciably between samples), the variation among the set of two or more results is due to sampling and analytical errors only. Similarly for exit gases: the variations between the values of N are independent of any changes in A, since no change in A occurs between taking the two or more samples of exit gas.

The method employed in the present example was to take a number of duplicate samples of inlet and exit gas, the duplicates being taken more or less simultaneously, and estimate $V(A)$ and $V(N)$ from the differences between the duplicates. This eliminates the effect of variations in A (and hence in N) between the separate tests, and the experimental errors in the determination of A and N are independent. The following values for the means and variances were found experimentally.

$$\bar{A} = 12.0 \qquad\qquad \bar{N} = 13.5$$

$$V(A) = 59.3 \times 10^{-4} \qquad V(N) = 92.2 \times 10^{-4}$$

$$\partial Y/\partial A = -(100)(13.5)/12^2 = -1,350/144 = -9.38$$

$$\partial Y/\partial N = 100/12 - 1.25 = 8.33 - 1.25 = 7.08$$

(Note that the differentials are evaluated at the mean values of A and N.)

$$V(Y) = (-9.38)^2 \times 59.3 \times 10^{-4} + (7.08)^2 \times 92.2 \times 10^{-4}$$
$$= 87.98 \times 59.3 \times 10^{-4} + 50.13 \times 92.2 \times 10^{-4}$$
$$= 0.522 + 0.462$$
$$= 0.984$$

$$S.D.(Y)^* = \sqrt{0.984} = 0.992\%$$

The mean value of Y was about 96%, so that the coefficient of variation is:

$$v = 0.992 \times 100/96$$
$$= 1.03\%$$

* That is, the standard deviation in the efficiency Y due to *experimental errors* in the determination of A and N.

E

Note that if the "percentage error" in A and N, i.e. their coefficients of variation, had been added, we should have found the coefficient of variation of Y as follows:

$$S.D.(A) = \sqrt{(59\cdot3 \times 10^{-4})} = 7\cdot7 \times 10^{-2} \qquad v(A) = 7\cdot7/12\cdot0 = 0\cdot64\%$$
$$S.D.(N) = \sqrt{(92\cdot2 \times 10^{-4})} = 9\cdot6 \times 10^{-2} \qquad v(N) = 9\cdot6/13\cdot5 = 0\cdot71\%$$
$$v(Y) \qquad\qquad = 1\cdot35\%$$

This is a serious overestimate of the error in Y and illustrates the importance of using the correct method. The error introduced is a maximum when variances are equal, assuming the separate quantities affect the result equally (this is not quite the case in the above example). The incorrect estimate is then high by 41%.

Appendix 3F

PROOF OF EQUATION (3·42)

Let the Universe mean be μ, the sample mean be $\bar{x}$, and the Universe variance σ^2. Then if x_i represents an observation in a sample of n:

$$(x_i - \mu) \equiv (x_i - \bar{x}) + (\bar{x} - \mu) \quad\dots\dots\dots\dots(3F\cdot1)$$
$$(x_i - \mu)^2 = (x_i - \bar{x})^2 + (\bar{x} - \mu)^2 + 2(x_i - \bar{x})(\bar{x} - \mu)\dots\dots(3F\cdot2)$$

Summing this equation over all values of i from 1 to n:

$$\Sigma(x_i - \mu)^2 = \Sigma(x_i - \bar{x})^2 + n(\bar{x} - \mu)^2 + 2(\bar{x} - \mu)\,\Sigma(x_i - \bar{x})$$

But $\qquad\qquad\qquad \Sigma(x_i - \bar{x}) = 0$, by definition of $\bar{x}$

Therefore $\qquad\qquad \Sigma(x_i - \mu)^2 = \Sigma(x_i - \bar{x})^2 + n(\bar{x} - \mu)^2\dots\dots\dots(3F\cdot3)$

If this calculation is repeated for a large number of samples, the mean value of $\Sigma(x_i - \mu)^2$ will tend to $n\sigma^2$ (by definition of σ^2) and the mean value of $n(\bar{x} - \mu)^2$ will similarly tend to n times the variance of $\bar{x}$, i.e. to $n(\sigma^2/n)$ [§ 3·71], whence

$$\Sigma(x_i - \bar{x})^2 + n(\sigma^2/n) \rightarrow n\sigma^2$$
$$\text{or} \qquad \Sigma(x_i - \bar{x})^2 \rightarrow (n - 1)\sigma^2$$
$$\text{and} \qquad V = \frac{\Sigma(x_i - \bar{x})^2}{n - 1} \rightarrow \sigma^2 \qquad\dots\dots\dots\dots\dots(3F\cdot4)$$

Thus V is an unbiased estimate of σ^2, i.e. its mean value over a large number of random samples tends to σ^2, being equal to σ^2 for an infinite number of samples.

CHAPTER 4

CONFIDENCE LIMITS
AND TESTS OF SIGNIFICANCE

WHEN a quantity such as the average yield is calculated from a limited sample of variable data the result is subject to error. The degree of uncertainty in the result can be expressed by a "confidence" interval within which the true value is almost certainly included. This chapter describes the calculation of confidence intervals for the mean, a standard deviation and the ratio of two standard deviations. This chapter also considers the associated tests of significance.

CONFIDENCE LIMITS

Introduction

4·1 When an estimate of some quantity has been made, for example an estimate of the composition of a chemical based on one or more analyses, it is desirable to know not only the estimated value, which is usually the most likely value, but also how precise this estimate is. A convenient way of expressing the precision is to state limits which, with a given probability, include the true value; it is then possible to state, for example, that the true value is unlikely to exceed some upper limit, or to be less than a lower limit, or to lie outside a pair of limits; this information may be more important than the estimate of the most likely value. Such limits are known as Confidence Limits, i.e. they are limits within which it can be stated, with a given degree of confidence, that the true value lies. The degree of confidence may be very high, say 99% certainty, or quite modest, say 80% or 90%, depending on the problem in hand. It is possible to calculate such limits for any statistic, such as the mean or standard deviation, provided the distribution of the observations is known. In this chapter methods are described for calculating the limits where the original data are Normally distributed. In the case of mean values, for the reasons given in § **3·52**, a close approximation is obtained even if the data are not Normally distributed; with the standard deviation, however, a departure from Normality may affect the confidence limits appreciably.

Confidence limits for a mean value

4·2 If the form of the distribution is known, and if the true mean and standard deviation are also known, it is possible, as was shown in § **2·44**, to make probability statements about the value of the mean of a number of observations. For a Normal Universe with mean μ and standard deviation σ, the probability that the mean of n observations will lie within the range $\mu - 3\sigma/\sqrt{n}$ to $\mu + 3\sigma/\sqrt{n}$ is 0·997. Conversely, if the true mean is unknown and the observed mean of n observations is $\bar{x}$, the probability that μ lies within the range $\bar{x} - 3\sigma/\sqrt{n}$ to $\bar{x} + 3\sigma/\sqrt{n}$ is also 0·997, i.e. the probability that this statement is true is 0·997. In other words, in repeated experiments of this sort, if we assert that the true value of μ lies within the limits $\bar{x} \pm 3\sigma/\sqrt{n}$ we shall be right in 99·7% of these assertions. These limits are thus the 99·7% Confidence Limits for the true mean, μ. We may assert, with 99·7% confidence, that μ lies somewhere in this range, the most probable value being $\bar{x}$. The interval between the limits is known as the Confidence Interval, and the degree of confidence (99·7% in the above example) as the Confidence Coefficient. For a smaller confidence coefficient the limits are closer, e.g. for 95% confidence they are $\bar{x} - 1·96\sigma/\sqrt{n}$ and $\bar{x} + 1·96\sigma/\sqrt{n}$, and so on. If it is necessary to be virtually certain of including the true value of the mean, a high confidence coefficient, and hence relatively wide limits, are necessary.

4·21 In some situations only one of the limits may be of interest, say the upper limit if all that is required is a sufficient assurance that μ does not exceed a stated value. The probability that μ exceeds $\bar{x} + 3\sigma/\sqrt{n}$ is 0·001, i.e. with 99·9% confidence μ is less than $\bar{x} + 3\sigma/\sqrt{n}$. In general the probability that μ exceeds $\bar{x} + u_a\sigma/\sqrt{n}$ is a, where u_a is the value of u given in Table A for the probability $P = a$, and we can state with $100(1 - a)\%$ confidence that μ is less than $\bar{x} + u_a\sigma/\sqrt{n}$. Similarly the probability that μ is greater than $\bar{x} - u_a\sigma/\sqrt{n}$ is $(1 - a)$. Where both upper and lower limits are required, the probability that μ lies within the range $\bar{x} - u_a\sigma/\sqrt{n}$ to $\bar{x} + u_a\sigma/\sqrt{n}$ is $(1 - 2a)$

$$\left. \begin{array}{l} \text{Lower Confidence Limit} = \bar{x} - u_a\sigma/\sqrt{n} \\ \text{Upper Confidence Limit} = \bar{x} + u_a\sigma/\sqrt{n} \\ \text{Confidence Coefficient} \quad = 100(1 - 2a)\% \end{array} \right\} \dots\dots\dots\dots(4\cdot1)$$

It is important to note that while u_a corresponds to a probability a, the confidence coefficient is $(1 - 2a)$. But if only one limit were required the associated confidence coefficient would be $(1 - a)$. When both limits are considered we shall refer to them as the $100(1 - 2a)\%$ confidence limits, or as the $100(1 - 2a)\%$ confidence interval.

Confidence limits for a mean value: Standard deviation estimated
4·22 It was assumed above that σ was known exactly; usually only an estimate, s, of σ is available, based on a limited number (ϕ) of degrees of freedom, and it is necessary to use this estimate in calculating the confidence limits. Since s itself is subject to some uncertainty the confidence limits for μ are further apart than they would be if σ were known exactly. This

uncertainty is allowed for by using, in place of u, the quantity t, which is tabulated in Table C. For a large number of degrees of freedom, say more than 20, the uncertainty in s is comparatively small, and t is practically identical with u, but as the number of degrees of freedom becomes smaller, t becomes progressively larger than u. The following table, for $a = 0.025$, illustrates the point.

ϕ				t
∞	..	..	..	.. $1.96 (= u)$
20	..	..	..	.. 2.09
10	..	..	..	.. 2.23
5	..	..	..	.. 2.57
2	..	..	..	.. 4.30
1	..	..	..	.. 12.71

The $100(1 - 2a)\%$ confidence limits are:

$$\left. \begin{array}{l} \text{Lower limit: } \bar{x} - t_a s/\sqrt{n} \\ \text{Upper limit: } \bar{x} + t_a s/\sqrt{n} \end{array} \right\} \quad \dots\dots\dots\dots\dots(4\cdot2)$$

where t_a is found from Table C, using the appropriate number of degrees of freedom.

Difference between two mean values

4·23   A problem that frequently arises is to assess the magnitude of the difference between two mean values, for example the yields of two alternative processes of manufacture or the compositions of two chemicals. The method of comparing the two is to calculate the difference between two observed means, $\bar{x}_1 - \bar{x}_2$, and the standard error of the difference. These values are used to calculate the confidence limits for the true difference, $\mu_1 - \mu_2$. If the lower limit is greater than zero it can be assumed that μ_1 is greater than μ_2, or if the upper limit is less than zero, that μ_2 is greater than μ_1. If the limits are too wide to lead to sufficiently reliable conclusions more observations must be taken. Note that these conclusions cannot be drawn directly from the confidence limits for the individual means.

Let the group means $\bar{x}_1$ and $\bar{x}_2$ be based on n_1 and n_2 observations from Universes with standard deviations σ_1 and σ_2 respectively.

4·231   The standard error of $\bar{x}_1 - \bar{x}_2$ is:

$$S.E.(\bar{x}_1 - \bar{x}_2) = \{\sigma_1^2/n_1 + \sigma_2^2/n_2\}^{\frac{1}{2}} \dots\dots\dots\dots(4\cdot3)$$

When σ_1 and σ_2 are equal this reduces to:

$$S.E.(\bar{x}_1 - \bar{x}_2) = \sigma(1/n_1 + 1/n_2)^{\frac{1}{2}} \dots\dots\dots\dots(4\cdot4)$$

The confidence limits are therefore:

$$(\bar{x}_1 - \bar{x}_2) \pm u_a \sigma(1/n_1 + 1/n_2)^{\frac{1}{2}} \dots\dots\dots\dots(4\cdot5)$$

If $n_1 = n_2$, this reduces to:

$$(\bar{x}_1 - \bar{x}_2) \pm u_a \sigma\sqrt{(2/n)} \dots\dots\dots\dots(4\cdot6)$$

4·232 If σ_1 and σ_2 are not known, estimates s_1 and s_2 are calculated in the usual way; if these do not differ greatly, and if it is reasonable to suppose that σ_1 and σ_2 are the same or nearly so, a common value is calculated as in § **3·341**. The confidence limits are then found as in Equation (4·5) or (4·6), substituting s for σ and t for u; s is based on $\phi = n_1 + n_2 - 2$ degrees of freedom, and this value is used in finding the appropriate value of t from Table C.

A difficulty arises when σ_1 and σ_2 cannot be assumed equal. An approximate solution is to calculate the standard error from:

$$S.E.(\bar{x}_1 - \bar{x}_2) = (s_1{}^2/n_1 + s_2{}^2/n_2)^{\frac{1}{2}} \ldots\ldots\ldots\ldots(4·7)$$

where $s_1{}^2$ and $s_2{}^2$ are the observed variances of the two sets of data. The approximate confidence limits are $(\bar{x}_1 - \bar{x}_2) \pm t_a\{S.E.(\bar{x}_1 - \bar{x}_2)\}$, but in finding t from Table C the value of ϕ is not $(n_1 + n_2 - 2)$ but is found [4·1] from:

$$\frac{1}{\phi} = \frac{1}{\phi_1}\left[\frac{s_1{}^2/n_1}{s_1{}^2/n_1 + s_2{}^2/n_2}\right]^2 + \frac{1}{\phi_2}\left[\frac{s_2{}^2/n_2}{s_1{}^2/n_1 + s_2{}^2/n_2}\right]^2 \ldots\ldots(4·8)$$

where the suffixes 1 and 2 refer to the two samples.* Note that $(s_1{}^2/n_1 + s_2{}^2/n_2)$ will already have been calculated. If $s_1{}^2$ is much greater than $s_2{}^2$, and n_1 and n_2 are not widely different, ϕ approximates to ϕ_1. If it is suspected that $s_1{}^2$ will be considerably greater than $s_2{}^2$ it is usually best to make n_1/n_2 about equal to $s_1{}^2/s_2{}^2$, so that the variances of the two sample means are approximately equal.

Example 4·1. Laboratory test for ease of filtration

4·24 In a plant manufacturing a nitrogenous fertiliser a main limitation to increased output was the rate of filtration, on rotary filters, to separate the fertiliser solution from insoluble by-products. Laboratory experiments were carried out in an attempt to make the magma more easily filtered, and a standard procedure was established for estimating ease of filtration, consisting simply of filtering a given volume through a standard filter paper under a standard suction and observing the time for filtration. It was first necessary to confirm that this test gave a reasonable indication of the ease of filtration on the plant filters. Samples of plant magma were taken at a time when filtering was judged to be "fair" and also at a time when it was judged to be "fairly good," this being part of a more extensive investigation covering other conditions also. The results of the laboratory tests were variable, but the average for the samples taken during the "fair" period was higher (i.e. poorer filtration) than for those in the "fairly good" period. It was necessary to estimate the magnitude of this difference, and also its limits of uncertainty, not only in assessing the results of the particular experiment but also in planning future trials.

---

*Slightly different limits, called "Fiducial Limits," are given by Behrens and Fisher; see [4·4] and [4·3].

The individual results are given in Table 4·1, and the necessary calculations beneath.

Table 4·1

LABORATORY FILTRATION TEST

	Filtration on Plant		
	Fair		Fairly Good
x_1	$x_1{}^2$	x_2	$x_2{}^2$
8	64	9	81
10	100	10	100
12	144	10	100
13	169	4	16
13	169	7	49
9	81	9	81
14	196		
Total 79	923	49	427

x = filtration time in seconds

$$\bar{x}_1 = 79/7 \qquad = 11\cdot29 \text{ sec.} \qquad \bar{x}_2 = 49/6 \qquad = 8\cdot17 \text{ sec.}$$
$$s_1{}^2 = \{923 - (79)^2/7\}/6 = 5\cdot24 \qquad s_2{}^2 = \{427 - (49)^2/6\}/5 = 5\cdot37$$
$$\phi_1 = 6 \qquad\qquad\qquad \phi_2 = 5$$
$$s_1 = \sqrt{5\cdot24} \qquad = 2\cdot29 \text{ sec.} \qquad s_2 = \sqrt{5\cdot37} \qquad = 2\cdot32 \text{ sec.}$$

Since s_1 and s_2 are almost identical, and since the standard deviations were not expected to be different, we use the combined estimate $s = 2\cdot30$ sec., based on $6 + 5 = 11$ degrees of freedom [§ **3·341**].

$$S.E.(\bar{x}_1 - \bar{x}_2) = 2\cdot30\sqrt{(\tfrac{1}{7} + \tfrac{1}{6})} = 1\cdot28 \text{ sec.}$$
$$\phi \qquad\qquad = 11 \quad ; \quad t_{0\cdot025} = 2\cdot20 \text{ (Table C)}$$
$$\bar{x}_1 - \bar{x}_2 \qquad = 11\cdot29 - 8\cdot17 = 3\cdot12 \text{ sec.}$$

The 95% confidence limits are:

$$3\cdot12 \pm 2\cdot20 \times 1\cdot28 = 0\cdot30 \text{ and } 5\cdot94 \text{ sec.}$$

It is thus reasonably certain that there is a real difference, in the expected direction. The estimate is, however, rather uncertain, and it would be desirable to increase the precision by carrying out more tests. It is clear, too, that several tests would be necessary before any particular magma could be classified with any reasonable degree of confidence.

The following considerations give a guide to the number of tests required. The standard error of the mean of n results carried out under uniform conditions is $2·30/\sqrt{n}$, and the 95% confidence limits are $\bar{x} \pm t_{0·025} \times 2·30/\sqrt{n}$. If we assume the estimate of 2·30 for the standard deviation to be free from error the confidence limits become

$$\bar{x} \pm u_{0·025} \times 2·30/\sqrt{n} = \bar{x} \pm 1·96 \times 2·30/\sqrt{n} = \bar{x} \pm 4·51/\sqrt{n}.$$

If for example it is desired to determine the time with 95% confidence correct to $\pm 1·5$ seconds, we have:

$$4·51/\sqrt{n} = 1·5$$
$$\sqrt{n} = 3·01$$
$$n = 9$$

So nine tests would be required.

The problems of determining the number of trials required is dealt with in more detail in Chapter 5.

Paired comparisons

4·25 When two processes are being compared it is desirable to keep all conditions constant, e.g. to use the same raw materials for both, so that the difference between the results is due only to the difference between the processes. It may be necessary to carry out several trials on each process in order to detect the difference with sufficient assurance, and it may not be possible to prepare sufficient raw material of uniform composition for the entire series of trials. The results of the trials on one process will vary because of experimental error, even if the raw material is constant; but if the raw material varies, the variation will be greater. Thus the standard error of each mean, and hence of the difference between the means, is increased by the use of several batches of raw material. The confidence limits for the true difference are made wider, and the comparison is less sensitive.

In suitable circumstances this difficulty can be overcome; for example, in comparing two plants, provided one batch of raw material is sufficient for at least one trial on each plant, a pair of trials may be carried out with each batch of raw material and the differences between the efficiencies noted. These differences, as distinct from the actual efficiencies, are the quantities studied, because there is no reason to believe that they are affected by variations between batches of raw material. Their standard deviation is the same as if the raw material were constant. This procedure may greatly reduce the number of trials required for a given degree of precision.

Example 4·2

4·26 Two analysts carried out simultaneous measurements of the percentage of ammonia in a plant gas on nine successive days to find the extent of the bias, if any, between their results. The gas composition varied somewhat, the variations being large compared with the analytical errors. In this case the differences between the simultaneous measurements are likely to have a smaller standard error than differences between measurements by the two operators carried out at different times. For this reason the tests were designed to permit "paired comparisons" and the statistical analysis is carried out on the differences between simultaneous measurements.

The results are shown in Table 4·2, the figures given being $100(N - 12)$ where $N = \%$ ammonia.

Table 4·2

PERCENTAGE AMMONIA IN PLANT GAS
TRANSFORMED DATA

Sample No.	Operator		$(x_2 - x_1)$ $= y$	y^2
	A	B		
	x_1	x_2		
1	4	18	14	196
2	37	37	0	0
3	35	38	3	9
4	43	36	− 7	49
5	34	47	13	169
6	36	48	12	144
7	48	57	9	81
8	33	28	− 5	25
9	33	42	9	81
Total　..	303	351	48	754
Mean　..	33·67	39·00	5·33	

The mean value $\bar{y}$ is 5·33, and the standard deviation of y, calculated in the usual way, is 7·89. The standard error of $\bar{y}$ is thus $7·89/\sqrt{9} = 2·63$. For $\phi = 8$ and $a = 0·025$, $t = 2·31$; the 95% confidence limits are therefore $5·33 \pm 2·31 \times 2·63 = 11·41$ and $- 0·75$. Although it is more likely than not that B gets on the average higher results than A, this is by no means certain. At worst, B's results are about 11·4 higher than A's, on the average, corresponding to 0·11% NH_3, which is not considered serious for this particular case.

The standard error of $\bar{y}$ is based on 8 degrees of freedom, whereas if the analysis had been carried out on the results of two completely independent sets of tests, the standard error of the difference between the means would have been based on 16 degrees of freedom. If there were no appreciable variation in ammonia content from sample to sample, the use of the difference method would have sacrificed 8 of the 16 degrees of freedom. This loss of degrees of freedom is the price that must be paid for eliminating the effect of sample-to-sample variation. If in Example 4·2 we treat the results as if they were from independent samples the standard deviation of the results, averaged over both analysts, is 11·8, and the confidence limits for the difference between the means would then be 17·2 and − 6·5. These are much wider than the limits already obtained for the mean difference, i.e. the elimination of the effect of sample-to-sample variation more than compensates for the loss of 8 degrees of freedom.

The conditions under which the "difference" method is used must be carefully noted. The two members of each pair must be naturally associated; it is not valid to pair the results arbitrarily, for example by arranging the two series in order of magnitude and pairing the results in that order. It should also be noted that when the experiment is designed for paired comparisons it should be analysed as such; we cannot then treat the results as if they were from two independent samples.

Confidence limits for the standard deviation

4·3 The standard deviation estimated from a sample is subject to some uncertainty, i.e. repeat estimates, using samples taken under the same conditions, would not be identical. It is desirable to know how reliable the estimate is, and this is best done by calculating the confidence limits. These limits are closer the greater the number of degrees of freedom on which the estimate is based. As will become apparent later, it is convenient to consider first the confidence limits for the ratio of two standard deviations; those for a single standard deviation are considered in § 4·33.

Confidence limits for the ratio of two standard deviations

4·31 Two standard deviations, both based on observations, are compared by calculating the ratio of the two estimates. The confidence limits of this ratio are obtained by the use of the pair of multipliers L_1 and L_2 given in Table H. Multiplying the ratio by L_1 gives the lower confidence limit, and by L_2 the upper confidence limit. Table H gives values of L_1 and L_2 for $\alpha = 0·01, 0·025, 0·05, 0·10$, i.e. for confidence coefficients of 98%, 95%, 90% and 80%. If only one limit is of interest the appropriate limit is calculated and its confidence coefficient is $100(1 - \alpha)\%$. Note that ϕ_N in Table H is the number of degrees of freedom for the numerator of the ratio s_1/s_2; ϕ_D is for the denominator. If the same procedure is carried out for s_2/s_1, the limits will be the exact reciprocals of those for s_1/s_2; the results are thus equivalent. Suppose for example that $s_1 = 1·5$, based on 10 degrees of freedom, and $s_2 = 1$, based on 20 degrees of freedom, and it is required to find the upper and lower 95% confidence limits. The ratio $s_1/s_2 = 1.5$. For $\phi_N = 10$, $\phi_D = 20$ and $a = 0.025$, $L_1 = 0.60$ and $L_2 = 1.85$.

$$\therefore \text{ Lower limit} = 1.5 \times 0.60 = 0.90$$
$$\text{Upper limit} = 1.5 \times 1.85 = 2.78$$

Alternatively:

$$s_2/s_1 = 0.67 \qquad \phi_N = 20 \qquad \phi_D = 10$$

$L_1 = 0.54$ and $L_2 = 1.66$.

$$\text{Lower limit} = 0.67 \times 0.54 = 0.36$$
$$\text{Upper limit} = 0.67 \times 1.66 = 1.11$$

The limits for s_1/s_2 are the reciprocals of these, i.e. 2·78 and 0·90, which are the same as before. Slight differences in the second decimal place may occur, since the figures have been rounded.

We can thus state, with 95% confidence, that σ_1 is between 0·90 times and 2·78 times σ_2.

Example 4·3

4·32 A relatively inexperienced analyst had been trained to carry out a routine test, and it was decided to compare him with an experienced man to find whether his results were as reproducible or whether he required a further period of training. It was thought that if the standard deviation of his results was not more than twice that of the experienced man he would be satisfactory. This can be decided by calculating the confidence limits for the ratio of the standard deviations, using a suitable confidence coefficient, say 95%, and concluding that the new analyst is suitable if the upper limit is less than 2.

The results of the experiment were as follows. A is the new analyst.

Analyst	A	B
Number of tests (n)	20	13
Variance (s^2)	294·7	139·0
Standard deviation (s)	17·2	11·8
Degrees of freedom $(\phi = n - 1)$	19	12

$$s_1/s_2 = 17.2/11.8 = 1.46$$
$$\phi_N = 19 \qquad \phi_D = 12$$

From Table H ($a = 0.025$), interpolating by inspection, $L_1 = 0.57$ and $L_2 = 1.66$. The 95% confidence limits are:

$$1.46 \times 0.57 = 0.83$$
$$1.46 \times 1.66 = 2.42$$

Since the upper limit is greater than 2, analyst A would not be considered suitable from these tests alone. However, the lower limit indicates that there is a reasonable probability that A is as good as B, and the only fair conclusion is that insufficient tests have been carried out to assess analyst A. Further tests are therefore necessary before a sufficiently reliable conclusion can be drawn. The number of tests required is about 24 for each analyst. The question of the number of tests required is dealt with more fully in Chapter 5.

Confidence limits for a single standard deviation

4·33 In Table H the values for ϕ_N or ϕ_D equal to infinity correspond to the case where one standard deviation is known exactly. Suppose $\phi_D = \infty$, then σ_2 is known exactly, and the ratio is uncertain only to the extent that σ_1 is uncertain; the confidence limits for σ_1 are clearly obtained by multiplying those for the ratio by the known value of σ_2. If $\sigma_2 = 1$, the confidence limits of the ratio are those of σ_1. To find the limits for a single standard deviation σ, therefore, we simply use the line of Table H for $\phi_D = \infty$, with ϕ_N equal to the number of degrees of freedom on which the estimate of σ is based. It will be seen that for a small number of degrees of freedom the limits are wide; for example, if $\phi = 4$ the upper 99% limit is seven times the lower; for $\phi = 2$ it is 23 times as great. Table H shows immediately how many observations are required to obtain a given precision, for example suppose that the upper limit should be not more than twice the estimate. For the 95% limit the number of observations is 11, since for $\phi = 10$, $L_2 = 1·98$, and for ϕ less than 10, L_2 is greater than 2.

The 95% confidence limits for the individual standard deviations in Example **4·3** are as follows.

	Analyst A	Analyst B
Estimate s	17·2	11·8
ϕ	19	12
L_1	0·76	0·72
L_2	1·47	1·65
Lower confidence limit ..	13·1	8·5
Upper confidence limit ..	25·3	19·5

Single- and double-sided limits

4·4 At this stage we may conveniently summarise the general procedure in calculating confidence limits, and the differentiation between single-sided and double-sided cases.

In calculating the limits of a confidence interval the procedure is to divide the whole range of possible values into three parts such that:

(i) There is a probability α that the true value of the statistic lies in the upper part of the range, i.e. above the upper limit.

(ii) There is a probability α that the true value lies in the lower part of the range, i.e. below the lower limit.

(iii) There is a probability $(1 - 2\alpha)$ that the true value lies in the centre part, i.e. between the two limits.

It follows that:

(iv) There is a probability $(1 - \alpha)$ that the true value lies below the upper limit.

(v) There is a probability $(1 - \alpha)$ that the true value lies above the lower limit.

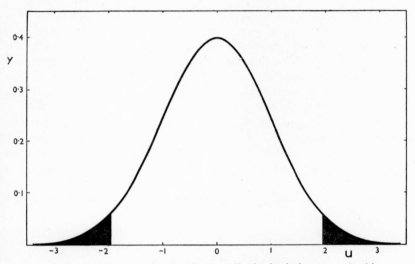

Fig. 4·1. 95% Confidence limits. Each shaded area = 2·5%

These relations are illustrated in Fig. 4·1, which shows a Normal distribution. The shaded area on the left is the part of the distribution below the lower limit; that on the right is the part above the upper limit. The clear area represents the confidence interval. The shaded areas each represent 2·5% of the total, and the clear area 95%.

The effect of non-Normality

4·5   It has been assumed so far that the data are Normally distributed, and Tables A, B, C, D and H have been calculated on this assumption. So far as mean values are concerned the assumption does not lead to serious error, since, as shown in § **2·42**, the means of even small samples are very nearly Normally distributed, even if the original data are not. But for the standard deviation, or the ratio of two standard deviations, if the data are not Normal the values given in Tables B, D and H may be appreciably in error; but even so, the values when used with caution are a useful guide. If sufficient information about the distribution is available, it may be possible to effect a transformation which gives a more nearly Normal distribution.

Confidence limits for standard deviation:
Distribution not assumed Normal

4·51   The method given in §§ 4·31 and 4·33 for finding confidence limits for a standard deviation, or a ratio of two standard deviations, is based on the assumption that the original data are Normally distributed. If in fact they are not, the calculated confidence limits may be very much too wide or too narrow, depending on the actual distribution. This question is discussed in [4·2], where a method is given which supplies approximate confidence limits whatever the nature of the distribution, i.e. it is a *distribution-free* method. As will be shown, this method has the disadvantage that the number of degrees of freedom available is very much less than the number of observations, so that unless a reasonably large number of observations are available the confidence limits are likely to be wide. Preferably, there should be 30 or more observations, but in the case of a ratio of two standard deviations the method can safely be used with somewhat fewer than 30 in each set. If these conditions are met it is worth while to use the distribution-free method unless it is known that the data are Normally distributed or very nearly so.

The method for the ratio of two standard deviations is as follows, that for a single standard deviation being treated as a special case.

4·511 (i) Divide each set of observations at random into small equal groups of say three to five observations, by using random numbers or by drawing numbered slips of paper.

(ii) Calculate the variance V for each of these groups, and take the logarithms. Let $y = \log V$.

(iii) Treat y as a new variable. Calculate its mean and standard deviation separately for each set, and find the confidence limits for $(\bar{y}_1 - \bar{y}_2)$ exactly as in § 4·23. The number of degrees of freedom used in finding the value of t is the total number of y's less two. Thus if groups of four are used, the number of degrees of freedom is reduced to about a quarter.

(iv) Take the antilogs of $(\bar{y}_1 - \bar{y}_2)$ and of the confidence limits. Then since $y = \log V$, $(\bar{y}_1 - \bar{y}_2)$ is an estimate of $\log(\sigma_1{}^2/\sigma_2{}^2)$, and the confidence limits are those for $\log(\sigma_1{}^2/\sigma_2{}^2)$. Thus the antilogs are the estimate and confidence limits of $\sigma_1{}^2/\sigma_2{}^2$ and their square roots are those of σ_1/σ_2.

If the data are in fact Normally distributed, the results obtained by this method will be much the same as those by the methods of § 4·31. If the data are not Normal the results by the two methods may be appreciably different.

The application to determine the confidence limits for a single standard deviation is obvious. An example is given in Appendix 4A, where the method is applied to the data of Appendix 3C. The two methods give very similar results, because the observations are approximately Normally distributed.

The number in each sub-group has been left vague because further research is required to determine the optimum value. When a large number of observations are available larger sub-groups can be taken, provided this does not reduce the number of sub-groups to too small a value, say less than 10 for each set. For sets with fewer than 30 observations it is advisable to take sub-groups of not more than four observations.

TESTS OF SIGNIFICANCE

4·6 A common procedure in present-day statistical analysis is to carry out a Test of Significance as an aid to the interpretation of experimental data. The reasoning behind such a test is best illustrated by a simple example.

Suppose that a process carried out by a standard method has a mean yield of μ_0, the standard deviation of batch yields being σ. A modification is suggested which it is thought might increase the yield, and in order to test whether this is so a series of n batches is prepared by the modified method, giving an average yield of $\bar{x}$. It can be assumed that σ will be the same with the modified as with the normal process. Suppose that in reality the modification has no effect on yield, in other words, that the true yield remains at μ_0. The observed mean may be greater than μ_0 simply because of sampling variations, and it is necessary to avoid the conclusion that the true mean has increased if in fact it has not. It is possible to calculate how large $\bar{x}$ is likely to be if the true mean is μ_0; for example it is unlikely (1 chance in 40) to exceed $\mu_0 + 1\cdot96\sigma/\sqrt{n}$. If it does exceed this value, the conclusion is reached that the true yield of the modified process, which we denote by μ_1, is greater than μ_0; if it does not, there is insufficient evidence to conclude that an increase has occurred, and the modified method cannot at this stage be adopted, though further tests might well be carried out before the modified process is finally accepted or rejected.

In the above illustration we are, in effect, testing the truth of a hypothesis, namely that the modified process has not produced an improvement in yield. Such a hypothesis is called a Null Hypothesis. In more general terms, the

Null Hypothesis takes the form that a parameter does not differ from a particular value. The procedure in a test of significance is to calculate the probability of finding a deviation as large as or larger than the observed deviation on the assumption that the Null Hypothesis is true. If this probability is sufficiently small, the Null Hypothesis is discredited.

The above illustration shows that tests of significance and confidence limits are closely related. The Null Hypothesis is that $\mu_1 - \mu_0 = 0$, μ_1 being the true yield for the modified process; from this we deduce that $\bar{x}$ has a probability a of exceeding $\mu_0 + u_a(\sigma/\sqrt{n})$, the value of u_a being obtained from Table A. But $\bar{x} > \mu_0 + u_a(\sigma/\sqrt{n})$ is equivalent to $\bar{x} - u_a(\sigma/\sqrt{n}) > \mu_0$, the left-hand side of which is the lower $100(1 - a)\%$ confidence limit for μ_1 [§ 4·21], and consequently the test of significance is identical with determining whether the lower confidence limit for μ_1 exceeds μ_0.

In this particular application we are only interested in the lower confidence limit. This is not always the case. Assuming the same Null Hypothesis, i.e. $\mu_1 - \mu_0 = 0$, is true, $\bar{x}$ has a probability a of being less than $\mu_0 - u_a(\sigma/\sqrt{n})$. This is equivalent to saying that $\bar{x} + u_a(\sigma/\sqrt{n})$ is less than μ_0, in other words that the upper $100(1 - a)\%$ confidence limit for μ_1 is less than μ_0. If, therefore, μ_0 lies *outside* the $100(1 - 2a)\%$ confidence limits for μ_1 the probability that this would happen if the Null Hypothesis were true is less than $2a$. A test of significance at a level $2a$ is thus a test of whether a particular value of μ_0 is included in the confidence limits of μ_1. Similar considerations apply in testing the significance of other statistics and no new principles are involved. Confidence limits are usually more useful than a test of significance because they give the complete range of values or hypotheses which can be regarded as consistent with the observations. More often than not, we are concerned with the complete range; however, there are situations where it is sufficient to test a Null Hypothesis, i.e. to test simply whether or not a given Hypothesis is acceptable.

Since the calculations are similar to those involved in calculating confidence limits, it is not necessary to give the methods of tests of significance in any great detail. It should be noted that a test of significance controls the risk of rejecting the Null Hypothesis when it is true, but has no provision for controlling the risk of not rejecting the Null Hypothesis when it is false.

Significance levels

4·61   When applying a test of significance we calculate the probability P that a given result would occur if the Null Hypothesis were true. If this probability is equal to or less than a given value a, the result is said to be significant at the level a. The appropriate level of significance will depend on the particular problem under consideration. Usually the value $P = 0·05$ gives sufficient assurance, but in certain circumstances a higher degree of assurance such as 0·01 may be required, while in others a less degree of assurance corresponding to 0·10 may be sufficient. When $P = 0·05$ the result is usually referred to as "significant" and when $P = 0·01$ as "highly significant." The determination of the appropriate significance level to use rests on the same considerations as those for determining the appropriate confidence coefficient, outlined in § **4·2**.

Significance of means

4·7   Two types of tests are involved in the significance of means, these being the Normal Test and the t-Test. The former applies when the standard deviation is known exactly, or is based on a large number of degrees of freedom (in practice > 30), and the latter when the standard deviation has to be estimated from the data and has a limited number ϕ of degrees of freedom. The Normal test is thus a particular case of the t-test when ϕ is large, and need not be considered separately.

The test is applied to the difference between two means μ_0 and μ_1, and there are two cases to consider, (i) μ_0 known and μ_1 estimated from a sample of n observations, (ii) μ_0 and μ_1 estimated from separate samples.

4·71   To test whether μ_1 differs significantly from a given value μ_0 when μ_1 is estimated from a sample of n observations, first calculate the sample mean $\bar{x}$ and form the difference $(\bar{x} - \mu_0)$. Let s be the estimate of the standard deviation based on ϕ degrees of freedom; when s is calculated from the sample, $\phi = (n - 1)$. Dividing $(\bar{x} - \mu_0)$ by its standard error $s/\sqrt{n}$, we have

$$t = (\bar{x} - \mu_0)/(s/\sqrt{n})$$

the significance of which can then be assessed by referring to Table C, using the appropriate number of degrees of freedom.

4·72   In testing whether μ_1 differs significantly from μ_0 when both μ_1 and μ_0 have to be estimated there are several possible situations, and these are discussed fully in § **4·23**. The only case we shall consider here is that in which it is reasonable to assume that the two Universes from which the samples are drawn have equal variances. The combined estimate s^2 of the true variance σ^2 will then be based on $\phi = (n_1 + n_0 - 2)$ degrees of freedom, n_1 and n_0 being the respective sample sizes.

The ratio of the difference between the two sample means, $\bar{x}_1 - \bar{x}_0$, to the standard error of this difference, $s\sqrt{(1/n_1 + 1/n_0)}$, is

$$t = \frac{(\bar{x}_1 - \bar{x}_0)}{s\sqrt{(1/n_1 + 1/n_0)}}$$

the numerical value of which is then referred to Table C.

F

The following results were obtained in § **4·24** for the data of Table 4·1:

$$\bar{x}_1 - \bar{x}_0 = 11·29 - 8·17 = 3·12$$

$$s = 2·30, \quad s\sqrt{\left(\frac{1}{n_1} + \frac{1}{n_0}\right)} = 2·3\sqrt{\left(\frac{1}{7} + \frac{1}{6}\right)} = 1·28$$

$$\phi = 7 + 6 - 2 = 11$$

Therefore $\qquad\qquad\qquad t = 3·12/1·28 = 2·44$

Referring to Table C, we find that for $\phi = 11$ values of t lying outside the interval $(- 2·20, + 2·20)$ are significant at the 0·05 level, 2·20 being the tabulated value of t corresponding to $P = 0·025$. The difference is therefore significant, and we conclude that the true means, μ_1 and μ_0, are probably different. To be adjudged highly significant the calculated t would have to exceed 3·11, the tabulated value corresponding to $P = 0·005$ and $\phi = 11$.

One-sided and two-sided tests

4·73   In the above example the alternative to the Null Hypothesis $\mu_1 - \mu_0 = 0$ is that $\mu_1 \neq \mu_0$, irrespective of whether μ_1 is greater than or less than μ_0. Since the Null Hypothesis may be wrongly rejected in favour of either of these possibilities, the test is said to be two-sided, and it is necessary to double the probabilities in Table C for the critical values of t.

If on the other hand the hypothesis to be tested is $\mu_1 \leqslant \mu_0$, the Null Hypothesis is wrongly rejected only if it appears that $\mu_1 > \mu_0$, and the test is said to be one-sided. The value of t required for significance must then exceed $t(P = 0·05, \phi)$. Referring to the above example, the calculated t is 2·44, and from Table C we find $t(P = 0·05, \phi = 11) = 1·80$ and $t(P = 0·01, \phi = 11) = 2·72$. The difference in means is therefore significant, though not highly significant, and we conclude that $\mu_1 > \mu_0$.

The F-test

4·8   The F-test is used for comparing two variances. Suppose it is required to compare the values of two variances σ_1^2 and σ_2^2 from estimates s_1^2 and s_2^2 based on ϕ_1 and ϕ_2 degrees of freedom respectively. If the alternative to the Null Hypothesis is $\sigma_1^2 > \sigma_2^2$, we calculate the ratio $F = s_1^2/s_2^2$ and refer to Table D for the critical values of F with $\phi_N = \phi_1$, and $\phi_D = \phi_2$. This represents a one-sided test. If on the other hand the alternative to the Null Hypothesis is simply $\sigma_1^2 \neq \sigma_2^2$ the test is double-sided, and we then calculate the ratio of the larger estimate to the smaller one, the probabilities in Table D being doubled to give the critical values for this ratio.

To determine whether a single variance is different from or greater than an assumed value σ^2 we calculate the ratio s^2/σ^2, where s^2 is an estimate based on ϕ degrees of freedom, and refer to Table D with $\phi_N = \phi_1$ and $\phi_D = \infty$, doubling the quoted probabilities in the case of a two-sided test.

Examples of the application of the F-test appear in later chapters, notably in Chapter 6 on the Analysis of Variance.

REFERENCES

[4·1] WELCH, B. L. "The Generalisation of 'Student's' Problems when Several Different Population Variances are Involved," *Biometrika*, **34** (1947), 28–35.

[4·2] BOX, G. E. P. "Non-Normality and Tests on Variances," *Ibid*, **40** (1953), 318–35.

[4·3] FISHER, R. A., and YATES, F. *Statistical Tables for Biological, Agricultural and Medical Research* (fifth edition). Oliver and Boyd (Edinburgh and London, 1957).

[4·4] FISHER, R. A. "The Comparison of Samples with Possibly Unequal Variances," *Annals of Eugenics*, **IX** (1939), 174–80.

APPENDIX 4A

CONFIDENCE LIMITS FOR A STANDARD DEVIATION; DATA NOT ASSUMED NORMAL

4A·1   Table 4A·1 shows the data of Table 3A·1, arranged in random groups of 5, together with the group variances and their logarithms.

Table 4A·1

Group	x					$V(x)$	$y = \log V$
1	− 3,	− 3,	0,	0,	3	6·3	0·80
2	3,	5,	5,	5,	9	4·8	0·68
3	− 2,	− 2,	− 1,	2,	6	11·8	1·07
4	− 1,	1,	3,	5,	6	8·2	0·91
5	− 4,	− 1,	0,	2,	2	6·2	0·79
6	− 3,	− 2,	− 1,	4,	4	11·3	1·05
7	− 7,	− 1,	1,	3,	8	30·2	1·48
8	− 5,	− 3,	0,	0,	7	20·7	1·32
9	− 4,	− 3,	− 3,	− 2,	0	2·3	0·36
10	− 6,	0,	4,	5,	6	24·2	1·38
11	− 3,	0,	0,	0,	4	6·2	0·79
12	− 4,	− 2,	− 1,	− 1,	4	8·7	0·94
13	− 2,	0,	0,	1,	7	11·7	1·07
14	− 5,	− 3,	2,	3,	4	15·7	1·20
15	− 6,	1,	6,	7,	7	31·5	1·50
16	− 2,	0,	0,	1,	2	2·2	0·34
17	− 6,	− 5,	− 3,	− 1,	1	8·2	0·91
18	− 6,	0,	1,	6,	8	30·2	1·48
19	− 1,	0,	1,	7,	1	9·8	0·99

The mean and standard deviation of y are calculated in the usual way.

$$\Sigma y = 19 \cdot 06 \qquad\qquad \bar{y} = 1 \cdot 003$$
$$\Sigma y^2 = 21 \cdot 2256$$
$$(\Sigma y)^2/19 = 19 \cdot 1202$$
$$\therefore \; \Sigma(y - \bar{y})^2 = \Sigma y^2 - (\Sigma y)^2/19 = 2 \cdot 1054$$
$$\therefore \; V(y) = 2 \cdot 1054/18 = 0 \cdot 1170$$
$$V(\bar{y}) = 0 \cdot 1170/19 = 0 \cdot 006158$$
$$\therefore \; \mathrm{SE}(\bar{y}) = 0 \cdot 0785$$
$$\phi = 18 \qquad t_{0 \cdot 025} = 2 \cdot 10$$
$$t \times \mathrm{SE}(\bar{y}) = 0 \cdot 165$$

The 95% confidence limits for $\log \sigma^2 = 1 \cdot 003 \pm 0 \cdot 165$
$$= 0 \cdot 838 \text{ and } 1 \cdot 168$$

Taking antilogs:

Estimate of σ^2 = antilog $1 \cdot 003 = 10 \cdot 07$

Lower confidence limit   = antilog $0 \cdot 838 = 6 \cdot 89$

Upper confidence limit   = antilog $1 \cdot 168 = 14 \cdot 72$

For σ we have:

Estimate $= 3 \cdot 17$

Lower confidence limit $= 2 \cdot 62$

Upper confidence limit $= 3 \cdot 84$

CHAPTER 5

STATISTICAL TESTS: CHOOSING THE NUMBER OF OBSERVATIONS

DECISIONS may often be taken in the light of evidence from a limited number of variable observations. This chapter is concerned with the problem of determining how many observations should be made so that the risk associated with any decision is acceptably small. When certain prior information is available it is possible to base this determination directly on the average cost of making wrong decisions. An alternative approach is given for use when, as frequently happens, this prior information is not available.

Introduction

5·1 The research worker in industry is frequently faced with the problem: How many observations should be made, given that from these observations a decision is to be taken which will result in financial loss if it is wrong?

Particular examples* of great practical importance arise in designing sampling inspection schemes and in planning plant trials in process development work. In sampling inspection the problem is to choose the number of tests that should be carried out in order to decide whether to accept or reject a consignment of material. In planning plant trials—that is, experiments on the production scale—the problem is to choose the number of trials that should be made to decide whether some modified method of manufacture should be accepted or rejected.

Because of random fluctuations in results there is always some risk that a wrong decision will be taken, however many observations are made. This risk becomes smaller as the number of observations is increased, but since observations cost money, taking too many observations can be as costly as taking too few.

In this chapter it will be shown how to calculate the optimum number of observations when certain background information is available and how to

---

* The problems discussed are particular instances of what are called decision function problems. A full discussion of these examples would involve not only the question of the optimum number of observations but also of the optimum *procedure* for making the test. A detailed discussion of this wider problem is not possible in the space available and at the elementary level of this textbook. In this account, therefore, it will be assumed that the test procedure is given and only the number of observations has to be decided.

arrive at a reasonable procedure when such background information is lacking.

5·11 The background information referred to above concerns two things:
  (i) The so-called *prior distribution*, which embodies knowledge available prior to making a series of tests or experiments.
  (ii) The *costs* of making wrong decisions and of experimentation.

We shall first consider the case where both sorts of information are available, illustrating the general principles which then apply in relation to the planning of a sampling inspection (acceptance testing) scheme. We next suppose, as frequently happens, that no information about the prior distribution is available but that information is available on costs. In this situation a procedure that may be regarded as a two-stage modification of the first procedure may be used; this is described and illustrated in relation to the planning of plant trials.

Finally the situation is considered in which neither information on the prior distribution nor information on costs is available. By what may be regarded as a further modification of the first procedure we arrive at methods which, although basically less satisfactory, have at least the advantage that they have been more thoroughly explored. With the first two methods we will consider only the single, but important, case in which the value of a mean is in question; the last procedure, however, is applied also to the problem of comparing variances.

PRIOR DISTRIBUTION AND COSTS KNOWN

A testing scheme

5·2 The general ideas that may be applied to the economic choice of numbers of observations, when the prior distribution and the costs are known, can best be illustrated by considering the particular example of an acceptance testing scheme.

The quality of a batch of a particular chemical delivered from a supplier is defined as the amount μ of an essential ingredient in the batch. According to the specification, μ, measured in suitable units, should be equal to 90, and in practice, if the mean $\bar{x}$ of chemical analyses of n samples from a given batch is greater than 90, the batch is accepted, and if it is less it is rejected. Assuming that the standard deviation of the error in the sampling and testing method is 1·0, the problem is to decide how many samples from each batch should be tested, i.e. how large n should be.

Outline of the method

5·21 The behaviour of any given scheme can be determined from the curves shown in Figure 5·1 (i) and Figure 5·1 (ii).

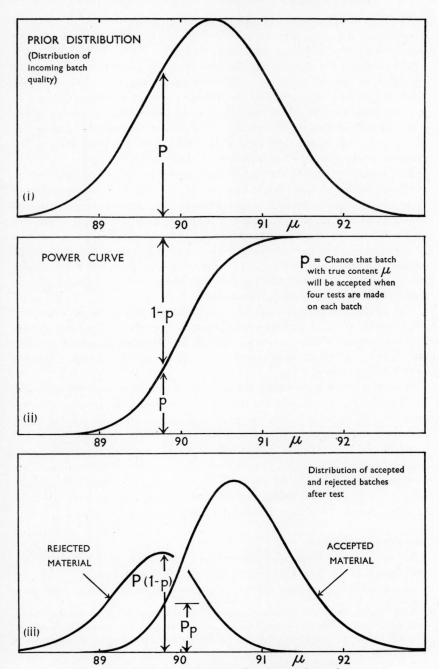

Fig. 5·1. Operation of a sampling inspection scheme

The first is the *incoming quality curve** or *prior distribution*. This curve characterises the material to be tested. It shows in fact how the true batch quality is distributed before the test is applied.

The second is the *operating characteristic curve** or *power curve*. This curve characterises the testing scheme; it shows the chance that material of any given quality will be accepted by the testing scheme as satisfactory.

From these two curves we can calculate the distribution of quality of the accepted batches and the distribution of quality of the rejected batches (see Figure 5·1 (iii)). Once these two distributions have been determined, the most economic number of observations is easily derived.

The process described may be likened to the sieving of particles where the sieve corresponds to the testing procedure. We have an aggregate of material and we want to divide it into two heaps, one heap containing material which is smaller than a certain size and the other containing material which is larger. The prior distribution corresponds to the size distribution of material before sieving. The sieve does not achieve a perfectly sharp "cut"; its "discrimination" is shown by the power curve. Knowing these two characteristic curves we can easily calculate the size distributions of the particles passing through the sieve and of those remaining in it.

The methods of calculating the prior distribution and the power curve and of combining these to obtain the distributions of quality of the accepted and rejected material will be described in what follows for the specific problem stated above. The best solution is then decided from economic considerations in the following way.

It is clear that by increasing the number of analytical tests we can make the discriminating power of our testing scheme, measured by the steepness of the power curve, as great as we please. We have to find the point at which the monetary advantage of increasing the discriminating power of the test is just offset by the increased cost of testing. In the method we are discussing this is done numerically by making the calculation for a series of trial values of n and choosing that which gives the lowest costs. Mathematical solutions are possible in particular instances; the numerical method which we give here, however, has the advantage that it can be applied perfectly generally.

The prior distribution

5·22 In sampling inspection problems the prior distribution is simply the distribution of the true quality μ of incoming batches. In practice this has to be determined from past records, on the assumption that future experience

---

* The expressions *incoming quality curve* and *operating characteristic curve* are terms used specifically when these methods are applied to sampling inspection schemes. The curves are particular instances of *prior distributions* and *power curves* respectively. These latter terms are used in a wider context.

will resemble past experience. Small changes in form of the prior distribution are found to have only a minor effect on the optimal values of n, and so it is not necessary to know the prior distribution very exactly.

We cannot use for the prior distribution the observed distribution of past test results *as it stands*, since this does not give the distribution of the true quality μ but rather the distribution of test observations which are subject to error. We have therefore to adjust the observed distribution of test results to allow for the effect of testing error. This may be done as follows. Suppose that k tests have normally been carried out on each batch and that the best estimate of the batch quality is taken to be the mean of these k test results. Suppose also that a large number, preferably several hundred, of these mean estimates of batch quality are available covering a typical period. A histogram is plotted from these results, and the mean and variance of the observed distribution, which we shall call the unadjusted distribution, are determined in the usual way. From these the mean and variance for the adjusted distributions may be calculated from the relationships:

Mean of adjusted distribution = Mean of unadjusted distribution
Variance of adjusted distribution = Variance of unadjusted distribution
— variance due to testing

Since k tests are performed, the variance due to testing is σ_T^2/k, where σ_T^2 is the variance of an individual test result.

A sufficient approximation to the distribution of μ will now be provided by a curve with the same mean as the adjusted distribution and of the same general shape but with spread reduced by a factor

$$\sqrt{\frac{\text{Variance of adjusted distribution}}{\text{Variance of unadjusted distribution}}}$$

In practice we can proceed by fitting a smooth curve by eye to the histogram and graphically constructing an adjusted curve of the same shape but with suitably reduced spread. Alternatively, in some cases the unadjusted curve may happen to be closely similar to some theoretical curve (e.g. the Normal curve), and the prior distribution can then be represented by the same type of curve with suitably reduced spread.

In the present instance we will assume that the testing procedure prior to the investigation has been to make one test on each batch and to accept or reject on this result. Past records of these results are available over a considerable period. A histogram plotted for 250 such values shows an approximately Normal distribution with mean 90·4 and variance 1·64. Since the testing error variance $\sigma_T^2 = 1\cdot0$ the adjusted curve has mean 90·4 and variance $1\cdot64 - 1\cdot00 = 0\cdot64$. We therefore take the prior distribution to be a Normal curve with mean 90·4 and standard deviation 0·8 as drawn in Figure 5·1 (i). A more precise method of adjustment of the observed distribution is given in [5·1].

We denote the ordinate of the prior distribution by P. Only the relative frequencies at various levels of μ are required in the calculations which follow. It is not essential, therefore, that the curve should be drawn on such a scale that its area is unity.

The power curve

5·23　The power curve shows, for a given test procedure, the chance p that batches with true quality μ will be accepted. We have assumed that our test procedure consists of performing n tests on each batch of material and accepting or rejecting the batch depending on whether the observed mean result $\bar{x}$ is higher or lower than 90. The derivation of the power curve for such a situation is given below.

For the reasons given in § **2·42** we may assume $\bar{x}$ to be Normally distributed. Consequently from a table of the Normal curve we can obtain the probability p that, for any given value of μ, $\bar{x}$ will exceed 90 and the batch will be accepted. We are given that in repeated sampling from a particular batch a single analytical result varies because of sampling and testing errors about the true batch value μ with standard deviation $\sigma_T = 1\cdot0$. The standard deviation of the mean of n analyses is therefore $\sigma_T/\sqrt{n} = 1/\sqrt{n}$. To find p we calculate $u = (90 - \mu)\sqrt{n}/\sigma_T$ and find from Table A the probability that u will attain this value or more. If u is positive p is less than 0·5, and is the entry in Table A; if it is negative p is greater than 0·5 and is found by subtracting the entry in Table A from unity, i.e. the entry is equal to $(1 - p)$. For instance, if 4 analyses are carried out and $\sigma_T = 1\cdot0$, then $u = 2(90 - \mu)$. The values of p obtained from Table A for values of μ between 88 and 92 are shown in Table 5·1 and are plotted in Figure 5·1 (ii).

Table 5·1

POWER CURVE—CALCULATION OF PROBABILITY OF
ACCEPTING A BATCH WITH MEAN QUALITY μ FOR $\sigma_T = 1$; $n = 4$

μ	u	p	μ	u	p
88·0	4·0	0·0000	90·2	− 0·4	0·6554
88·2	3·6	0·0002	90·4	− 0·8	0·7881
88·4	3·2	0·0007	90·6	− 1·2	0·8449
88·6	2·8	0·0026	90·8	− 1·6	0·9452
88·8	2·4	0·0082	91·0	− 2·0	0·9772
89·0	2·0	0·0228	91·2	− 2·4	0·9918
89·2	1·6	0·0548	91·4	− 2·8	0·9974
89·4	1·2	0·1151	91·6	− 3·2	0·9993
89·6	0·8	0·2119	91·8	− 3·6	0·9998
89·8	0·4	0·3446	92·0	− 4·0	1·0000
90·0	0·0	0·5000			

The power curves corresponding to $n = 1$, 4 and 16 are shown in Figure 5·2, from which we see the comparative discriminating power of tests based on different numbers of observations. The steeper is the curve, the greater is the discriminating power of the test. The "ideal" power curve would be a

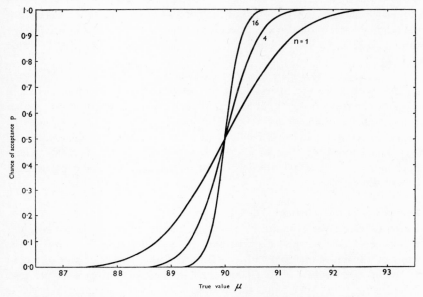

Fig. 5·2. Power curves for various values of n with $\bar{x}_0 = 90$, $\sigma = 1$

vertical line at $\mu = 90$; this would give certain acceptance for $\mu > 90$ and certain rejection for $\mu < 90$. Such a curve could only occur, however, if there were no testing error or if an infinite number of analyses were done.

The distribution of outgoing quality

5·24   The relative frequency with which batches of quality μ are offered and *accepted* is obtained by multiplying the ordinate P of the prior distribution, which is the relative frequency with which a batch of quality μ is offered, by the ordinate p of the power curve which is the probability that, having been offered, a batch with quality μ will be accepted; plotting the product Pp against μ then gives the distribution of the quality of accepted batches. For the present example this is shown by the curve on the right-hand side of Figure 5·1 (iii). Similarly the distribution of rejected batches is obtained by plotting $P(1 - p)$ against μ; this is shown on the left-hand side of Figure 5·1 (iii). The complete diagram shows how the incoming population of batches is split up by the test into two portions. The areas under the distribution curves for accepted and rejected material show the proportions which fall into these two categories. For the example considered in which 4 repeat tests are performed on each batch these areas are $0·664A$ and $0·336A$ respectively, where A is the area under the prior distribution curve. The mean of the distribution of accepted material is 90·772 and the mean of the distribution of rejected material is 89·661. Thus the effect of the testing scheme is to split the original batches into an accepted group (66·4% of the whole) with average value 90·772 and a rejected group (33·6% of the whole) with average value 89·661.

Because the test is subject to error we do not get a perfect "cut-off" between batches with a content of less than 90 and batches with a content of more than 90. In fact the 66·4% of accepted batches is made up of 59·8% with a content greater than 90 and 6·6% with a content of less than 90, and the 33·6% of rejected batches is made up of 24·2% of batches with a content of less than 90 and 9·4% of batches with a content greater than 90. These percentages are obtained from the areas of the distributions lying on each side of the value $\mu = 90$.

Economics of the scheme

5·25 To assess the economic implications of the scheme we must consider the value of the accepted material and the cost of testing it. Suppose the value of a batch of material with content μ is £100μ (e.g. the value of a consignment with content 90 is £9,000), and the cost of testing is £1 per test. Then using 4 tests per batch the average value of the accepted material is £90·772 × 100 = £9,077·2 per batch. Now, the cost of testing is £4 per batch, and since only 66·4% of batches are accepted the cost of testing per accepted batch is £4/0·664 = £6. Thus if we debit the cost of testing, the

Table 5·2

Number of tests n	0	1	2	3	4	5	6
Percentage accepted ..	100	62·3	64·6	65·7	66·4	66·9	67·2
Average value in £'s of accepted batches ..	9040·0	9070·4	9074·5	9076·2	9077·2	9077·8	9078·3
Cost of testing per accepted batch	—	1·6	3·1	4·6	6·0	7·5	8·9
Net value in £'s	9040·0	9068·8	9071·4	9071·6	9071·2	9070·3	9069·4

net value per accepted batch using this scheme is £9071·2. Proceeding in this way for various numbers of tests Table 5·2 is constructed.

We see that in this particular case there is a considerable monetary advantage (about £30 per batch) in testing the batches rather than in not testing them, and that there is a gain of almost £3 per batch by using 3 tests per batch rather than one, but no advantage is obtained by using more than 3 tests.

Practical calculation of an optimal scheme

5·26   The exact evaluation of all the quantities considered above would be a laborious and difficult task. Fortunately sufficient accuracy can usually be achieved by simple arithmetic. We shall illustrate this by showing in the case $n = 4$ detailed calculations for the distribution of accepted material, the proportion of accepted batches, and the average value of accepted batches. The quantities required are set out in Table 5·3. In column (i) of this table the mean value for the batch is given from $\mu = 87·5$ to $\mu = 93·3$ at intervals of 0·2. This allows between 20 and 30 ordinates to be calculated over the range in which the distribution curves have appreciable frequencies. Column (ii) shows the ordinate of the prior distribution curve. In the present example this is simply the ordinate of a Normal curve with mean 90·4 and standard deviation 0·8, and is readily derived from Table 1 of [5·6]. As we have explained, an empirical curve could have been used equally well. Since we are concerned only with relative frequency it is not necessary to scale this curve so that the area beneath it is unity. Column (iii) shows the ordinate of the power curve for each value of μ. This is obtained in the manner already discussed in § **5·23**. The ordinates of the distribution of accepted batches are obtained in column (iv) by multiplying together the entries in columns (ii) and (iii). Column (v) shows the value G in £'s per batch of material with content μ.

The proportion of batches accepted is given by
$$\Sigma Pp/\Sigma P = 2·6566/3·9994 = 0·6642$$
The average value of accepted material is given by
$$\Sigma PpG/\Sigma Pp = 24{,}114·5/2·6566 = 9{,}077·2$$
As mentioned in the footnote to § **5·1**, we have supposed in the above example that the testing procedure was decided in advance and only the effect of changing n was to be studied. In practice we would often be interested also in the effect of changing the critical rejection level $\bar{x}_0$, which we have taken to be 90 in this example. This could be studied in the same manner as has been used to find the effect of changing n. At the expenditure of some labour jointly optimal values of n and $\bar{x}_0$ could be determined.

5·27   In the example given the cost is a simple linear function of μ. This will not always be so. Thus in the situation described it could have happened that a batch was worth a certain fixed amount if μ was greater than 90 and

Table 5·3

QUANTITIES USED IN CALCULATING THE OPTIMAL SCHEME

(i)	(ii)	(iii)	(iv)	(v)
μ	P	p	Pp	G
87·5	0·0006	0·000	0·0000	8,750
87·7	0·0013	0·000	0·0000	8,770
87·9	0·0030	0·000	0·0000	8,790
88·1	0·0064	0·000	0·0000	8,810
88·3	0·0127	0·000	0·0000	8,830
88·5	0·0238	0·001	0·0000	8,850
88·7	0·0417	0·005	0·0002	8,870
88·9	0·0688	0·014	0·0010	8,890
89·1	0·1065	0·036	0·0038	8,910
89·3	0·1550	0·081	0·0126	8,930
89·5	0·2119	0·159	0·0337	8,950
89·7	0·2721	0·274	0·0746	8,970
89·9	0·3282	0·421	0·1382	8,990
90·1	0·3719	0·579	0·2153	9,010
90·3	0·3958	0·726	0·2874	9,030
90·5	0·3958	0·841	0·3329	9,050
90·7	0·3719	0·919	0·3418	9,070
90·9	0·3282	0·964	0·3164	9,090
91·1	0·2721	0·986	0·2683	9,110
91·3	0·2119	0·995	0·2108	9,130
91·5	0·1550	0·999	0·1548	9,150
91·7	0·1065	1·000	0·1065	9,170
91·9	0·0688	1·000	0·0688	9,190
92·1	0·0417	1·000	0·0417	9,210
92·3	0·0238	1·000	0·0238	9,230
92·5	0·0127	1·000	0·0127	9,250
92·7	0·0064	1·000	0·0064	9,270
92·9	0·0030	1·000	0·0030	9,290
93·1	0·0013	1·000	0·0013	9,310
93·3	0·0006	1·000	0·0006	9,330

$$\Sigma P = 3\cdot9994 \qquad \Sigma Pp = 2\cdot6566$$
$$\Sigma PpG = 24,114\cdot5$$
$$\Sigma Pp/\Sigma P = 0\cdot6642$$
$$\Sigma PpG/\Sigma Pp = 9,077\cdot19$$

nothing otherwise. Another possibility would be that if μ was less than 90 the loss was proportional to $90 - \mu$ except when μ fell below some limit μ_0, when the loss was much greater. This case might arise if material with $\mu < \mu_0$ could seriously upset the process.

Whatever the nature of the cost function, the method described above can be immediately applied. The average value of the accepted material can always be evaluated once the value of the material for each value of μ and the distribution of the accepted material are known.

The type of approach discussed is applicable to a number of parallel situations. It will be seen that the method not only allows the most economic scheme to be found, but in the course of the calculations all the characteristics of any proposed scheme are revealed. We can calculate, for example, what proportion of the material we reject will be rightly rejected and what proportion will be wrongly rejected. Knowledge of these values may be of considerable use in negotiations with the producer. It should not be forgotten that the introduction of an inspection scheme will probably have the effect of encouraging the producer to improve his material. He may, for example, introduce a testing scheme himself which reduces the lower tail of the incoming quality curve, or he may raise the mean level of his whole production. The prior distribution, therefore, may change, and the consumer should always be conscious of this possibility and of the advantages to be gained by changing his scheme if a revised calculation shows this to be desirable.

PRIOR DISTRIBUTION UNKNOWN

Planning of plant trials

5·3   In principle the method discussed above for the sampling inspection scheme could be used in a variety of situations, some of which would not at first sight appear to be related to it. For example, suppose that an experiment on a plant was to be conducted to try out some suggested modification, and the problem was that of deciding how many trials should be done before finally accepting or rejecting the modification.

Suppose, to correspond to the previous example, that

(i) the normal plant efficiency is 90 units;

(ii) the true level of process efficiency when the modification is used is μ;

(iii) the result x of a single trial varies about μ with standard deviation $\sigma = 1$ unit;

(iv) the capital value of an improvement to some value μ is £$100(\mu - 90)$;

(v) the cost of an experiment is £1 per trial.

Arithmetically we then have the same problem as before, and in principle it could be solved in the same way.

If we try to apply this technique, however, we are immediately faced with the practical question "What should we take for the prior distribution?" In the sampling inspection example the prior distribution was an observable entity—the distribution of quality of incoming batches. In the present problem, however, it is much more nebulous. We might proceed by asking those most directly concerned with the process modification what increase in yield they thought was most likely (thus fixing the mode of the prior distribution) and what were the largest and smallest increases they thought possible (thus getting some idea of the range). Although such an approach might be thought to be too indefinite, it can in fact often be usefully applied. At least we know that this approach makes full use of expert opinion and that we have worked out the logical consequences of that opinion.

A modification to this approach which does not specifically involve the prior distribution and which has considerable practical appeal is due to Yates [5·3] and Grundy, Healy and Rees [5·4] and [5·5]. They use a two-stage procedure. A first sample of n_1 observations is taken and a calculation is made. This calculation tells us either—

    (i) to accept or reject the modification without further test, or

    (ii) to take n_2 further observations and then to accept the modification if the mean of all results shows an apparent positive effect (however small) and to reject if the mean of all the results shows an apparent negative effect.

The method can be arrived at by assuming that prior to the first sample nothing is known of the magnitude of the effect which might be found, and we therefore assume the same initial probability for all values of μ. The "effective" prior distribution for the second sample utilises the information gained from the first sample. We shall describe here the important case where the capital value of an improvement is given by $£k'(\mu - \mu_0)$, where μ is the mean value obtained using the modification and μ_0 is the mean value obtained using the normal process. Suppose—

    (i) there are n_1 observations in the first sample with mean $\bar{x}_1$;

    (ii) there are n_2 observations in the second sample with mean $\bar{x}_2$;

    (iii) the mean of all the $n_1 + n_2$ observations is $\bar{x}$;

    (iv) the standard deviation is known and equal to σ;

    (v) the cost of experimentation is $£k$ per observation;

    (vi) the capital value of an improvement from μ_0 to μ is $£k'(\mu - \mu_0)$.

It is shown [5·5] that the course of action to be adopted depends on a quantity

$$\lambda = \frac{k'}{kn_1} \frac{\sigma}{\sqrt{n_1}}$$

It is seen that the ratio k'/k compares the value of the expected gain from the experiment with the cost of experimentation. We would expect, therefore, that when the value of λ is large, and much is therefore at stake, larger numbers of observations would be justified, and in fact this is found to be the case.

The procedure is as follows. The value of λ appropriate to the particular experiment is first calculated. The quantity $u = \dfrac{\bar{x}_1 - \mu_0}{\sigma/\sqrt{n_1}}$ is then referred to Table 5·4 below. If $|u|$ exceeds the critical value there given for the appropriate value of λ the modification is accepted, if $\bar{x}_1 - \mu_0$ is positive, or rejected, if $\bar{x}_1 - \mu_0$ is negative, without further test.

Table 5·4

CRITICAL VALUE OF $|u|$

Value of λ	100	200	500	1,000	2,000
Critical value of $|u|$ ..	1·30	1·52	1·81	2·02	2·22

If $|u|$ is not as large as its critical value, further evidence is needed. A further sample of size $n_2 = cn_1$ should therefore be taken. The size of c depends on u as well as on λ and is given by the entries in Table 5·5.

Table 5·5

PROPORTIONATE SIZE OF SECOND SAMPLE

Value of $|u|$	Value of λ				
	100	200	500	1,000	2,000
	Value of $c = n_2/n_1$				
0	3·9	5·3	9·1	13·0	19·0
0·5	3·7	5·0	8·3	12·0	18·0
1·0	3·0	3·8	6·5	10·0	14·0
1·5	—	2·0	4·3	6·7	10·0
2·0	—	—	—	3·0	5·5

To return to the example quoted at the beginning of this section, $\sigma = 1$, $k' = 100$ and $k = 1$. If one trial only was performed in the first sample $n_1 = 1$, and $\lambda = 100$. From Table 5·4, therefore, if the observed value was greater than $90 + 1·30$ we should accept without further testing, and if it was less than $90 - 1·30$ we should reject without further testing. If an intermediate value was observed we should consult Table 5·5. It will be seen that we should then have to take either 3 or 4 further observations and base our decisions on the sign of $\bar{x} - 90$ where $\bar{x}$ was the mean of the whole group.

The above example is somewhat unrealistic; the values of σ and λ are unusually small for a plant trial, and it is most unlikely that a first sample would contain only one observation. The following is a more typical example.

G

Suppose that a 1% increase in yield would save £10,800 per annum and such an improvement would be written off over a 5-year period, thus representing £54,000 in capital value per 1%. This makes $k' = 54,000$. Suppose that each experiment costs £20 to perform, i.e. $k = 20$, and further that $\sigma = 5$. A first sample of $n_1 = 9$ trials is performed, so that $\lambda = \dfrac{54,000}{20 \times 9} \times \dfrac{5}{3} = 500$.

Suppose that an average improvement of 1% was observed in these trials. We then have $u = 0.6$, and from Table 5·4 we see that no immediate decision can be taken. Entering Table 5·5 with $u = 0.6$ and $\lambda = 500$, we find that c is about 8·0, and we should then recommend that $8.0 \times 9 = 72$ further observations be made. The modification would be judged on the sign of $\bar{x} - \mu_0$, where $\bar{x}$ is the mean for the entire group of 81 observations.

PRIOR DISTRIBUTION AND COSTS UNKNOWN

Many problems occur in which not only can no firm information be obtained about the prior distribution but the costs also are unknown or difficult to assess. These can be dealt with in the manner illustrated below.

Planning laboratory experiments on dye receptivity

5·4 Suppose laboratory experiments were being conducted to study possible methods for increasing the dye receptivity of a synthetic fibre. It is reasonably certain that if such experiments were successful they would be of monetary value; frequently, however, so much would depend on unforeseeable factors that it might be extremely difficult to guess even the order of the quantities involved. Furthermore, the real cost of experimenting would involve not only direct expenses but also the cost of denying facilities to other projects which might yield even greater gain. In these circumstances the approach outlined above would become difficult or even impossible. We can, however, still make some attempt to choose the size of experiment intelligently by selecting the scheme that gives an acceptable power curve.

To use Figure 5·2 once more, let us suppose that the known standard deviation of observations on dye receptivity is $\sigma = 1$ unit, and that it is decided to use a procedure whereby n tests are performed and the method accepted if $\bar{x}$, the mean of the tests, is greater than $\bar{x}_0 = 90$ and rejected otherwise. Then the graphs marked $n = 1$, $n = 4$, $n = 16$ are the appropriate power curves when 1, 4 and 16 tests respectively are made. These curves show the "sensitivity" of each test procedure. As would be expected, the larger the number of observations, the steeper the power curve and the more sensitive the test.

The effect of changing the critical level $\bar{x}_0$ is to shift the power curve an equal amount along the horizontal axis; for example if we decided to put the critical level $\bar{x}_0$ equal to 91 instead of to 90 the effect would be to shift the power curve along the horizontal axis by one unit. It will be seen, therefore, that by suitably adjusting the values of n and $\bar{x}_0$ the characteristics of the test as measured by the slope and position of the power curve may be chosen at will. The experimenter can therefore proceed by first deciding on the sort of power curve he wants and then finding values of n and $\bar{x}_0$ which approximately satisfy these requirements.

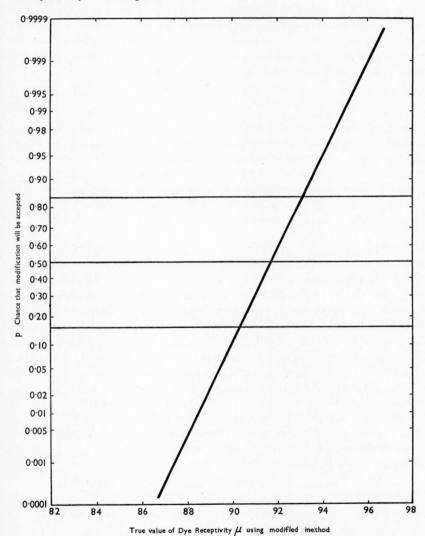

Fig. 5·3. Power curve plotted on Normal probability paper

In the example we are here considering, the power curve is simply a cumulative Normal distribution. This curve is most conveniently plotted on Normal Probability Paper, the vertical axis of which scales the probability so that any cumulative Normal curve becomes a straight line instead of the usual S-shaped curve.

In practice, therefore, the experimenter can proceed by drawing the power curve which he feels will best meet his requirements as a straight line on Normal probability paper. The values of $\bar{x}_0$ and n required to give such a power curve can then be obtained immediately from the plotted line. If μ_p is used to denote the value of μ corresponding to the probability of acceptance p, the required values of $\bar{x}_0$ and n are given by

$$\bar{x}_0 = \mu_{0\cdot50} \quad\dots\dots\dots\dots\dots\dots\dots\dots(5\cdot1)$$
$$n = \sigma^2/(\mu_{0\cdot50} - \mu_{0\cdot84})^2 \quad\dots\dots\dots\dots\dots\dots(5\cdot11)$$

where σ is the experimental error standard deviation. Expression $(5\cdot11)$ is derived from the fact that the standard deviation of the mean of the n tests is given by the reciprocal of the slope of the power curve drawn on Normal probability paper, i.e. $\sigma/\sqrt{n} = 1/\text{slope}$. Since an actual probability displacement of $0\cdot34$ on either side of $p = 0\cdot50$ corresponds to a unit displacement on the Normal probability scale, the slope is most conveniently evaluated from either $1/(\mu_{0\cdot84} - \mu_{0\cdot50})$ or $1/(\mu_{0\cdot50} - \mu_{0\cdot16})$.

Example

5·41 Suppose that the experimental error standard deviation σ is equal to 5 and that after some consideration the experimenter decides that a power curve like that in Figure 5·3 would be acceptable. Reading off some typical values it will be seen that, if a test is employed which has such a power curve, then when the true dye receptivity is as low as 88 there will only be a chance of about $0\cdot3\%$ of being led to believe that a real improvement has occurred. When the true dye receptivity is 89 this chance rises to about 2%; at 90 (when the modified method is of the same effectiveness as the standard method) it is 10%. At the value $91\cdot75$ the chances of accepting or rejecting the modification are equal. When the modified method gives a true dye receptivity of 94 the chance of accepting the modified method will be 95%, and this chance rises to 99% and $99\cdot9\%$ respectively for dye receptivities of 95 and 96.

To determine the values of $\bar{x}_0$ and n we read off the values $\mu_{0\cdot50} = 91\cdot75$ and $\mu_{0\cdot84} = 93\cdot10$, whence

$$\bar{x}_0 = 91\cdot75$$
$$n = (5/1\cdot35)^2 = 13\cdot7$$

A test with about the required characteristics is therefore provided by making 14 repeat tests. The modification should be accepted if the mean result exceeds $91\cdot75$ and rejected otherwise.

Relation to prior distribution and costs

5·42 In practice, if the power curve which the experimenter draws leads to a value of n which he feels is too large, he may decide to modify the requirements expressed by the power curve. In this way by trial and error he will eventually reach the compromise which he thinks is most reasonable. In this process of choice he will of course to some extent be subjectively taking into account such factors as the prior distribution of the amount of improvement to be expected, the possible monetary gains and losses, and the cost of experiments.

The procedure from the point of view of significance testing

5·43 An alternative—and more customary—approach to this problem is via significance tests [§ **4·6**]. In the above example, for instance, we are in effect performing an ordinary significance test, having first taken the precaution of ensuring that the sample size is large enough for important improvements nearly always to be detected.

To see that this is so it should first be noted that the power curve is fully defined as soon as we specify any two points on it. This means that although it is always wisest to plot the complete power curve, it is sufficient from the point of view of specifying the scheme for the experimenter to state the chance of accepting the proposed method for two specific values of μ. The values of $\bar{x}_0$ and n which produce a power curve passing through these two points can then be calculated.

In an example such as that now being considered it is customary to choose the two specific values of μ to be the "standard value" μ_0 and some larger value $\mu_1 = \mu_0 + \delta$ where δ is the difference that it is "important to detect." The hypothesis $\mu = \mu_0$ is then called the "Null Hypothesis," i.e. the hypothesis that the modification has no effect, and the hypothesis $\mu = \mu_1 (= \mu_0 + \delta)$ is called an "alternative hypothesis." The probabilities, i.e. the ordinates on the power curve associated with these two values of μ, are denoted by α and $1 - \beta$ respectively. The probability α is the chance that we shall conclude that an improvement on the standard value has occurred when it has not, i.e. that we shall wrongly reject the Null Hypothesis. It is in fact the familiar "significance level" and is sometimes called the chance of an error of the "first kind."

The probability β is the chance that we shall conclude that no improvement has occurred when in fact a change as large as δ has occurred, i.e. the chance that we shall wrongly accept the Null Hypothesis when in fact an important difference has occurred. This value β is sometimes called the chance of an error of the "second kind."

It is readily demonstrated that if the standard deviation is σ, then the number of observations n and the critical value $\bar{x}_0$ appropriate to ensure that the power curve passes through the points (α, μ_0), and $(1 - \beta, \mu_0 + \delta)$ are

$$n = \{(u_\alpha + u_\beta)\sigma/\delta\}^2 \quad\dots\dots\dots\dots\dots\dots\dots\dots\dots(5·2)$$

$$\bar{x}_0 = \mu_0 + u_\alpha\sigma/\sqrt{n} \quad\dots\dots\dots\dots\dots\dots\dots\dots(5·21)$$

or equivalently $\bar{x}_0 = \{u_\alpha(\mu_0 + \delta) + u_\beta\mu_0\}/(u_\alpha + u_\beta) \dots\dots\dots\dots(5·22)$

where u_α and u_β are Normal deviates associated with the probabilities α and β.

The quantity $\bar{x}_0 = \mu_0 + u_\alpha\sigma/\sqrt{n}$ in Equation (5·21) is the familiar value with which $\bar{x}$ must be compared in a simple test of significance at the α level of probability. Thus what we are doing is to make an ordinary test of significance at the probability level α, having chosen n large enough to ensure that there is only a small probability β of an improvement of size δ being overlooked.

Example

5·44 Suppose as before that $\mu_0 = 90$, $\sigma = 5$, and that it has been decided that the probability of wrongly asserting that an improvement has occurred should be not more than $\alpha = 0·10$. Suppose further than an increase of $\delta = 4$ units would be of such importance that we want the probability of failing to detect it to be not more than $\beta = 0·05$. From Table A we find $u_\alpha = u_{0·10} = 1·28$ and $u_\beta = u_{0·05} = 1·64$. Thus we have, on substituting in Equations (5·2) and (5·21):

$$n = \{(1·28 + 1·64)1·25\}^2 = 3·65^2 = 13·3$$

$$\bar{x}_0 = 90 + 1·28 \times 5/3·65 = 91·75$$

It will be noted that, since the points $(0·10, 90)$, $(0·95, 94)$ are both on the power curve of Figure 5·3, this scheme and the previous one discussed in § **5·41** are in fact identical. The slight departure from the value of n found before arises from the slight uncertainty in reading the graph. Our scheme is therefore equivalent to testing whether the mean of a sample of 14 observations is significantly greater than 90; if it is, the modification is accepted; if not, the modification is rejected.

Single- and double-sided tests

5·45 In the above example we were concerned only with whether μ had or had not increased. A decrease in the mean was of no special interest, since the action required (that of rejecting the modification) would be the same whether a harmful negative effect or no effect whatever were produced by the modification. Such a test is called a *single-sided* test. In other circumstances we might be interested in a change in either direction. For example, the analysis of a chemical may have to lie within given limits, plus or minus, an excessive deviation in either direction being undesirable. This is called a *double-sided* test.

Example: Specification of an organic product

5·46 The specification for a particular organic product states that its true hydroxyl value μ should lie within the range $13·4 \pm 0·2\%$ by weight. As a result of many sets of repeat determinations the standard deviation of the error due to sampling and testing was known to be 0·085%. A procedure for testing the product was required which would ensure with high probability that off-grade material would not be despatched and that good material would not be rejected.

For the single-sided situation the test procedure was specified by two values, n and $\bar{x}_0$. In the double-sided test, on the other hand, we clearly need three values, these being the number n of repeat tests to be performed on each consignment, and *two* critical values which we may denote by $\bar{x}_{0-}$ and $\bar{x}_{0+}$. So long as $\bar{x}$ lies between the values $\bar{x}_{0-}$ and $\bar{x}_{0+}$ we conclude that no important change has occurred from the value μ_0; when $\bar{x}$ exceeds $\bar{x}_{0+}$ we conclude that it is out of specification on the *high* side, while if it falls short of $\bar{x}_{0-}$ we conclude that it is out of specification on the *low* side.

The procedure we adopt is equivalent to applying two separate tests, one for an increase and one for a decrease. The power curve for the joint test has the appearance shown in Figure 5·4. The full line representing the joint power curve simply shows the sum of the two probabilities read from the two straight-line graphs. These straight-line graphs are the power curves for the separate tests and are shown by dotted lines where they are distinguishable from the full line. For the low values of μ almost the whole contribution to the probability of rejection comes from the chance that the product will not be accepted because the mean $\bar{x}$ has *too low* a value. This chance is represented by the straight line on the left of the diagram. Conversely for high values of μ almost the whole contribution to the probability of rejection arises from the chance that the product will not be accepted because the mean $\bar{x}$ of the results has too high a value. This chance is represented by the straight line on the right-hand side of the diagram. Only in the neighbourhood of the minimum value is the influence of both probabilities felt, and the value at the minimum corresponding to μ_0, where the straight lines cross, is in fact twice the value read from either straight-line graph. This corresponds to the fact that when $\mu = \mu_0$ the probability α that the consignment will be (wrongly) rejected is made up of two parts—a chance $\frac{1}{2}\alpha$ that it will be rejected because $\bar{x}$ exceeds $\bar{x}_{0+}$ and a chance $\frac{1}{2}\alpha$ that it will be rejected because $\bar{x}$ falls short of $\bar{x}_{0-}$.

To devise a suitable scheme, therefore, the experimenter should as before first draw the power curve that he feels will be suitable. This is done by drawing two straight lines in a V shape on Normal probability paper, equally inclined to the vertical and crossing at the value $\mu = \mu_0$. He does this bearing in mind the fact that the probability of rejection at $\mu = \mu_0$ will be twice the value shown at the intersection of the straight lines, and apart from the region around μ_0 the power curve will closely follow the straight lines. The values of n and $\bar{x}_0$ for a test corresponding to each separate straight line power curve are

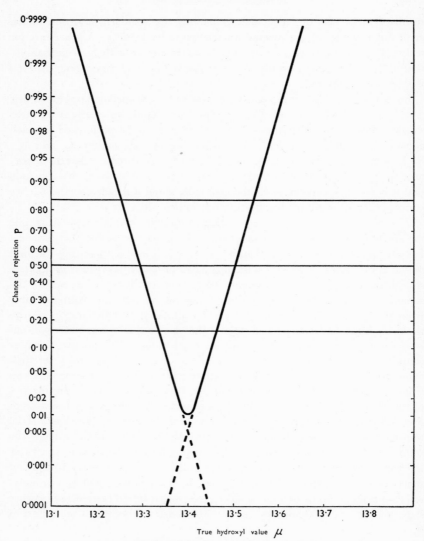

Fig. 5·4. Power curve for double-sided test

then determined. The value of n is of course the same for each test, and this is the value to be adopted. The two values of $\bar{x}_0$ are labelled $\bar{x}_{0+}$ and $\bar{x}_{0-}$, and these supply the required pair of critical values.

For example, suppose the experimenter decided that a power curve like that in Figure 5·4 would meet his requirements. To determine the appropriate test we note from the straight line on the right-hand side of the figure that $\mu_{0\cdot50} = 13\cdot505$ and $\mu_{0\cdot84} = 13\cdot545$. Since we are told that $\sigma = 0\cdot085$ we have from Formulae (*5·1*) and (*5·11*)

$$\bar{x}_{0+} = 13\cdot505$$
$$n = (0\cdot085/0\cdot040)^2 = 2\cdot125^2 = 4\cdot5$$

Similarly from the left-hand straight line we have $\mu_{0\cdot50} = 13\cdot295$ and $\mu_{0\cdot84} = 13\cdot255$, whence

$$\bar{x}_{0-} = 13\cdot295$$
$$n = (0\cdot085/0\cdot040)^2 = 4\cdot5 \text{ (as before)}$$

The value $\bar{x}_{0-}$ could alternatively be obtained by symmetry.

Five analyses are therefore required. Since n has been rounded up to 5, the risks will be rather less than those specified.

Consider this example from the alternative viewpoint of the significance test. Three points are now needed to define the power curve, and these are taken to be $(\beta, \mu_0 - \delta)$, (α, μ_0) and $(\beta, \mu_0 + \delta)$. The value β is dependent on the risk we are prepared to run of failing to detect an important difference $\pm \delta$ from the value μ_0. As before, α is the risk we are prepared to run of wrongly asserting that the Null Hypothesis $\mu = \mu_0$ is untrue. It is composed of a part $\tfrac{1}{2}\alpha$, which is the risk of rejecting the Null Hypothesis and saying that an *increase* in μ has occurred, and of a second part $\tfrac{1}{2}\alpha$ which is the risk of rejecting the Null Hypothesis and saying that a *decrease* in μ has occurred. Using Formulae (*5·2*) and (*5·21*):

$$n = \{(u_{\frac{1}{2}\alpha} + u_\beta)\sigma/\delta\}^2 \quad \dots\dots\dots\dots\dots\dots(5\cdot3)$$
$$\bar{x}_{0+} = \mu_0 + u_{\frac{1}{2}\alpha}\sigma/\sqrt{n} \dots\dots\dots\dots\dots\dots\dots(5\cdot31)$$
$$\bar{x}_{0-} = \mu_0 - u_{\frac{1}{2}\alpha}\sigma/\sqrt{n} \dots\dots\dots\dots\dots\dots\dots(5\cdot32)$$

The requirements could be expressed by saying that n observations should be made, where n is given by Formula (*5·3*), and if the mean $\bar{x}$ is greater than μ_0 it should be tested at the level $\tfrac{1}{2}\alpha$ to find whether it is significantly greater than μ_0, whereas if it is less it should be tested at the level $\tfrac{1}{2}\alpha$ to see if it is significantly less than μ_0.

The scheme we have given above would have been arrived at, for example, if it had been decided that if the true hydroxyl value μ_0 were 13·4 the risk of rejection should be not more than $\alpha = 0\cdot01$, and if it deviated from 13·4 by more than $\delta = 0\cdot2$, that is if the product was outside specification, the risk of acceptance (and hence passing the batch for despatch) should be not more than $\beta = 0\cdot01$.

Since $u_{\frac{1}{2}\alpha} = u_{0\cdot005} = 2\cdot58$; $u_\beta = u_{0\cdot01} = 2\cdot33$, we have

$$n = \{0\cdot425(2\cdot58 + 2\cdot33)\}^2 = (2\cdot087)^2 = 4\cdot4$$
$$\bar{x}_{0+} = 13\cdot4 + 2\cdot58 \times 0\cdot085/2\cdot087 = 13\cdot505$$
$$\bar{x}_{0-} = 13\cdot4 - 2\cdot58 \times 0\cdot085/2\cdot087 = 13\cdot295$$

Again, apart from a small difference in n due to uncertainty in reading the graph, the results are identical with those obtained before.

Comparison of two means

5·5 So far we have discussed only the situation where a single method giving a true mean value μ was to be evaluated. This was done by comparing the observed mean $\bar{x}$ with a critical level $\bar{x}_0$, or in the case of a "two-sided situation" with two critical levels $\bar{x}_{0-}$ and $\bar{x}_{0+}$. Frequently we have two methods to compare. Suppose μ_1 is the true mean for the first method and μ_2 the true mean for the second. Then, since the quantity of interest is the difference $\mu = \mu_2 - \mu_1$, the problem becomes of the same form as discussed before. In fact we have to consider the observed difference $\bar{x} = \bar{x}_2 - \bar{x}_1$ in relation to a critical value of the difference $\bar{x}_0$ (or in the case of a two-sided situation to two critical values $\bar{x}_{0-}$ and $\bar{x}_{0+}$). The experimenter proceeds as before by first plotting on Normal probability paper the power curve which he feels the test should have. From this the required test specification is readily derived.

Single-sided test situation

5·51 Consider the single-sided situation first. Here the question asked is of the kind "Is the mean value obtained from method 2 greater by an important amount than the mean obtained from method 1?" To resolve this question predetermined numbers of observations n_1 and n_2 would be made with the two methods, and the mean difference $\bar{x} = \bar{x}_2 - \bar{x}_1$ in the results would be compared with a critical value $\bar{x}_0$. If $\bar{x}$ was greater than $\bar{x}_0$ the conclusion would be drawn that method 2 was better, otherwise it would be concluded that no real difference of importance existed. The power curve would show the chance of reaching the conclusion that method 2 was better than method 1 for any value of μ, the true difference.

As before, the critical value $\bar{x}_0$ of the difference would be given by reading off the value $\mu_{0·50}$ from the chosen power curve. Also, since the standard deviation of the observed mean difference $\bar{x}_2 - \bar{x}_1$ is $(\sigma_1^2/n_1 + \sigma_2^2/n_2)^{\frac{1}{2}}$, the values of n_1 and n_2 necessary to give the chosen power curve would be such as to satisfy Equation (5·11), that is,

$$(\sigma_1^2/n_1 + \sigma_2^2/n_2)^{\frac{1}{2}} = \mu_{0·84} - \mu_{0·50} \quad \cdots \cdots \cdots \cdots (5·4)$$

We have assumed that σ_1 and σ_2, the standard deviations of observations arising from the two methods, are known in advance. Clearly a variety of values of n_1 and n_2 can be found which satisfy (5·4). It is readily shown that the smallest total $(n_1 + n_2)$ is obtained by arranging that $n_1/n_2 = \sigma_1/\sigma_2$. In this case

$$n_1 = \sigma_1(\sigma_1 + \sigma_2)/(\mu_{0·84} - \mu_{0·50})^2 \quad \cdots \cdots \cdots \cdots (5·41)$$
$$n_2 = \sigma_2(\sigma_1 + \sigma_2)/(\mu_{0·84} - \mu_{0·50})^2 \quad \cdots \cdots \cdots \cdots (5·42)$$

Often σ_1 and σ_2 would be expected to be equal; if their common value is denoted by σ the number of observations is then given by

$$n_1 = n_2 = 2\sigma^2/(\mu_{0·84} - \mu_{0·50})^2 \quad \cdots \cdots \cdots \cdots (5·43)$$

Double-sided test situation

5·52   When the question is "Is there evidence that method 2 *differs* from method 1 by an important amount?" we have the double-sided test situation where we are equally interested in a negative and a positive difference μ. We deal with this situation exactly as before. A V-shaped power curve built up from two straight lines equally inclined to the vertical is drawn on Normal probability paper. The critical values $\bar{x}_{0-}$ and $\bar{x}_{0+}$ may be read off immediately as the points on the component straight lines corresponding to the 0·50 probability ordinate. Appropriate values for n_1 and n_2 are obtained as before, using Equation (5·4) and substituting values of $\mu_{0·84}$ and $\mu_{0·50}$ from either of the straight-line components of the V-shaped power curve.

Procedure from the viewpoint of significance testing

5·53   Consideration from the viewpoint of significance testing closely follows that discussed above. In this approach the test procedure is chosen to give a power curve passing through the points $(\alpha, 0)$ and $(1 - \beta, \delta)$ in the single-sided test situation, or $(1 - \beta, - \delta)$, $(\alpha, 0)$ and $(1 - \beta, \delta)$ in the double-sided test situation. This is done as usual by choosing first the difference δ which it is important to detect, and then assigning suitable values to α and β.

In the single-sided situation the appropriate formulae from which n_1, n_2 and $\bar{x}_0$ can be calculated are

$$\sigma_1{}^2/n_1 + \sigma_2{}^2/n_2 = \delta^2/(u_\alpha + u_\beta)^2 \dots\dots\dots\dots\dots(5\cdot5)$$
$$\bar{x}_0 = u_\alpha(\sigma_1{}^2/n_1 + \sigma_2{}^2/n_2)^{\frac{1}{2}} \dots\dots\dots\dots\dots(5\cdot51)$$

For the double-sided situation they are

$$\sigma_1{}^2/n_1 + \sigma_2{}^2/n_2 = \delta^2/(u_{\frac{1}{2}\alpha} + u_\beta)^2 \dots\dots\dots\dots(5\cdot52)$$
$$\bar{x}_0 = \pm\, u_{\frac{1}{2}\alpha}(\sigma_1{}^2/n_1 + \sigma_2{}^2/n_2)^{\frac{1}{2}} \dots\dots\dots\dots(5\cdot53)$$

As before, important special cases of the formulae occur when n_1/n_2 is put equal to σ_1/σ_2 and when $\sigma_1 = \sigma_2$.

Standard deviation not precisely known

5·6   It is obvious that if nothing is known of the standard deviation we can make no statement whatever about the number of observations needed. Conversely when σ, or in the case of two groups σ_1 and σ_2, are precisely known the number of observations to provide a test with a given power curve can be calculated exactly. We have supposed that values of the standard deviation postulated in advance were entirely reliable and were used not only in planning the experiment but also in making the test itself. In practice the information concerning σ prior to the experiment is seldom exact and in some cases amounts to little more than a guess. For this reason, having obtained the number of observations by the method described, the experimenter may choose to make the actual significance test using the estimates of the standard deviation obtained from the results themselves. To test the Null Hypothesis it will then be appropriate to use the t-test rather than the Normal Curve test. For example, if this were done in comparing a mean $\bar{x}$ with the standard value μ_0 the actual critical value used would not be $\bar{x}_0 = \mu_0 + u_a\sigma/\sqrt{n}$ as in Equation $(5\cdot21)$ but $\bar{x}_0 = \mu_0 + t_a s/\sqrt{n}$ where t_a is the deviate of the t-distribution corresponding to the probability a as given by Table C. By proceeding in this way the experimenter ensures that the risk is precisely a that the Null Hypothesis will be wrongly rejected and therefore ensures that the ordinate of the power curve is correct at the point $\mu = \mu_0$. Whether or not the true power curve is close to that desired at other values of μ will entirely depend on the accuracy of the initial estimate of σ. When it is clear from an unexpectedly large size of the estimate s that σ has been underestimated a further sample should be taken using the estimate s to decide its magnitude. The two sets of observations should then be combined in making the final test. This use of the ordinary significance tables in making a two-stage test is not strictly valid but provides a fair approximation in most cases.

Choosing the number of observations in comparing standard deviations

5·7 Not infrequently the quantity of interest is not the mean but the variability or spread associated with a given measurement or method. For example, we may wish to compare the precisions of two analytical methods, or the variabilities in strength of yarn produced by two different methods.

When the original observations are approximately Normally distributed an appropriate criterion for the comparison of variability is the variance ratio $F = s_1^2/s_2^2$, or equivalently the ratio of the standard deviations $L = s_1/s_2$ $= \sqrt{F}$, or again equivalently the logarithm of this latter ratio $z = \ln (s_1/s_2)$ $= \frac{1}{2} \ln F$, where ln denotes the Napierian logarithm. Since these three criteria are all functions of s_1/s_2, exactly the same results will be obtained whichever is used. However, it is most convenient to use the quantity z for the purpose of deciding the number of observations because, unlike the other criteria, z is approximately Normally distributed with variance independent of the ratio σ_1/σ_2 of the true values. This approximation is satisfactory provided the numbers of degrees of freedom ϕ_1 and ϕ_2 on which the estimates s_1 and s_2 are based are not too small, say each not less than 10. Since also the mean value of z is linearly related to $\ln (\sigma_1/\sigma_2)$ the power curve for the variance test can be approximately represented by a straight line on Logarithmic Probability Paper as shown in Figure 5·5. Using this fact we can apply the same method as before to determine the appropriate numbers of observations.

Comparison of analytical methods

5·71 Suppose for example that two methods of analysis are to be compared. Suppose method 1 is simpler to perform than method 2, and consequently it is felt that method 1 should be chosen unless it can be demonstrated that

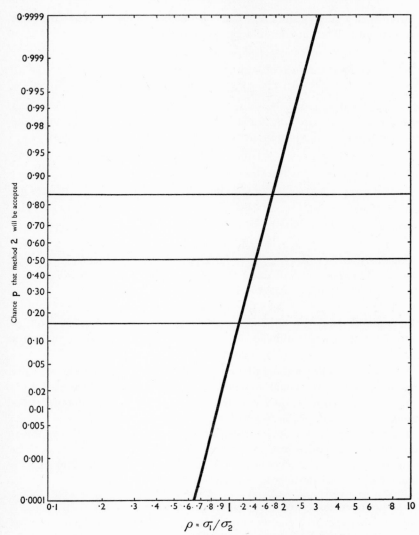

Fig. 5·5. Power curve for comparison of standard deviations

it is considerably less accurate than method 2. The subjective feelings contained in this statement may be expressed by the experimenter in quantitative form by drawing a graph on logarithmic probability paper like that shown in Figure 5·5. This incorporates the experimenter's ideas on what he feels the chances of accepting method 2 should be for various values of the ratio $\rho = \sigma_1/\sigma_2$.

From such a graph a suitable scheme can be determined in much the same way as before. The variance of z can be shown to be

$$\sigma_z{}^2 = \tfrac{1}{2}\{1/(\phi_1 - 1) + 1/(\phi_2 - 1)\}$$

Also the required variance of z implied by the choice of power curve is

$$\sigma_z{}^2 = (\ln \rho_{0\cdot84} - \ln \rho_{0\cdot50})^2$$

where $\rho_{0\cdot84}$ and $\rho_{0\cdot50}$ are the values of ρ corresponding to the probabilities 0·84 and 0·50. By equating these two expressions we obtain the following equation, from which appropriate values of ϕ_1 and ϕ_2 can be obtained:

$$\tfrac{1}{2}\{1/(\phi_1 - 1) + 1/(\phi_2 - 1)\} = \{\ln (\rho_{0\cdot84}/\rho_{0\cdot50})\}^2 \quad \dots \dots (5\cdot6)$$

and the critical value for the observed z is

$$z_0 = \ln \rho_{0\cdot50} \quad \dots \dots \dots \dots \dots \dots (5\cdot61)$$

The smallest total number of observations is obtained when $\phi_1 = \phi_2$. Denoting this common value by ϕ, it follows from Equation $(5\cdot6)$ that

$$\phi = 1 + 1/\{\ln (\rho_{0\cdot84}/\rho_{0\cdot50})\}^2 \quad \dots \dots \dots \dots (5\cdot62)$$

For this specific example $\rho_{0\cdot84} = 1\cdot73$, $\rho_{0\cdot50} = 1\cdot40$, whence $\ln (\rho_{0\cdot84}/\rho_{0\cdot50}) = 0\cdot21$. Thus we need to make sufficient observations to obtain variance estimates each having ϕ degrees of freedom where

$$\phi = 1 + 1/0\cdot21^2 = 23\cdot7$$

The required number n of observations in each group is therefore 24·7, or 25 to the nearest whole number, and the critical value for making the test is

$$z_0 = \ln 1\cdot40 = 0\cdot34$$

Thus 25 observations should be made with each method of analysis. The quantity $z = \ln (s_1/s_2)$ should then be calculated and method 2 accepted if the value of z exceeds 0·34, otherwise rejected. Equivalently we may refer the ratio $s_1{}^2/s_2{}^2$ to tables of the F-distribution.

The procedure for the double-sided situation simply involves the combination of two single-sided test procedures. When a single estimate s_1 is to be compared with a "precisely known" value σ_2 the approximate value of ϕ_1 is obtained simply by putting $\phi_2 = \infty$ in Equation $(5\cdot6)$.

Procedure from the viewpoint of significance testing

5·72 In this approach the test procedure is chosen to give a power curve passing through the points $(\alpha, 1)$ and $(1 - \beta, R)$, where R is a ratio of the standard deviations which is important in the sense that we wish to run only a small risk β of failing to detect it.

Appropriate values of ϕ_1 and ϕ_2 are then related by

$$\tfrac{1}{2}\{1/(\phi_1 - 1) + 1/(\phi_2 - 1)\} = \{(\ln R)/(u_\alpha + u_\beta)\}^2 \quad \dots \dots (5\cdot7)$$

and the critical value of z is

$$z_0 = \frac{1}{\sqrt{2}}u_\alpha\{1/(\phi_1 - 1) + 1/(\phi_2 - 1)\}^{\frac{1}{2}} \dots \dots \dots \dots (5\cdot71)$$

If it is decided to make the groups of equal size, the common value ϕ is given by

$$\phi = 1 + \left\{ \frac{u_a + u_\beta}{\ln R} \right\}^2$$

and

$$z_0 = u_a/(\phi - 1)^{\frac{1}{2}}$$

For the double-sided situation we require the power curve to pass through the three points $(1 - \beta, 1/R)$, $(a, 1)$ and $(1 - \beta, R)$ and the appropriate formulae are obtained by replacing a by $\frac{1}{2}a$ in Equations (5·7) and (5·71).

To illustrate the use of these formulae, suppose that in the previous example the experimenter had decided that if the standard deviations σ_1 and σ_2 were equal (that is, ρ was unity) he would wish to run only a small risk $a = 0.05$ of choosing method 2. If on the other hand σ_1 was twice as large as σ_2, so that $\rho = 2$, he would wish to take a risk of only $\beta = 0.05$ of not choosing method 2. Substituting these values, we have

$$\phi = 1 + \left(\frac{3.29}{0.693} \right)^2 = 1 + 4.75^2$$

$$= 23.6$$

whence

$$n = 24.6$$

The conclusion is as before that we should include 25 observations in each group. This is to be expected, since the power curve of Figure 5·5 passes through the points $(0.05, 1)$ and $(0.95, 2)$.

The value z_0 is 0.346, and the final comparison of z with z_0 is of course equivalent to a test of significance at the level a and can be carried out without approximation either by employing the exact z tables as given, for example, in [5·7] or by using either of the equivalent tests with the criteria $F = s_1{}^2/s_2{}^2$ or $L = s_1/s_2$.

REFERENCES

[5·1] BRUNT, D. *The Combination of Observations*. Cambridge University Press (1931).

[5·2] BARNARD, G. A. "Sampling Inspection and Statistical Decisions," *J. Roy. Stat. Soc.*, B, **16**, 151 (1954).

[5·3] YATES, F. "Principles governing the Amount of Experimentation in Developmental Work," *Nature*, **170**, 138 (1952).

[5·4] GRUNDY, P. M., HEALY, M. J. R., and REES, D. H. "Decision between Two Alternatives—How Many Experiments?" *Biometrics*, **10**, 317 (1954).

[5·5] GRUNDY, P. M., HEALY, M. J. R., and REES, D. H. "Economic Choice of Amount of Experimentation," *J. Roy. Stat. Soc.*, B, **18**, 32 (1956).

[5·6] PEARSON, E. S., and HARTLEY, H. O. *Biometrika Tables for Statisticians*, **1**. Cambridge University Press (1954).

[5·7] FISHER, R. A., and YATES, F. *Statistical Tables for Biological, Agricultural and Medical Research* (fifth edition). Oliver and Boyd (Edinburgh and London, 1957).

CHAPTER 6

ANALYSIS OF VARIANCE

In this chapter the Analysis of Variance is described. This is a
technique by which the variations associated with defined sources
may be isolated and estimated. For example, a group of chemical
test results from different samples of the same material may contain differences associated with sampling as well as differences
associated with the test itself. The Analysis of Variance technique
allows the sampling variation and the testing variation to be
separated and their magnitudes estimated.

Introduction

6·1 In this chapter we consider those situations in which a result or an
observation is subject to a number of sources of variation, and the problem is
to separate and estimate these sources of variation. For instance, to assess
the average purity of a chemical product in bulk, a chemist will carry out
analyses on one or more samples taken from the bulk. The method of
analysis may not be perfectly reproducible, and so repeat analyses will vary;
the material, also, may not be perfectly homogeneous, and so repeat samples
will differ among themselves. If in such a case one analysis on one sample is
used as an estimate of the average purity of the bulk, this estimate will be
subject to two types of errors, that arising in the analysis and that arising in
the sampling.

Similar problems may arise in all types of processes—testing processes or
manufacturing processes—which involve more than one stage. For instance,
the test for the effectiveness of a waterproofing treatment involves three
distinct stages, each of which contributes to the overall error of the test.
These sources of error are:

(i) Variation in the fabric which has to be treated with the waterproofing
agent.

(ii) Variation in applying the treatment.

(iii) Error in the assessment of the water repellency.

In manufacturing processes there are usually three types of variation
which contribute to the variation in yield or quality of the final product.
These are:

(i) Variation in the quality of one or more of the raw materials.

(ii) Variation in operating conditions of the process at one or more stages.

(iii) Error arising in sampling and testing the finished product or in
estimating the yield.

Additive property of variances

6·11 When two or more independent sources of variation operate, the resulting variance is the sum of the separate variances [§ **3·71**]. The two types of errors which arise when estimating the property of a bulk chemical are:

(i) Errors of sampling with variance denoted by σ_1^2.

(ii) Errors of analysis with variance denoted by σ_0^2.

These sources of error operate independently, and the total variation may be obtained by simple addition of the two. This means that, when the result of one analysis on one random sample is used as an estimate of the quality of the bulk, this estimate will have an error variance of:

$$\sigma^2 = \sigma_1^2 + \sigma_0^2 \quad \dots\dots\dots\dots\dots\dots\dots\dots\dots (6\cdot1)$$

To determine the variances exactly would require an infinite number of observations; in practice the variances can only be estimated from a finite number of observations, and it is these estimates which have to be used in Formula $(6\cdot1)$ to derive an estimate of the combined variance. The additive property applies to the true values of the variances, and is never completely realised by estimates based on a finite number of observations. Errors of estimation can be considerable for small samples.

Estimates of variances are denoted by the symbol s^2 with the appropriate suffix. The estimate of the variance for one analysis on one sample is then:

$$s^2 = s_1^2 + s_0^2 \quad \dots\dots\dots\dots\dots\dots\dots\dots (6\cdot11)$$

When n analyses are carried out on the sample and the results averaged, the variance from this source is reduced to σ_0^2/n, and the variance of the mean result when used as an estimate of the average value of the bulk is:

$$\sigma_1^2 + \sigma_0^2/n$$

When m samples are taken from the bulk and n analyses carried out on each, the variance of the mean is:

$$(\sigma_1^2 + \sigma_0^2/n)/m = \sigma_1^2/m + \sigma_0^2/nm$$

It will be noted that the divisor of σ_1^2 is the total number of samples, and the divisor of σ_0^2 is the total number of analyses. To use these formulae in practice we have to substitute estimated values for the σ's. When different numbers of analyses are made on the samples the result is more complicated, and the appropriate treatment is considered in Appendix 6A. It is worth while mentioning here that the precision of a result from any sampling and testing scheme can be assessed and the best scheme derived. This also is considered in Appendix 6A and in § **6·53**.

Types of classification

6·2 The Analysis of Variance is essentially a method of analysing the variance to which a response is subject, into its various components corresponding to the sources of variation which can be identified. The data must

H

clearly contain information on any given source of variation before its contribution can be estimated, and as a rule these components are best estimated from experiments which have been designed for this purpose. The procedure to be used in the application of the Analysis of Variance will depend on the number and nature of the independent causes of variation which can be identified. It is always possible to classify the data with respect to each such source of variation, and a complete classification is a necessary first step in the analysis.

There are two general types of classification with which we shall deal in this book. One type has already been illustrated in the sampling and testing example discussed in § **6·11**, in which a bulk chemical is sampled a number of times and repeat analyses are carried out on each. This scheme can be represented by a series of branching lines as in Figure 6·1. This is called the Hierarchic Classification.

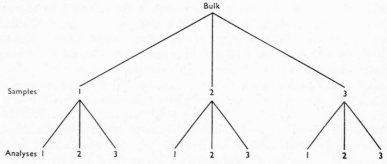

Fig. 6·1. Hierarchic classification

6·21   The second general type of classification, called the Cross-Classification, is one in which each observation can be classified independently with respect to all sources of variation. For example, in comparing three analytical methods

Table 6·1

TWO-WAY CROSS-CLASSIFICATION

Method of Analysis	Laboratory				
	I	2	3	4	5
I					
2					
3					

for assessing the amount of a particular impurity in a product, samples from the same material were analysed by the three methods in five laboratories. There are here two sources of variations—laboratory and method of analysis—and these can be displayed by means of a two-way table.

The results obtained from each laboratory can be entered in the appropriate cells of Table 6·1; they are then classified with respect to both methods and laboratories. Classification can still be carried out when some laboratories do not use all three methods; in such a case a proportion of cells in the table will be blank. This type of classification can readily be extended to three or more sources of variation. For example, if more than one sample or material is analysed, a table such as the above can be constructed for each sample and a three-way table results. The data are then classified with respect to three sources of variation.

6·22 More complicated classifications exist which are combinations of these two basic types, for example a two-way table in which some cells contain two or more observations.

The most satisfactory way to acquire a working knowledge and understanding of the methods used in Analysis of Variance is to work out fully a number of typical examples. The treatment in this chapter is of limited scope, intended mainly to illustrate principles and basic methods of analysis; the examples, however, are of the kind most frequently encountered in the chemical industry. Two of these are of the hierarchic type, the first with one criterion of classification and the second with two. The third is the simplest form of a cross-classification, and the final example is also a cross-classification but with several results in each cell; it is the simplest form combining both methods of classification. Further examples involving a larger number of sources of variations are treated in "Design and Analysis."

Nature of variation

6·23 Irrespective of the way in which the data may be classified, there are two kinds of problems to which the Analysis of Variance has been applied, and these are distinguished by the nature of the separate sources of variation. In one, the individual items examined can be regarded as a random sample from a Universe of such items, and the purpose of the analysis is to estimate the variance of the Universe. The first illustration given above is of this type, since the repeat analytical tests on each sample of material can be regarded as random elements from a Universe of analytical tests whose variation is completely specified by the variance σ_0^2. Similarly, the repeat samples from the bulk can be regarded as random elements from a Universe of such samples whose variation is completely specified by the variance σ_1^2. The purpose of the experiment is to estimate σ_0^2 and σ_1^2.

In the other kind of problem we are interested in specific comparisons between the items tested. For instance, suppose it is necessary to compare the purity of batches of a chemical product manufactured by three different processes and that each batch is sampled and analysed several times. The source of variation which we can designate as "between batches," which may be assumed to be due mainly to changes in the method of manufacture, is of a different kind from that due to sampling and analytical errors. Even if a Universe of batches can be postulated it is of no interest, because we require only to compare the three specific batches with each other; that is, we require to compare means and not to estimate variances—a simple extension of the problem of comparing two group means which was considered in Chapter 4.

The two problems dealt with by the Analysis of Variance are referred to respectively as Estimation of Variances and Comparison of Mean Values. The arithmetical procedures are similar for the two cases; they differ only in the final stage and in the interpretation.

SEPARATION AND ESTIMATION OF VARIANCES

Analysis of variance of hierarchic data

6·3 The simplest form of hierarchic data involves only one classification, and an illustration has already been given [§ **6·11**] in which several samples are taken from a bulk suspected to be variable, and a number of analytical tests carried out on each sample. The purpose of the analysis is to separate and estimate the variances due to testing and to sampling. Only the general principles involved in the derivation of the methods of analysis will be dealt with here; the full step-by-step details of the recommended methods are given in Appendix 6B.

Estimation of analytical error variance

6·31 Suppose there are k samples and n repeat analyses on each, giving a total number of analyses $N = kn$. The analytical error is responsible for the variation in the repeat analyses on each sample; denote its variance by σ_0^2. A method of estimating σ_0^2 has already been considered in § 3·31, and a summary is given as follows:

Denote the observations on the ith sample by $(x_{i1}, x_{i2}, \ldots, x_{in})$ with mean $\bar{x}_i$. The sum of squares about the mean is $\sum\limits_{j=1}^{n} (x_{ij} - \bar{x}_i)^2$, which has $n - 1$ degrees of freedom. The estimate of the variance of analytical error based on this sample is then $\sum\limits_{j=1}^{n} (x_{ij} - \bar{x}_i)^2/(n - 1)$. A similar expression can be obtained for each sample, and on the reasonable assumption that the analytical error does not vary from sample to sample, the variances may be combined as shown in § **3·341**. Accordingly σ_0^2 is estimated by:

Total of the sums of squares about the sample means

$$\overline{\text{Total of the degrees of freedom}}$$

$$= \sum_{i=1}^{k} \sum_{j=1}^{n} (x_{ij} - \bar{x}_i)^2 / k(n-1) \dots \dots (6 \cdot 2)$$

The numerator is referred to as the sum of squares within samples. An alternative expression for this more convenient for computation is:

$$\sum_{i=1}^{k} \sum_{j=1}^{n} x_{ij}^2 - \sum_{i=1}^{k} (\sum_{j=1}^{n} x_{ij})^2 / n \dots \dots \dots \dots \dots (6 \cdot 21)$$

The first term is the sum of squares of each of the nk observations and the second is the sum of the squares of each sample total divided by n.

In combining the sums of squares within each sample to obtain an estimate of the experimental error, the tacit assumption is made that the system of chance causes resulting in the experimental error is the same for all the samples. There is usually no reason for supposing that this is not the case in sampling and testing problems. Even if there is reason for expecting the variances to differ for the various groups, the estimate for σ_0^2 will still be an estimate of the average experimental error variance.

Such situations could arise when different analysts or different methods of analysis are used. It may then be required to compare the variances for the different analysts or methods; this is a separate problem which has already been considered for two sets of results in § **4·31**. An extension of the method for comparing the variances from more than two sets is considered in Appendix 6D.

Estimation of the sampling error variance

6·32   Let the means of the samples be $\bar{x}_1, \bar{x}_2, \ldots, \bar{x}_k$ and the grand mean $\bar{x}$. The variance between the sample means is simply

$$\sum_{i=1}^{k} (\bar{x}_i - \bar{x})^2 / (k-1) \dots \dots \dots \dots \dots (6 \cdot 3)$$

Denoting the variance due to sampling error by σ_1^2, the variance of the mean of n tests on any one sample is:

$$\sigma_1^2 + \sigma_0^2 / n \dots \dots \dots \dots \dots \dots (6 \cdot 4)$$

Expression $(6 \cdot 3)$ is therefore an estimate of $(6 \cdot 4)$. If we multiply $(6 \cdot 3)$ and $(6 \cdot 4)$ by n we obtain:

$$n \sum_{i=1}^{k} (\bar{x}_i - \bar{x})^2 / (k-1) \rightarrow n\sigma_1^2 + \sigma_0^2 \dots \dots \dots \dots (6 \cdot 5)$$

where the arrow denotes "is an estimate of."*

* An arrow is sometimes also used in this book to denote "is estimated by," but it is clear from the context which is meant.

The expression $n \sum\limits_{i=1}^{k} (\bar{x}_i - \bar{x})^2$ is referred to as "the sum of squares between samples." An alternative expression for this sum of squares more suitable for computing is:

$$\sum_{i=1}^{k} (\sum_{j=1}^{n} x_{ij})^2/n - (\sum_{i=1}^{k} \sum_{j=1}^{n} x_{ij})^2/nk \quad \ldots\ldots\ldots\ldots\ldots(6·51)$$

Previously, Equation (6·2), we obtained:

$$\sum_{i=1}^{k} \sum_{j=1}^{n} (x_{ij} - \bar{x}_i)^2/k(n-1) \rightarrow \sigma_0^2 \quad \ldots\ldots\ldots\ldots\ldots(6·6)$$

An estimate of σ_1^2 may be obtained by solving (6·5) and (6·6). This will be dealt with more fully in § **6·35**.

6·33 Another expression required is "the total sum of squares"; this is the sum of squares of all the nk observations about the grand mean $\bar{x}$, which has $(nk - 1)$ degrees of freedom.

$$\text{Total sum of squares} = \sum_{i=1}^{k} \sum_{j=1}^{n} (x_{ij} - \bar{x})^2 \quad \ldots\ldots\ldots\ldots(6·7)$$

An alternative expression more suitable for computing is:

$$\sum_{i=1}^{k} \sum_{j=1}^{n} x_{ij}^2 - (\sum_{i=1}^{k} \sum_{j=1}^{n} x_{ij})^2/nk \quad \ldots\ldots\ldots\ldots\ldots(6·71)$$

In the expressions (6·21), (6·51) and (6·71) for the sums of squares the first terms are referred to as "the crude sum of squares" and the second terms as "the correction for the mean." It is seen that the divisor in each of the second terms is the number of observations making up the total which is squared. This is true in all hierarchic data, whether the numbers in each group are equal or unequal.

The step-by-step details of the method of analysis most suitable for numerical calculation are given in Appendix 6B·1.

Analysis of Variance table

6·34 The sums of squares and degrees of freedom "between samples," "within samples" and "total" may be set out in tabular form, called the Analysis of Variance Table, as in Table 6·2.

All three sums of squares and degrees of freedom have been derived independently. It is seen that the degrees of freedom for "Total" is the sum of the other two. When the alternative expressions (6·21), (6·51) and (6·71) are substituted for the sums of squares, it is also seen that the sum of squares for "Total" is the sum of the other two sums of squares. This is an important result: it is an expression of the additive property* of the sum of squares and

---

* This additive property of the sums of squares arises from the particular arrangement of the experiment, and cases exist where this additive property does not hold ["Design and Analysis," Chapters 6 and 11]. In all the examples dealt with in this chapter the sums of squares are additive.

Table 6·2

ANALYSIS OF VARIANCE

Source of Variation	Sum of Squares	Degrees of Freedom	Mean Square	Quantity estimated by Mean Square
Between samples	$n \sum\limits_{i=1}^{k} (\bar{x}_i - \bar{x})^2 = S_1$	$k - 1$	$S_1/(k - 1)$ $(= M_1)$	$\sigma_0{}^2 + n\sigma_1{}^2$
Within samples	$\sum\limits_{i=1}^{k} \sum\limits_{j=1}^{n} (x_{ij} - \bar{x}_i)^2 = S_0$	$k(n - 1)$	$S_0/k(n - 1)$ $(= M_0)$	$\sigma_0{}^2$
Total.. ..	$\sum\limits_{i=1}^{k} \sum\limits_{j=1}^{n} (x_{ij} - \bar{x})^2$	$nk - 1$		

of the degrees of freedom, and is of considerable importance in the Analysis of Variance technique, as will be seen in the numerical examples which follow. This arrangement of the computation, besides making clear the additive property of the sums of squares, enables a useful comparison to be made between the mean squares. The implications of this will be considered more fully in a later section.

Estimates of variances and their confidence limits

6·35 The main purpose of the Analysis of Variance is to estimate σ_0 and σ_1. It is clear from the Analysis of Variance table how these estimates may be derived. Denote by M_1 the mean square between samples, and by M_0 the mean square within samples. Then:

$$M_0 \to \sigma_0{}^2$$
$$(M_1 - M_0)/n \to \sigma_1{}^2$$

or in terms of the standard deviations:

$$\sqrt{M_0} \to \sigma_0$$
$$\sqrt{\{(M_1 - M_0)/n\}} \to \sigma_1$$

One of the most important functions of statistical methods is to provide estimates and their confidence limits. *Estimates are of little value unless we can attach at least approximate confidence limits to them.* The confidence limits for the estimate of σ_0 can be readily derived from Table H at the end of the volume [§ 4·33] by entering with $k(n - 1)$ degrees of freedom. If the multipliers for probability a are denoted by $L_1(a)$ and $L_2(a)$, then the $100(1 - 2a)\%$ confidence limits are:

$$L_1(a)\sqrt{M_0}, \qquad L_2(a)\sqrt{M_0}$$

The estimate of σ_1^2 is derived from a difference between two mean squares, and its exact confidence limits are not easy to calculate. However, exact confidence limits can be calculated for the ratio σ_1^2/σ_0^2, and multiplying these limits by the estimate of σ_0^2 will give approximate confidence limits for σ_1^2 which are sufficiently accurate for most practical purposes when, as is usually the case, the estimate of σ_0^2 is based on 10 or more degrees of freedom.

The confidence limits for the ratio σ_1^2/σ_0^2 are considered in detail in Appendix 6C, the following being a summary of the procedure:

Let $M_1/M_0 = $ ratio of the two mean squares.

$\phi_1 = $ degrees of freedom of M_1 ($= k - 1$ in Table 6·2).

$\phi_0 = $ degrees of freedom of M_0 ($= k(n - 1)$ in Table 6·2).

$L_1(a) = $ the multiplier for the lower confidence limit of the ratio of two standard deviations based on ϕ_1 and ϕ_0 degrees of freedom for probability a.

$L_2(a) = $ the corresponding multiplier for the upper confidence limit.

Then the $100(1 - 2a)\%$ confidence limits (i.e. the lower $100(1 - a)\%$ and the upper $100(1 - a)\%$ limits) for σ_1^2/σ_0^2 are

$$\frac{1}{n}\left(\frac{M_1 L_1^2}{M_0} - 1\right) \text{ and } \frac{1}{n}\left(\frac{M_1 L_2^2}{M_0} - 1\right)$$

Now, M_0 is the estimate of σ_0^2, and therefore the lower and upper confidence limits for σ_1 may be approximated by:

$$\sqrt{\{(M_1 L_1^2 - M_0)/n\}} \text{ and } \sqrt{\{(M_1 L_2^2 - M_0)/n\}}$$

the estimate for σ_1 being:

$$\sqrt{\{(M_1 - M_0)/n\}}$$

When $M_1 L_1^2 \leqslant M_0$ the lower limit must be taken as zero.

Numerical applications of the above confidence limits are given in the examples which follow.

Although these confidence limits are a little too narrow, because full allowance has not been made for the errors in using M_0 as an estimate of σ_0^2, they are sufficiently good for most practical purposes, but caution must be exercised in their interpretation when M_0 is based on fewer than 10 degrees of freedom.

Example 6·1

6·4 Before examining the further uses of the Analysis of Variance it will be helpful to illustrate the derivation of the variance components by means of a numerical example.

This example deals with an investigation to find out how much the variation from batch to batch in the quality of an intermediate product (H-acid) contributes to the variation in the yield of a dyestuff (Naphthalene Black 12B) made from it. In the experiment six samples of the intermediate, representing different batches of works manufacture, were obtained, and five preparations of the dyestuff were made in the laboratory from each sample. The equivalent yield of each preparation as grammes of standard colour was determined by dye-trial, and the results are recorded in Table 6·3.

Table 6·3

YIELDS OF NAPHTHALENE BLACK 12B

Sample No. of H-acid ..	1	2	3	4	5	6
Individual yields in grammes of standard colour	1,545	1,540	1,595	1,445	1,595	1,520
	1,440	1,555	1,550	1,440	1,630	1,455
	1,440	1,490	1,605	1,595	1,515	1,450
	1,520	1,560	1,510	1,465	1,635	1,480
	1,580	1,495	1,560	1,545	1,625	1,445
Mean	1,505	1,528	1,564	1,498	1,600	1,470

Grand mean $= 1,527 \cdot 5$ g.

The experimental error, or simply "error," is measured by the variation between the five preparations from each sample of H-acid.

Table 6·31

(Based on Table 6·3)

Sample No. of H-acid ..	1	2	3	4	5	6	
Yield − 1,400 ..	145	140	195	45	195	120	
	40	155	150	40	230	55	
	40	90	205	195	115	50	
	120	160	110	65	235	80	
	180	95	160	145	225	45	Total
1) Sum $= S$ ..	525	640	820	490	1,000	350	3,825
2) Crude Sum of Squares ..	71,025	86,350	140,250	66,900	210,000	28,350	602,875
3) Correction $= S^2/5$ ..	55,125	81,920	134,480	48,020	200,000	24,500	544,045
4) (2) − (3) = Sum of Squares about Sample Mean ..	15,900	4,430	5,770	18,880	10,000	3,850	58,830
5) Degrees of freedom ..	4	4	4	4	4	4	24

The arithmetical computations are simplified by subtracting a constant quantity from each yield so that we deal with smaller numbers. This does not affect the estimates of the variances, since these are functions of the deviations from the means. The calculation of the sum of squares for each sample is shown in Table 6·31; the initial figures in this table are derived by subtracting 1,400 from each observation.

We derive:

Sum of squares of the deviations of the observations
    from the sample means (called sum of squares
    within samples) $= 58{,}830$

Degrees of freedom within samples $= 24$ (i.e. 4 for each
                                                       sample)

Variance within samples (i.e. experimental error
    variance) $= 58{,}830/24 = 2{,}451$

To derive the other sums of squares required for the Analysis of Variance we make use of Formulae (*6·51*) and (*6·71*). The calculations are:

Correction for the grand mean $= (3{,}825)^2/30 = 487{,}687{·}5$

Sum of squares between samples $=$ total of row (**3**) less the correction for
    the grand mean $= 544{,}045 - 487{,}687{·}5 = 56{,}357{·}5$

Finally:

Sum of squares of all 30 observations about the grand mean (called the
    Total Sum of Squares) $=$ total of row (**2**) less the correction for the
    mean $= 602{,}875 - 487{,}687{·}5 = 115{,}187{·}5.$

When applying the Analysis of Variance for the first few times it is instructive to record the results in detail as in Table 6·31. However, the details given for each sample in rows (**2**), (**3**), (**4**), and (**5**) are not always required, and it is usually sufficient to quote only the quantities in the Total column.

The above calculations lead to the Analysis of Variance Table 6·32.

Note that in this table the sum of the "sums of squares" and the sum of the "degrees of freedom" of rows (**1**) and (**2**) are respectively equal to the corresponding values in the row marked Total and that these quantities have been calculated independently.

This additive property of the sums of squares may be used to simplify the arithmetical computations. Thus it is not necessary to calculate all three sums of squares: two are sufficient, and the third may be derived using the additive property. The easiest to calculate are the total sum of squares and the sum of squares between samples.

The additive property of the sums of squares is very useful in the Analysis of Variance and becomes increasingly so for more complex examples. It should not be confused with the additive law of the combined effect of several independent variances. The former is governed by an algebraic identity and must apply to any arithmetically correct calculations, while the

Table 6·32
ANALYSIS OF VARIANCE
(Based on Table 6·31)

	Source of Variation	Sum of Squares	Degrees of Freedom	Mean Square	Quantity estimated by the Mean Square*
(1)	Between Samples..	56,357·5	5	11,272	$\sigma_0^2 + 5\sigma_1^2$
(2)	Within Samples ..	58,830·0	24	2,451	σ_0^2
	Total	115,187·5	29	(3,972)	

* The multiplier for σ_1^2 is the number of observations for each sample.

latter is a property of "true" variances of infinite Universes, and is never completely realised by practical estimates of variances, which are necessarily based on a finite number of observations.

Estimates of variances

6·41 From Table 6·32 we readily deduce:

$$\sigma_0^2 \to 2,451$$
$$\sigma_1^2 \to (11,272 - 2,451)/5 = 1,764$$

Expressed as standard deviations:

$$\sigma_0 \to 49·5$$
$$\sigma_1 \to 42·0$$

These are respectively the estimates of the standard deviations of the experimental error and of the variation between batches of H-acid.

Confidence limits

6·42 For 24 degrees of freedom the factors for the 95% confidence limits for the estimate of σ_0 derived from Table H are 0·78 and 1·39 [§ **6·35**]. These give 38·6 and 68·8 for the 95% confidence limits of σ_0.

The approximate 95% confidence limits for σ_1 are derived using the formulae of § **6·35**. From Table H we find that for $\phi_1 = 5$, $\phi_0 = 24$, $\alpha = 0·025$:

$$L_1^2(0·025) = (0·56)^2 = 0·314$$
$$L_2^2(0·025) = (2·51)^2 = 6·30$$

whence

Lower limit $= \sqrt{\{(11,272 \times 0·314 - 2,451)/5\}} = \sqrt{217} \quad = 14·7$
Upper limit $= \sqrt{\{(11,272 \times 6·30 \ - 2,451)/5\}} = \sqrt{13,713} = 117$

Thus the confidence limits for σ_1 are 14·7 and 117. These limits are much wider than those for the estimate of σ_0. This was to be expected, because (i) the number of degrees of freedom, 5, for the mean square between samples is much smaller than that for the experimental error, and (ii) the estimate of σ_1 is derived from a difference between two mean squares, between samples and within samples, and this increases the variance of the estimate.

Test of significance

6·43 In some problems the possibility that a given source of variation has had no effect has to be considered. For instance, in Example 6·1 one purpose of the experiment might have been to find out whether or not the variation in the observed yield from batch to batch could be accounted for by experimental error. Setting up the Null Hypothesis that there is no batch-to-batch variation, i.e. that $\sigma_1^2 = 0$, it is evident from Table 6·32 that on this hypothesis the mean square between samples is also an estimate of σ_0^2. There are then two independent estimates of σ_0^2, one from the mean square within samples and the other from the mean square between samples.

We may now test whether these two estimates differ significantly, i.e. whether they differ by more than can be reasonably explained on the grounds of errors in the estimates. This is done by taking the ratio of the mean square between samples to the mean square within samples—called the F-ratio [§ **4·8**]—and referring to the F-tables (see Table D at the end of the volume). A significant value of F discredits the Null Hypothesis.

When the observations are distributed Normally, the ratio of the two mean squares is distributed exactly as F and depends only on the degrees of freedom of the mean squares. This is also sufficiently close to the truth even when the distribution of the observations departs markedly from the Normal form, provided the numbers of analyses on each sample do not differ widely. There is an important distinction between the application of the F-test to the comparison of mean squares in an Analysis of Variance table and the application to the comparison of two variances calculated from different sets of observations, e.g. when comparing the variability of two analytical methods. The latter is highly dependent on the form of the distribution of the observations, and when this departs from Normality, even to a relatively small extent, the F-test has to be interpreted with caution [§ **4·5**].

Applying the F-test to the two mean squares of Table 6·32 we have:

$$F = \frac{\text{Mean square between samples}}{\text{Mean square within samples}} = 4\cdot60$$

For 5 and 24 degrees of freedom the 0·05 and 0·01 values of F are respectively 2·62 and 3·90. The observed ratio of 4·60 is greater than either of these, hence the hypothesis that $\sigma_1^2 = 0$ is discredited, and it is concluded that real variations exist in the quality of H-acid from batch to batch.

Note on test of significance in relation to Table 6·32

6·44 It should be clearly understood that the F-test applied to Table 6·32 tests the hypothesis that σ_1^2 is zero, and such a test will have a meaning only when it is reasonable to make this hypothesis. In most applications of the Analysis of Variance to sampling and testing problems, repeat samples are taken only when the material is expected or suspected to be variable, and in such circumstances a Null Hypothesis that the sampling error variance is zero is illogical. We know that a sampling error exists, though it may be small, and the purpose of the analysis is to estimate its magnitude and determine the confidence limits.

There are some problems, however, involving an Analysis of Variance for which it is reasonable to set up a Null Hypothesis. For instance, when a blender is used to obtain a bulk quantity of uniform material from a number of batches which are liable to vary, the material from such a blend is expected to be uniform, and only on rare occasions when something has gone wrong would the material not be homogeneous. When testing a number of samples from such a material it would be reasonable to set up the Null Hypothesis that σ_1^2 is zero and to interpret a significant value of F as indicating that something had gone wrong in the blending operation.

Hierarchic classification with three sources of variation

6·5 A sampling and testing example containing three sources of variation will now be considered. The example refers to deliveries of a chemical paste product contained in casks where, in addition to sampling and testing errors, there are variations in quality between deliveries which require to be estimated.

Example 6·2.

As a routine, three casks selected at random from each delivery were sampled, and the samples were kept for reference. It was desired to estimate the variability in the paste strength from cask to cask and from one delivery to another. Ten of the delivery batches were chosen at random and two analytical tests carried out on each of the 30 samples. In order to ensure that the tests were independent, all 60 strength determinations were carried out in a random order. The resulting data are given in Table 6·4.

To illustrate the method of analysis of the data we will first consider the more general case of k deliveries, n casks per delivery, and q tests per cask.

Denote the analytical error variance by σ_0^2, the cask-to-cask variance by σ_1^2, and the variance between deliveries by σ_2^2. For each cask the average of the q strength determinations will have a variance of $\sigma_1^2 + \sigma_0^2/q$ due to these two sources of variation. Consider the table of data formed by the averages

Table 6·4

% PASTE STRENGTH OF SAMPLES

Batch	Cask 1		Cask 2		Cask 3	
1	62·8	62·6	60·1	62·3	62·7	63·1
2	60·0	61·4	57·5	56·9	61·1	58·9
3	58·7	57·5	63·9	63·1	65·4	63·7
4	57·1	56·4	56·9	58·6	64·7	64·5
5	55·1	55·1	54·7	54·2	58·8	57·5
6	63·4	64·9	59·3	58·1	60·5	60·0
7	62·5	62·6	61·0	58·7	56·9	57·7
8	59·2	59·4	65·2	66·0	64·8	64·1
9	54·8	54·8	64·0	64·0	57·7	56·8
10	58·3	59·3	59·2	59·2	58·9	56·6

of the tests on each cask: there are k deliveries and n results per delivery; such a classification is identical with that of § **6·2**. Analysing these means will give an Analysis of Variance table similar to Table 6·32 but with σ_1^2 replaced by σ_2^2, and σ_0^2 replaced by $\sigma_1^2 + \sigma_0^2/q$ in the column representing "quantity estimated by the mean squares." In order to make the coefficient of σ_0^2 unity all sums of squares have to be multiplied by q, and we obtain the following analysis for the total variation between the casks:

Source of Variation	Sum of Squares	Degrees of Freedom	Mean Square	Quantity estimated by Mean Square
Between Deliveries	$qn \sum\limits_{i=1}^{k} (\bar{x}_i - \bar{x})^2$	$k - 1$		$\sigma_0^2 + q\sigma_1^2 + nq\sigma_2^2$
Between Casks Within Deliveries	$q \sum\limits_{i=1}^{k} \sum\limits_{j=1}^{n} (\bar{x}_{ij} - \bar{x}_i)^2$	$k(n - 1)$		$\sigma_0^2 + q\sigma_1^2$
Total Between Casks	$q \sum\limits_{i=1}^{k} \sum\limits_{j=1}^{n} (\bar{x}_{ij} - \bar{x})^2$	$nk - 1$		

The information in this table is sufficient to estimate σ_2^2.

To complete the analysis we note that there are q tests on each of the nk casks, and the variance within these tests estimates σ_0^2 directly. The estimate is based on $nk(q - 1)$ degrees of freedom. The completed Analysis of Variance table then reads:

Table 6·41

ANALYSIS OF VARIANCE OF HIERARCHIC DATA
WITH THREE SOURCES OF VARIATION

Source of Variation	Sum of Squares	Degrees of Freedom	Mean Square	Quantity estimated by Mean Square
Between Deliveries ..	$qn \sum_{i=1}^{k} (\bar{x}_i - \bar{x})^2$	$k - 1$		$\sigma_0^2 + q\sigma_1^2 + nq\sigma_2^2$
Between Casks Within Deliveries	$q \sum_{i=1}^{k} \sum_{j=1}^{n} (\bar{x}_{ij} - \bar{x}_i)^2$	$k(n - 1)$		$\sigma_0^2 + q\sigma_1^2$
Total Between Casks	$q \sum_{i=1}^{k} \sum_{j=1}^{n} (\bar{x}_{ij} - \bar{x})^2$	$nk - 1$		
Analytical Error ..	$\sum_{i=1}^{k} \sum_{j=1}^{n} \sum_{t=1}^{q} (x_{ijt} - \bar{x}_{ij})^2$	$nk(q - 1)$		σ_0^2
Total	$\sum_{i=1}^{k} \sum_{j=1}^{n} \sum_{t=1}^{q} (x_{ijt} - \bar{x})^2$	$nkq - 1$		

For the purpose of computation the following alternative expressions for the sums of squares are preferable:

$$qn \sum_{i=1}^{k} (\bar{x}_i - \bar{x})^2 = \sum_{i=1}^{k} S_i^2/qn - S^2/qnk \ldots\ldots\ldots\ldots(6\cdot81)$$

where S_i is the total of the qn tests on the ith batch and S the grand total of the qnk tests. $\sum_{i=1}^{k} S_i^2/qn$ is frequently referred to as the crude sum of squares between deliveries and S^2/qnk the correction for the grand mean.

$$q \sum_{i=1}^{k} \sum_{j=1}^{n} (\bar{x}_{ij} - \bar{x}_i)^2 = \sum_{i=1}^{k} \sum_{j=1}^{n} S_{ij}^2/q - \sum_{i=1}^{k} S_i^2/qn\ldots\ldots\ldots(6\cdot82)$$

where S_{ij} is the sum of the q observations for the jth cask in the ith batch.

$$q \sum_{i=1}^{k} \sum_{j=1}^{n} (\bar{x}_{i,} - \bar{x})^2 = \sum_{i=1}^{k} \sum_{j=1}^{n} S_{ij}^2/q - S^2/qnk \ldots\ldots\ldots(6\cdot83)$$

$$\sum_{i=1}^{k} \sum_{j=1}^{n} \sum_{t=1}^{q} (x_{ijt} - \bar{x}_{ij})^2 = \sum_{i=1}^{k} \sum_{j=1}^{n} \sum_{t=1}^{q} x_{ijt}^2 - \sum_{i=1}^{k} \sum_{j=1}^{n} S_{ij}^2/q \ldots.(6\cdot84)$$

where $\sum_{i=1}^{k} \sum_{j=1}^{n} \sum_{t=1}^{q} x_{ijt}^2$ is the actual (crude) sum of squares of the qnk observations.

$$\sum_{=1}^{k} \sum_{j=1}^{n} \sum_{t=1}^{q} (x_{ijt} - \bar{x})^2 = \sum_{i=1}^{k} \sum_{j=1}^{n} \sum_{t=1}^{q} x_{ijt}^2 - S^2/qnk \ldots\ldots(6\cdot85)$$

Expressed in these alternative forms, the additive property of the sums of squares is apparent. It is sufficient, therefore, to calculate $(6·81)$, $(6·83)$ and $(6·85)$ and derive $(6·82)$ and $(6·84)$ by subtraction. These correspond respectively to rows (1), (3), (5), (2) and (4) of Table 6·41. In presenting the final Analysis of Variance table row (3) is usually omitted.

The general method of analysis set out in a form most convenient for numerical calculation is given in Appendix 6B·2.

It is clear from the quantities estimated by the mean squares that to test the hypothesis that σ_2^2 is zero we compare the mean squares of (1) and (2), and to test the hypothesis that σ_1^2 is zero we compare the mean squares of (2) and (4). Usually the problem is not one of testing these hypotheses but of estimating the variances σ_0^2, σ_1^2 and σ_2^2. σ_0^2 is given directly by (4), σ_1^2 is derived from the difference of the mean squares (2) and (4), and σ_2^2 is derived from the difference of the mean squares (1) and (2).

Analysis of data of Example 6·2

6·51   To simplify the arithmetic, subtract 50 from the observations of Table 6·4. This gives:

Table 6·42

% STRENGTH LESS 50

Batch	Cask 1		Total	Cask 2		Total	Cask 3		Total	Total per Batch
	Observations		Total	Observations		Total	Observations		Total	
1	12·8	12·6	25·4	10·1	12·3	22·4	12·7	13·1	25·8	73·6
2	10·0	11·4	21·4	7·5	6·9	14·4	11·1	8·9	20·0	55·8
3	8·7	7·5	16·2	13·9	13·1	27·0	15·4	13·7	29·1	72·3
4	7·1	6·4	13·5	6·9	8·6	15·5	14·7	14·5	29·2	58·2
5	5·1	5·1	10·2	4·7	4·2	8·9	8·8	7·5	16·3	35·4
6	13·4	14·9	28·3	9·3	8·1	17·4	10·5	10·0	20·5	66·2
7	12·5	12·6	25·1	11·0	8·7	19·7	6·9	7·7	14·6	59·4
8	9·2	9·4	18·6	15·2	16·0	31·2	14·8	14·1	28·9	78·7
9	4·8	4·8	9·6	14·0	14·0	28·0	7·7	6·8	14·5	52·1
10	8·3	9·3	17·6	9·2	9·2	18·4	8·9	6·6	15·5	51·5

Total number of observations = 60   603·2

The various sums of squares are calculated using the formulae $(6·81)$, $(6·83)$ and $(6·85)$ as follows:

Source of Variation	Crude Sum of Squares	Correction for the Mean	Corrected Sum of Squares	Degrees of Freedom
(6·85) Total ..	$12·8^2 + 12·6^2 + \ldots$ $+ 6·6^2 = 6,682·82$	$(603·2)^2/60$ $= 6,064·17$	618·65	$60 - 1$ $= 59$
(6·81) Between Batches	$(73·6^2 + 55·8^2 + \ldots$ $+ 51·5^2)/6$ $= 6,311·57$	6,064·17	247·40	$10 - 1$ $= 9$
(6·83) Sum of Squares Between all Casks	$(25·4^2 + 21·4^2 + \ldots$ $+ 14·5^2 + 15·5^2)/2$ $= 6,662·48$	6,064·17	598·31	$30 - 1$ $= 29$

(6·83) is the sum of squares between all 30 casks; the sum of squares and degrees of freedom for the variation between casks within batches are derived by subtracting (6·81) from (6·83), and the sum of squares and degrees of freedom within casks are derived by subtracting (6·83) from (6·85).

This leads to the following Analysis of Variance table:

Table 6·5

ANALYSIS OF VARIANCE

Source of Variation	Sum of Squares	Degrees of Freedom	Mean Square	Quantity estimated by Mean Square
Between Batches	247·40	9	27·49	$\sigma_0^2 + 2\sigma_1^2 + 6\sigma_2^2$
Between Casks Within Batches..	350·91	20	17·55	$\sigma_0^2 + 2\sigma_1^2$
Within Casks	20·34	30	0·68	σ_0^2
Total	618·65	59		

A simple check on the calculations in the above table is provided in this case because each cask has only two readings; the sum of squares of the differences for each cask divided by 2 thus provides an alternative expression for the sum of squares within casks. It is $(0·2^2 + 1·4^2 + \ldots + 0·5^2 + 2·3^2)/2 = 40·68/2 = 20·34$. This agreement with the entry in Table 6·5 furnishes the check.

I

Estimates of $\sigma_0{}^2$, $\sigma_1{}^2$ and $\sigma_2{}^2$ are obtained by solving the following "equations":

$$\sigma_0{}^2 + 2\sigma_1{}^2 + 6\sigma_2{}^2 \to 27\!\cdot\!49$$
$$\sigma_0{}^2 + 2\sigma_1{}^2 \qquad\quad \to 17\!\cdot\!55$$
$$\sigma_0{}^2 \qquad\qquad\quad \to 0\!\cdot\!68$$

The estimates are:

Variance between batches $= \sigma_2{}^2 \to 1\!\cdot\!66$; $\quad \sigma_2 \to 1\!\cdot\!29$

Variance between casks $\;= \sigma_1{}^2 \to 8\!\cdot\!44$; $\quad \sigma_1 \to 2\!\cdot\!91$

Testing error variance $\;= \sigma_0{}^2 \to 0\!\cdot\!68$; $\quad \sigma_0 \to 0\!\cdot\!82$

It is seen that the cask-to-cask variation is by far the largest. If it is required to test the Null Hypothesis that the apparent variation between batches is due to the variation between casks and to analytical error, then the mean square of 27·49 based on 9 degrees of freedom must be compared with the mean square of 17·55 based on 20 degrees of freedom. The F-ratio is 1·57, and from Table D it is seen that a ratio of 2·39 is required for significance at the 0·05 level and 1·96 at the 0·10 level. There is thus insufficient evidence to enable us to reject the Null Hypothesis.

Confidence Limits

6·52 σ_0 is based on 30 degrees of freedom, and the factors for the 95% confidence limits obtained from Table H for $\alpha = 0\!\cdot\!025$ are 0·80 and 1·34. These give 0·66 and 1·10 for the 95% confidence limits of σ_0. To calculate the confidence limits for σ_1/σ_0 we require the following quantities from Table H:

$$L_1{}^2(0\!\cdot\!025, 20, 30) = 0\!\cdot\!67^2 = 0\!\cdot\!45; \quad L_2{}^2(0\!\cdot\!025, 20, 30) = 1\!\cdot\!53^2 = 2\!\cdot\!34$$

Referring to the Analysis of Variance Table 6·5 for the values of the mean squares and to the formulae of § **6·35**, we obtain the following approximations for the 95% confidence limits for σ_1:

$$\sqrt{\{(17\!\cdot\!55 \times 0\!\cdot\!45 - 0\!\cdot\!68)/2\}} = \sqrt{3\!\cdot\!60} = 1\!\cdot\!89$$
and
$$\sqrt{\{(17\!\cdot\!55 \times 2\!\cdot\!34 - 0\!\cdot\!68)/2\}} = \sqrt{20\!\cdot\!19} = 4\!\cdot\!49$$

the estimate for σ_1 being 2·91.

The confidence limits for σ_2 are derived from the confidence limits for $\sigma_2{}^2/\sigma_1{}^2$ in much the same way as the confidence limits for σ_1 are derived from the confidence limits for $\sigma_1{}^2/\sigma_0{}^2$.

The estimate and approximate 95% confidence limits for σ_2 are:

$$\sigma_2 \to 1\!\cdot\!29$$

Lower limit $= 0$ (Since the quantity under the square root sign
is negative, this limit is taken to be zero.)

Upper limit $= \sqrt{\{(27\!\cdot\!49 \times 3\!\cdot\!69 - 17\!\cdot\!55)/6\}} = \sqrt{13\!\cdot\!98} = 3\!\cdot\!74$

As expected, σ_2 is subject to larger errors of estimation than σ_1 or σ_0.

Precision of sampling and testing schemes

6·53 The precision of a sampling and testing scheme can be readily determined from the above estimates of the sampling and testing errors. For example:

Scheme 1

Sample 4 casks and test each sample once:

Variance of mean $= (\sigma_1{}^2 + \sigma_0{}^2)/4 = (8\!\cdot\!44/4) + (0\!\cdot\!68/4) = 2\!\cdot\!28$

S.E. of mean $\quad= \sqrt{2\!\cdot\!28} = 1\!\cdot\!51$

Scheme 2

Sample 10 casks, blend the samples and test twice:

Variance of mean $= (8\!\cdot\!44/10) + (0\!\cdot\!68/2) = 1\!\cdot\!18$

S.E. of mean $\quad= \sqrt{1\!\cdot\!18} = 1\!\cdot\!09$

If sampling is cheaper than analytical testing, the second scheme, in addition to giving a smaller standard error, may be cheaper. The cost of any scheme can be readily calculated, given the costs of sampling and testing. For further consideration of the economics of sampling and testing see "Design and Analysis", Chapter 4.

General hierarchic classification

6·54 The analysis for a larger number of sources of variation can be carried out in stages in a similar way, and no new principle is involved. Once the method of analysis is understood for three sources of variation its extension to any larger number presents no difficulty.

Unequal numbers of observations in the groups

6·55 The analysis is simplest when the experiment is balanced, i.e. when there are the same number of samples in each batch, the same number of tests on each sample, etc. The examples discussed previously satisfy this condition. It is not always possible or even desirable to use a balanced experiment, and in such a case some modifications have to be introduced in the analysis. The calculations of the sums of squares are similar, provided the alternative expression introduced to simplify the computations, e.g. expressions *(6·81)*, *(6·82)*, *(6·83)*, etc., are used, and that each total squared is divided by the number of observations involved in the total. For example, in hierarchic data with two sources of variation, let k be the number of samples and n_i the number of tests on the ith sample, then the crude sum of squares between samples is $\sum_{i=1}^{k} S_i{}^2/n_i$ where S_i is the sum of the observations on the ith sample.

The quantities estimated by the mean squares in the case of unequal numbers are a little more complicated. For three sources of variations these quantities may be written:

Mean square between batches $= M_2 \to \sigma_0{}^2 + \bar{n}_2\sigma_1{}^2 + \bar{n}_3\sigma_2{}^2$ d.f. $= \phi_2$

Mean square between samples $= M_1 \to \sigma_0{}^2 + \bar{n}_1\sigma_1{}^2$ d.f. $= \phi_1$
(within batch)

Mean square within samples $= M_0 \to \sigma_0{}^2$ d.f. $= \phi_0$

The coefficients $\bar{n}_1$, $\bar{n}_2$ and $\bar{n}_3$ are functions of the numbers of samples in the batches and the numbers of tests on the samples. Frequently $\bar{n}_1$ and $\bar{n}_2$ may be approximated by the mean number of tests per sample and $\bar{n}_3$ by the mean number of tests per batch. The exact formulae are given in Appendix 6B.

One disadvantage in a balanced hierarchic design is that $\sigma_1{}^2$ is estimated with appreciably less accuracy than $\sigma_0{}^2$, and $\sigma_2{}^2$ with appreciably less accuracy than $\sigma_1{}^2$, etc. A balanced design will have to involve at least twice as many samples as batches and at least twice as many tests as samples; in order to obtain a reasonably accurate estimate of $\sigma_2{}^2$ this may mean multiplying the number of tests to a prohibitive number. One way of getting over the difficulty is to use an unbalanced design such as the following:

In this scheme two samples are taken from each batch; one of the samples is tested once only and the other twice. For this arrangement, if there are n batches, there will be $(n - 1)$ degrees of freedom for batches, n for samples and n for analytical testing. This is not necessarily the most efficient arrangement, but it is better for some purposes than the balanced arrangement with the same number $3n$ of analytical tests.

A method is required which will enable the efficiencies of various arrangements to be compared. Unfortunately it is not practicable to lay down precise rules for doing this, but the following considerations will assist.

We may take the ratio of the upper confidence limit to the actual estimate as a reasonable measure of the precision of an estimate. For $\sigma_0{}^2$ this ratio depends only on the degrees of freedom and may be obtained directly from Table H at the end of the volume. For $\sigma_1{}^2$ the ratio is:

$$(M_1 L_2{}^2 - M_0)/(M_1 - M_0)$$

where L_2 is the factor for the upper confidence limit for ϕ_1 and ϕ_0 degrees of freedom and the appropriate level of α. Denote this ratio by Q. Substituting for M_0 and M_1 their expected values σ_0^2 and $\sigma_0^2 + \bar{n}_1\sigma_1^2$ respectively, Q reduces to:

$$Q = [(1 + \bar{n}_1R_1)L_2^2 - 1]/\bar{n}_1R_1 = L_2^2 + (L_2^2 - 1)/\bar{n}_1R_1$$

where R_1 is the ratio σ_1^2/σ_0^2. This formula gives the exact ratio of the upper confidence limit of σ_1^2/σ_0^2 to the estimated value of this ratio. Frequently $(L_2^2 - 1)/\bar{n}_1R_1$ will be found to be small compared with L_2^2, and it can then be ignored; in such cases the ratio is given directly by the value of L_2^2 corresponding to the probability level chosen, and will depend only on the degrees of freedom of the mean squares.

The corresponding ratio for σ_2^2 is more complicated, but for the designs usually used (such as those considered in App. 6G) a sufficiently accurate measure is obtained by using the above formula with R_1 replaced by R_2, where $R_2 = \sigma_2^2/(\sigma_0^2 + \bar{n}_1\sigma_1^2)$, $\bar{n}_1$ replaced by $\bar{n}_3$, and L_2 by the value for ϕ_2 and ϕ_1 degrees of freedom. For a completely balanced design $\bar{n}_2 = \bar{n}_1$, and the formula gives the exact measure. The designs generally used in practice are balanced or nearly so and the error involved in taking $\bar{n}_2 = \bar{n}_1$ is very small, so that the above formula may be used as an approximation to the ratio. The correct formula for unbalanced designs is given in App. 6C, and in App. 6G five different arrangements for estimating σ_2^2, σ_1^2 and σ_0^2 (which are respectively the variance between batches, the variance between samples and the analytical error variance) are assessed and compared, each design being based on a total of about 48 analyses but with different numbers of batches, numbers of samples per batch and numbers of tests per sample. The conclusion from this is that no design emerges which is best for estimating all of the variances; the design which is best for estimating σ_2^2 is not the best for estimating σ_1^2, etc. Design 5, in which three samples are taken from each batch, two samples analysed twice and the other once, is a reasonable compromise. However, the final choice in any particular case will have to take other considerations into account, e.g. the cost of the design and whether or not some variances are required to be estimated more accurately than others.

Cross-classifications

Two-way cross-classifications: Example 6·3

6·6 In a two-way cross-classification the data can be arranged in a rectangular table with r rows and c columns. The results of such an experiment are shown in Table 6·6. The investigation which it represents is taken from penicillin testing. The particular problem was to assess the variability between samples of penicillin by the *B. subtilis* plate method. In this method of test a bulk-inoculated nutrient agar medium is poured into a Petri dish of approximately 9 cm. diameter, known as a plate. When the medium has set, six small hollow cylinders or pots (about 0·4 cm. in diameter) are cemented on to the surface at equally spaced intervals. A few drops of the penicillin solutions to be compared are placed in the respective cylinders, and the whole plate is placed in an incubator for a given time. Penicillin diffuses from the pots into the agar, and this produces a clear circular zone of inhibition of growth of the organisms, which can be readily measured. The diameter of

Table 6·6

24-PLATE COMPARATIVE TEST ON SAMPLES OF PENICILLIN
(Circle diameter less 20 mm.)

Plate No.	Penicillin Samples						Total	Mean
	1	2	3	4	5	6		
1	7	3	6	3	3	1	23	3·83
2	7	3	6	3	3	1	23	3·83
3	5	1	5	4	4	0	19	3·17
4	6	3	5	3	3	0	20	3·33
5	5	2	6	2	3	0	18	3·00
6	4	2	5	3	2	— 1	15	2·50
7	4	0	3	1	2	— 1	9	1·50
8	6	2	6	4	4	1	23	3·83
9	4	1	4	2	2	0	13	2·17
10	4	1	4	3	2	— 1	13	2·17
11	6	3	6	4	4	1	24	4·00
12	5	2	6	4	4	0	21	3·50
13	6	4	6	4	5	2	27	4·50
14	6	3	6	3	3	0	21	3·50
15	6	3	5	4	4	2	24	4·00
16	5	2	5	3	3	0	18	3·00
17	5	1	4	3	3	0	16	2·67
18	5	2	4	3	3	— 1	16	2·67
19	4	1	3	1	1	— 1	9	1·50
20	6	3	6	4	4	1	24	4·00
21	5	1	4	2	2	— 2	12	2·00
22	5	2	5	2	2	0	16	2·67
23	4	1	4	2	4	— 1	14	2·33
24	4	1	4	2	1	— 2	10	1·67
Total ..	124	47	118	69	71	— 1	428	
Mean ..	5·17	1·96	4·92	2·88	2·96	— 0·04	Grand mean = 2·97	

the zone is related in a known way to the concentration of penicillin in the solutions.

In this example the six samples were compared on twenty-four replicate plates. The circle diameters (in millimetres) of the zones of inhibition are given in Table 6·6. A constant quantity (20 mm.) has been subtracted from each observation in order to simplify the arithmetic; this, of course, does not affect the results.

When analysing such a table of results we have to consider three sources of variation: that between columns (samples of penicillin), that between rows (plates), and that due to testing error. It is assumed that there is a Universe of samples of penicillin and a Universe of plates, and one purpose of the experiment is to estimate their variances. Denote these variances respectively by σ_c^2, σ_r^2 and σ_0^2. The variance σ_c^2 may be regarded as a sampling variance, σ_r^2 as the component of error due to variation between plates and σ_0^2 as the remainder of the error. Apart from experimental error, the differences between any two samples are expected to be the same for all the plates. This implies that the deviation δ of any single result from the grand mean can be regarded as a sum of the three separate components corresponding respectively to the operation of σ_c^2, σ_r^2 and σ_0^2:

$$\delta = \delta_c + \delta_r + \delta_0$$

Each sample of penicillin in Table 6·6 can be regarded as having been tested 24 times, and if for the moment the variation between plates is ignored and the tests are regarded as independent, we can construct an Analysis of Variance between and within samples in the usual way. If the grand mean is denoted by $\bar{X}$, a sample (column) mean by C_i and the number of plates (that is, the number in each column) by r, then the sum of squares between samples is $r \sum\limits_{i=1}^{c} (C_i - \bar{X})^2$ based on $c - 1$ degrees of freedom, where c is the number of samples (columns). For Table 6·6 this comes to 449, based on 5 degrees of freedom.

In a similar way the table can be regarded as consisting of 24 plates all tested six times, and we may calculate the sum of squares between plates (rows). If a row mean is denoted by R_j, this sum of squares is $c \sum\limits_{j=1}^{r} (R_j - \bar{X})^2$ based on $r - 1$ degrees of freedom. For the data of Table 6·6 this comes to 106, based on 23 degrees of freedom.

The sum of squares for all individual results is 590. From these figures we construct the Analysis of Variance Table 6·61.

The remainder sum of squares and degrees of freedom are obtained by subtraction from the total.

The calculations can be summarised as follows:

Correction for the mean $= (428)^2/144 = 1,272$

Total sum of squares
$$= \{7^2 + 3^2 + \ldots + 1^2 + (-2)^2\} - 1{,}272 = 590 \qquad \text{d.f.} = 143$$
Sum of squares between plates
$$= (23^2 + 23^2 + \ldots + 14^2 + 10^2)/6 - 1{,}272 = 106 \qquad \text{d.f.} = 23$$
Sum of squares between samples
$$= \{124^2 + 47^2 + \ldots + 71^2 + (-1)^2\}/24 - 1{,}272 = 449 \quad \text{d.f.} = 5$$

Table 6·61

ANALYSIS OF VARIANCE

(Based on Table 6·6)

Source of Variation	Sum of Squares	Degrees of Freedom	Mean Square
Between Samples	449	5	89·8
Between Plates	106	23	4·6
Remainder = (Error)	35	115	0·30
Total	590	143	

6·61 Since there are 24 plates and 6 samples per plate, the mean squares estimate the following quantities:

$$\text{Between samples: } \sigma_0^2 + 24\sigma_c^2$$
$$\text{Between plates: } \quad \sigma_0^2 + 6\sigma_r^2$$
$$\text{Remainder: } \qquad \sigma_0^2$$

We note that the variance between plates does not enter into the quantity estimated by the mean square between samples, and *vice versa*; this is because all the plates are common to every sample, so that the differences between the means of the samples are unaffected by the differences between the plates, and *vice versa*.

Using the mean squares of Table 6·61 and the expressions of the quantities estimated by them, we readily derive the following estimates:

$$\sigma_0^2 \to 0{\cdot}30 \qquad\qquad\qquad \sigma_0 \to 0{\cdot}55$$
$$\sigma_c^2 \to (89{\cdot}8 - 0{\cdot}30)/24 = 3{\cdot}73 \qquad \sigma_c \to 1{\cdot}93$$
$$\sigma_r^2 \to (4{\cdot}6 - 0{\cdot}30)/6 \;\; = 0{\cdot}72 \qquad \sigma_r \to 0{\cdot}85$$

The confidence limits may be calculated, using the same formulae as those used in the simple hierarchic classification.

Referring to Table H, we find that for 115 degrees of freedom the factors for $a = 0{\cdot}025$ are 0·89 and 1·44, whence the 95% confidence limits of σ_0 are 0·49 and 0·79.

Following the procedure of § **6·35** to find approximate 95% confidence limits for σ_c we look up the values of L_1 and L_2 in Table H for 5 and 115 degrees of freedom and obtain $L_1 = 0.61$ and $L_2 = 2.46$, giving $L_1^2 = 0.372$ and $L_2^2 = 6.05$. The 95% confidence limits for σ_c are therefore:

$$\sqrt{\{(89.8 \times 0.372 - 0.30)/24\}} \quad \text{and} \quad \sqrt{\{(89.8 \times 6.05 - 0.30)/24\}}$$

i.e. 1·17 and 4·76. Similarly, the 95% confidence limits for σ_r are:

$$\sqrt{\{(4.6 \times 0.562 - 0.30)/6\}} \quad \text{and} \quad \sqrt{\{(4.6 \times 2.04 - 0.30)/6\}}$$

i.e. 0·62 and 1·23.

Because of the larger number of degrees of freedom available for the error variance these limits are narrower than those obtained in previous examples.

Test of significance

6·611 If it is required to test the hypothesis $\sigma_c^2 = 0$ we compare the mean square between samples with the remainder mean square, and for the hypothesis $\sigma_r^2 = 0$ we compare the mean square between plates with the remainder mean square. Usually, however, the problem is not one of testing hypotheses but of separating and estimating the variances.

Sums of squares

6·612 The identity which expresses the additive property of the sums of squares is derived and proved in Appendix 6E. This identity is of interest because it shows that the remainder sum of squares is the sum of squares of the deviations of the observations from the values expected on the assumption that the sample "effect" and the plate "effect" are additive. A sample effect is defined as the difference between the sample mean and the grand mean. Thus, for example, the mean of sample 1 is 2·20 mm. greater than the grand mean and represents an "effect" of + 2·20 mm. Further, the mean of the first plate is 0·86 mm. above the grand mean and represents an "effect" of + 0·86 mm. On the assumption of an additive law for the effects of samples and plates we would expect sample 1 on plate 1 to be $2.20 + 0.86 = 3.06$ above the grand mean of 22·97. This gives an expected value of 26·03 mm. The actual value is 27·00 mm., which deviates from the expected by 0·97 mm. The residual quantities remaining after the effect of rows and columns have been allowed for are used to estimate the experimental error variance σ_0^2. This will be explained more fully in § **6·63**.

The additive property of the sums of squares shows that:

(i) Sum of squares within samples = Sum of squares between plates + Remainder sum of squares.

(ii) Sum of squares within plates = Sum of squares between samples + Remainder sum of squares.

General two-way classification

6·62 The analysis of the general two-way cross-classification with m rows and n columns is carried out similarly; the step-by-step details are set out in a form convenient for computational purposes in Appendix 6E.

Interaction

6·63 In the analysis of a two-way table the remainder sum of squares is the sum of squares of the deviations of the observations from the values expected on the assumption that the effects of the variations due to rows and to columns are additive. The remainder mean square is generally referred to as the Interaction Mean Square. When, as in the previous example, the residuals after allowing for the effect of rows and columns are due to experimental error, the interaction mean square is an estimate of the experimental error variance.

The hypothesis that the effects are additive is discredited when the remainder mean square is significantly greater than that expected from the experimental error variance; the sources of variation represented by the rows and columns are then said to interact. In order that this hypothesis can be tested a separate estimate of the error variance is needed, usually obtained from previous experiments or by replication.

The simplest example of an interaction is shown by a 2×2 table. Consider, for example, two samples of penicillin compared by each of two different methods. The true results by each method on each sample are depicted as follows:

Method	Penicillin Sample	
	A	B
1	a_1	b_1
2	a_2	b_2

An interaction is a consistent effect such as would arise if sample A is more effective than B with one method and not with the other. The difference between A and B by method 1 is $d_1 = (a_1 - b_1)$, and by method 2 is $d_2 = (a_2 - b_2)$. If d_1 and d_2 differ, then the samples and methods are said to interact and the extent of the difference $(d_1 - d_2)$ is a measure of the interaction.

The true values are, of course, unknown and have to be estimated experimentally. Suppose n repeat observations have been carried out on each sample by each method, and let the means be $(\bar{x}_1, \bar{x}_2)$ for sample A and $(\bar{y}_1, \bar{y}_2)$ for sample B. The interaction is then estimated by $d = (\bar{x}_1 - \bar{y}_1) - (\bar{x}_2 - \bar{y}_2)$. The error variance σ_0^2 can be estimated from the replicate tests and will be based on $4(n - 1)$ degrees of freedom.

The table is symmetrical, and we could equally well consider the differential effect of the methods for the two samples; thus for A the estimate of the effect of methods is $(\bar{x}_1 - \bar{x}_2)$, and for B it is $(\bar{y}_1 - \bar{y}_2)$. The difference between these is $(\bar{x}_1 - \bar{x}_2) - (\bar{y}_1 - \bar{y}_2)$, which is identical with the expression obtained previously.

The significance of the differential effect can be readily ascertained in the following manner. The variance of each mean is σ_0^2/n and that of the difference $(\bar{x}_1 - \bar{y}_1)$ is $2\sigma_0^2/n$. The variance of $(\bar{x}_2 - \bar{y}_2)$ is also $2\sigma_0^2/n$, and therefore the variance of the difference between them is $4\sigma_0^2/n$. We must substitute for σ_0^2 its estimate s_0^2 based on $4(n-1)$ degrees of freedom. The standard error of the interaction d is then $2s_0/\sqrt{n}$, and the significance of d is determined from:

$$t = d/(2s_0/\sqrt{n})$$

which is based on $4(n-1)$ degrees of freedom. If D is significant, the Null Hypothesis of no interaction is discredited.

When there are more than two columns or rows the interaction cannot be estimated in the above simple way; it is necessary to calculate the appropriate mean square and to compare it with the error mean square. An example of this is considered in a later section [§ **6·74**].

COMPARISON OF MEANS

6·7   It was pointed out in § **6·23** that there were two basic types of problems which could be dealt with by the technique of the Analysis of Variance. Up to now we have considered only the one in which the items in each classification are random elements from a Universe of such items, and the only measures of interest are the variances of these Universes. The method analyses the variance into its separate components and enables these components to be estimated and the confidence limits calculated.

The other type of problem is that of comparing the specific values of certain items as opposed to the estimation of the variance of a Universe of such items. This is not strictly an Analysis of Variance problem, since we are not concerned with variances except that of experimental error, but nevertheless the same technique of analysis up to the point of deriving the mean squares may be usefully employed. This second class of problem is called Comparison of Means. An illustration will now be considered.

In the example of Table 6·3 the six samples of H-acid represented batches from bulk manufacture (i.e. a Universe of batches) and we required to estimate the variance of this Universe. This estimate, together with that of experimental error (the variance within batches) and their confidence limits give a complete analysis of the data.

Suppose now that we were interested in specific comparison between the samples of H-acid; this would be so if the six samples represented material prepared by different processes or obtained from different suppliers. The main interest would then lie in comparing one material with another and ultimately in choosing the most suitable one. There would be little point in estimating the variance of a Universe of different materials, because it would have little meaning in relation to the investigation. It is possible, of course, to follow the normal procedure of the Analysis of Variance, but the quantity estimated by the mean square between samples would not then contain σ_1^2, because such a quantity does not exist. The σ_1^2 of a normal Analysis of Variance would have to be replaced by $\sum_{i=1}^{k}(M_i - \bar{M})^2/(k-1)$, where M_i is the true mean of the ith sample and $\bar{M}$ the mean of the M_i's. This expression is a measure of the overall variation between the given samples, and if an overall test of significance is required for this variation it is provided by a comparison of the mean squares. The main purpose of such an Analysis of Variance is, however, to supply a valid estimate of error for the comparisons between the means of the samples of H-acid. This estimate of error is given by the mean square within samples.

The problem is seen to be an extension of the one considered in § 4·23, in which two group means were compared; the only difference here is that there are more than two means to compare. It will be recalled that for two group means, each based on n observations, the $100(1-2a)\%$ confidence limits for the difference are:

$$(\bar{x}_1 - \bar{x}_2) \pm t_{a\phi}s\sqrt{(2/n)}$$

where s is the estimate of σ_0 based on $\phi\,(= 2n - 2)$ degrees of freedom, and $t_{a\phi}$ the corresponding value of t for the probability a.

6·71 An obvious extension when there are more than two groups is to compare the groups two at a time, using the combined variance within all the groups as the estimate of error—in other words, using the estimate of σ_0^2 derived in the Analysis of Variance Table. Suppose there are k group means $\bar{x}_1, \bar{x}_2, \ldots, \bar{x}_k$, each based on n observations; the $100(1-2a)\%$ confidence limits for the comparisons are then:

$$(\bar{x}_i - \bar{x}_j) \pm t_{a\phi}s\sqrt{(2/n)}$$

where s is the estimate of σ_0 based on ϕ degrees of freedom (in this case $\phi = k(n-1)$).

If the purpose of the experiment is to make specific comparisons of this sort, i.e. if the experimenter can specify beforehand what comparisons he is going to make, then the above confidence limits may be applied to each comparison as though they were independent. This means that there is a risk $2a$ of any one set of confidence limits not containing the true difference, and in the long run only in $100(2a)\%$ of the total number of such comparisons made will the confidence limits not contain the true difference. If we work with 95% confidence limits, then in the long run only in one case out of 20 will the confidence interval for the difference between a pair of means not contain the true difference; in one case in 40 the true difference will exceed the upper limit, and in one case in 40 the true difference will be below the lower limit. In an experiment in which k groups are compared there are $k(k-1)/2$ possible pairs, so that the chance that the confidence limits for one or more of these differences will not contain the true value may be quite high. There is in principle no difference between making n specific comparisons between several samples in one experiment and making these comparisons one at a time in each of n experiments on pairs of samples. What must be guarded against is to select only those comparisons which are suggested by the data. For instance, if only the highest and the lowest results are compared there is a high chance of a misleading conclusion being reached, and the proportion of wrong conclusions due to the error of the first kind for such comparisons may be very high.

One application of these multiple comparisons is to chemotherapeutic research, in which a biological test is used as a screen for a large number of compounds. Usually several compounds are compared with a control in each application of the test. An effect is defined as the difference between the mean of a treated group and that of the control. Those compounds which show an effect above a certain predetermined value will be retained for further examination, but those showing a smaller effect will be discarded. The only comparisons normally made are between a treatment mean and the control.

To be of technical importance a compound should have a true effect greater than a given amount d. A critical value c for an observed effect is chosen so that if an effect less than c is observed the compound is concluded to be not effective, and if greater than c the compound is concluded to be effective. In such screening tests there is a risk of observing an effect greater than c from a compound which really has no effect. This is the error of the first kind which gives rise to false positives. There is also a risk of a false negative, i.e. of observing an effect less than c when the compound has a true effect greater than d and so is of potential interest. This corresponds to the error of the second kind. The confidence limits can be used to control these risks in the following manner [Ch. 5]. Suppose we are prepared to take a risk a of a false negative and a similar risk of a false positive, then the distance between the $100(1-2a)\%$ confidence limits should be equal to d, and since the limits will be symmetrical about the observed value the critical value c should be taken at $d/2$. The number of observations on each group must then be chosen to give a $100(1-2a)\%$ confidence interval of d. This can be readily determined when the standard error is known or when an estimate is available from previous trials.

6·711   There are other kinds of experiments in which the experimenter, although requiring to compare the sample means in pairs, may require to choose the confidence limits so that the chance of any one or more of these limits in each experiment being wrong is $2a$. The experiment is then considered as an entity and not as a complex of smaller ones, and the experimenter wishes to ensure that in only $100(2a)\%$ *of such experiments* will any wrong conclusions be reached.

The confidence limits must then be wider than those used previously. Suitable limits have been derived by J. W. Tukey and are given as follows:

There are k means $\bar{x}_1, \bar{x}_2, \ldots, \bar{x}_k$ to compare, each mean being based on n observations. The confidence interval for any difference $\bar{x}_i - \bar{x}_j$ is:

$$(\bar{x}_i - \bar{x}_j) \pm q_{ak\phi}s/\sqrt{n}$$

where s^2 is the estimate of the variance within the groups based on ϕ degrees of freedom, a is the significance level, e.g. the $0\cdot025$ level, and the quantity q is given in the table of the "Studentised Range" (Table 29 of Biometrika Tables [6·2]) and is the upper $100a\%$ probability limit of the range of k observations from a Normal Universe divided by the standard deviation estimated independently of the observations with ϕ degrees of freedom. Other tests exist which have advantages in certain circumstances, and a full discussion will be found in [6·1].

Illustrations of multiple confidence intervals and Tukey's test

6·72   The following illustrations are intended to show in what circumstances the two types of confidence interval discussed respectively in §§ **6·7** and **6·71** should be used:

   (i) Assume that in Example 6·1 the six samples represented six different qualities of H-acid (e.g. six different suppliers) and that sample 1 represented the one in current use (e.g. own manufacture). It was required to find out if higher yields could be obtained from any of the other qualities.

Here the correct procedure is to compare each mean with that of the control (sample 1), using confidence limits derived from the t-table. The standard deviation of each observation is $49\cdot5$ [§ **6·41**], whence the standard error of a difference between sample means is $49\cdot5\sqrt{(2/5)} = 31\cdot3$. The $0\cdot025$ value of t for 24 degrees of freedom is $2\cdot06$. The 95% confidence limits to be attached to any observed difference are then $\pm 64\cdot5$; in other words, there is a chance of 1 in 40 (or less) of being wrong if it is concluded that a real improvement has occurred when the observed difference in means is $64\cdot5$ (or more). Two samples, 3 and 5, are thus seen to be better than the control.

   (ii) The six samples of Example 6·1 are assumed to represent six consecutive batches of current manufacture. Is there justification for carrying out an analytical investigation on some of the batches for the purpose of discovering causes of variation in yield?

Here we are not interested in specific comparison. When the experiment was planned there was no reason for carrying out particular comparisons between particular batches. Here it is required to ascertain which differences between batches are too large to be explained as having arisen from experimental error.

Tukey's test may be applied here. For the 0·05 level, and $k = 6$, $\phi = 24$, the value of q is 4·38 (see Table 29 [6·2]). The confidence limits for the largest difference are then $\pm 4\cdot38 \times 22 = \pm 96$, where 22 is the standard error of a mean. The differences between the means of samples 4 and 5 and of samples 5 and 6 exceed this value. There is therefore sufficient reason for carrying out an analytical investigation.

Application to Example 6·3

6·73 In Table 6·61 the quantity estimated by the mean square for samples is obtained on the assumption that the samples can be regarded as representative of a Universe of samples, and this gives a meaning to σ_c^2. If, however, the samples cannot be so regarded, e.g. when the samples represent specific grades of the material, then σ_c^2 no longer has a meaning and it has to be replaced by the expression $\sum\limits_{i=1}^{c}(C_i - \bar{X})^2/(c-1)$ where c is the number of samples. The main purpose of the experiment is then to compare the six samples.

In this example there is a meaning to the variance between plates, because the plates used in the test are a sample from a much larger number of such plates. However, this source of error has been eliminated in the comparisons of the samples.

The remainder mean square is 0·30, which corresponds to a standard deviation of $\sqrt{0\cdot30} = 0\cdot55$ mm. The standard error of each sample mean over the twenty-four plates is therefore $0\cdot55/\sqrt{24} = 0\cdot11$ mm. This is the standard error to use to compare sample means. The means are:

$$A = 25\cdot17 \qquad B = 21\cdot96 \qquad C = 24\cdot92$$
$$D = 22\cdot88 \qquad E = 22\cdot96 \qquad F = 19\cdot96$$

Assume that one of the samples, A, is a standard material and we require to compare each of the other samples with it. For this purpose we calculate the difference between the means of A and each of B to F and their confidence limits. The error mean square is 0·30 based on 115 degrees of freedom; therefore the 95% confidence limits of each difference are

$$\pm 1\cdot98\sqrt{(0\cdot30 \times 2/24)} = \pm 0\cdot31.$$

All the samples except C are thus seen to differ significantly from A.

Example 6·4. Testing of cement mortar

6·74 This example is of a type which combines a simple hierarchic classification with a two-way cross-classification and is, in fact, a two-way cross-classification with repeat tests in each cell.

A sample of Portland cement was mixed and reduced in a sampling machine to small samples for testing. The cement mortar was "gauged" (i.e. mixed with water and worked for a standard time) by each of three gaugers and cast into $\frac{1}{2}$ in. cube moulds. The cubes were removed from the moulds after twenty-four hours, stored at 18° C. for seven days, and then tested for compressive strength. Three testers or "breakers" were employed. The source of variation examined were:

(a) Between the three gaugers.
(b) Between the three breakers.
(c) Between repeat tests, i.e. testing error.

Between gaugers some variation might be expected, since the personal factor is strong unless the operation is carefully standardised. Between breakers (i.e. the assistants operating the testing machine) there should normally be no variation, since the machine is automatic. In this case an old machine was in use, and one object of the test was to find whether personal factors in the preliminary adjustment of the machine could cause variations in the results. Each gauger gauged twelve cubes, each set of twelve cubes was divided into three sets of four, and each breaker tested one such set from each gauger. The results are shown in Table 6·7. The figures were about 5,000 lb./sq. in. To save arithmetic 5,000 has been subtracted from each, and since the figures were recorded to the nearest 10 lb./sq. in. the differences were divided by 10.

Table 6·7
TESTS ON SAMPLES OF PORTLAND CEMENT

	Breaker 1		Breaker 2		Breaker 3		Means
Gauger 1	28	52	− 66	− 60	− 84	18	4·83
	− 24	80	2	120	32	− 40	
Gauger 2	− 58	28	34	− 12	− 82	− 20	3·17
	58	− 10	− 4	120	− 40	− 52	
Gauger 3	36	116	72	− 24	− 54	− 7	33·58
	68	50	62	56	− 32	60	
Means ..	35·33		25·00		− 25·08		11·75

6·741 The first stage in the analysis is to construct Table 6·71, in which each entry is the sum of the corresponding repeat tests in Table 6·7.

Table 6·71

TABLE OF SUMS DERIVED FROM TABLE 6·7

	Breaker 1	Breaker 2	Breaker 3	Total
Gauger 1	136	− 4	− 74	58
Gauger 2	18	138	− 194	− 38
Gauger 3	270	166	− 33	403
Total ..	424	300	− 301	423

The estimate of the error variance $\sigma_0{}^2$ is obtained directly from the variance within the groups of four repeat tests.

The variance of the entries in Table 6·71 is $4\sigma_0{}^2$, since each entry is a sum of four independent observations. If, therefore, the two-way table of totals (Table 6·71) is analysed in the usual way, the quantities estimated by the mean squares will include the quantity $4\sigma_0{}^2$. Each sum of squares must therefore be divided by 4 in order to make the coefficient of $\sigma_0{}^2$ unity.

The computation is almost automatic if we follow the rule for all calculations involved in Analysis of Variance, namely that when determining the crude sum of squares of similar quantities which are sums of individual observations, each square has to be divided by the number of observations contained in it.

The details of the calculations of the sums of squares are:

(i) Correction for the mean $= (423)^2/36 = 4{,}970$

(ii) Total sum of squares of all 36 observations
$$= \{28^2 + 52^2 + \ldots + 60^2\} - 4{,}970 = 114{,}819 \qquad \text{d.f.} = 35$$

(iii) Total sum of squares between the 9 sub-groups
$$= \{136^2 + (-4)^2 + \ldots + 166^2 + (-33)^2\}/4 - 4{,}970$$
$$= 40{,}664 \qquad \text{d.f.} = 8$$

(iv) Sum of squares between breakers
$$= \{424^2 + 300^2 + (-301)^2\}/12 - 4{,}970 = 25{,}061 \qquad \text{d.f.} = 2$$

(v) Sum of squares between gaugers
$$= \{58^2 + (-38)^2 + 403^2\}/12 - 4{,}970 = 8{,}965 \qquad \text{d.f.} = 2$$

The Analysis of Variance table may then be constructed as in Table 6·72.

6·742   The sum of squares and degrees of freedom within sub-groups were found by subtracting (iii) from (ii) and the interaction of gaugers and breakers by subtracting the sum of (iv) and (v) from (iii). The row in brackets is usually omitted.

K

Table 6·72

ANALYSIS OF VARIANCE

Sources of Variation	Sum of Squares	Degrees of Freedom	Mean Square	Quantities estimated by the Mean Squares
Between Gaugers ..	8,965	2	4,482	$\sigma_0^2 + 12\Sigma(G_i - \bar{X})^2/2$
Between Breakers ..	25,061	2	12,530	$\sigma_0^2 + 12\Sigma(B_i - \bar{X})^2/2$
Interaction of Gaugers and Breakers	6,638	4	1,659	$\sigma_0^2 + 4\Sigma\Sigma(x_{ij} - G_i$ $- B_j + \bar{X})^2$
(Total Between Sub-groups)	(40,664)	(8)		
Within Sub-groups ..	74,155	27	2,746	σ_0^2
Total	114,819	35		

The quantities estimated by the mean squares given in Table 6·72 can be readily determined from the following considerations. Assume that there is no error and that the true values for each cell of Table 6·7 are as follows:

	x_{11}	x_{12}	x_{13}	G_1
	x_{21}	x_{22}	x_{23}	G_2
	x_{31}	x_{33}	x_{34}	G_4
Means	B_1	B_2	B_3	$\bar{X}$

Each entry must be multiplied by 4 to obtain the results corresponding to Table 6·71. The row and column means have then to be multiplied by 12 and the grand mean by 36 to give the corresponding totals. Carrying out the identical procedure of § **6·741** on these quantities will give mean squares the same as the expressions of Table 6·72 with σ_0^2 omitted. σ_0^2 has now to be added to allow for the errors in the determinations of the breaking strengths in order to give the quantities estimated by the mean squares in the analysis of the observations.

Interpretation

6·75 The interaction mean square does not differ significantly from the error mean square; in fact it is smaller, but not significantly so. All the apparent interaction between breakers and gaugers can therefore be fully explained by the experimental error, and the assumption that no real interaction exists is fully justified. An interaction could arise if testers were biased so that a tester (i.e. breaker) obtained better results with cubes made by a certain gauger than with the others, not due to any real difference but because he carried out the test in such a way as to show better results. In practice a bias should be ruled out, if possible, in the design of the experiment.

We are interested in assessing whether any real variation exists between the breakers and the gaugers, and therefore it is appropriate to assess the significance of the mean squares. The F-test shows that the variation between gaugers is not significant, but the variation between breakers is significant at $P = 0·05$.

The application of Tukey's test is, however, more informative because it gives directly the confidence limits of the differences between the means. To apply this test we refer to Table 29 [6·2] to obtain the value of q for $\phi = 27$, $k = 3$ and $\alpha = 0·025$. This is found to be 3·51. The standard deviation of each mean is $\sqrt{(2,746/12)} = 15·1$, and therefore the 95% confidence limits of any difference between two means are $\pm 53·0$. The differences in the mean values obtained by the three gaugers are all less than this value, which confirms the conclusion already arrived at that there is insufficient evidence to presume that the gaugers were different. On the other hand, breaker 3 is seen to differ from breaker 1 because the difference in their means exceeds 53·0.

6·751 In this problem we are concerned with the comparison between the three gaugers and the three breakers. If, however, the problem was one in which we were interested in the Universe of gaugers and breakers, then the summation terms in the quantities estimated by the mean squares in Table 6·72 would be replaced by $\sigma_G{}^2$ (for gaugers), $\sigma_B{}^2$ (for breakers) and $\sigma_I{}^2$ (for interaction). The variance $\sigma_I{}^2$ represents a variable bias, and if this is appreciable it would be an additional testing error which would have to be taken into account in assessing the significance of the variation between breakers and gaugers. It would then be necessary to assess the significance of the first two mean squares of Table 6·72 against the interaction and not against the error variance. Had the interaction been significant it would have been necessary to investigate the experimental conditions to identify the possible causes and eliminate them in future tests. Even when the interaction is not significant it is, of course, perfectly valid to assess the first two mean squares against the interaction mean square, but we almost invariably lose precision in so doing, since there are fewer degrees of freedom for interaction than for error.

Many textbooks recommend that any mean square which is not significant be combined with the error mean square to give a new error mean square based on a larger number of degrees of freedom. The combination of non-significant mean squares should be carried out with discretion and not as a general rule; it should be restricted to those mean squares corresponding to effects which from prior considerations are not expected to be appreciable, but whenever possible the experiment should be carried out on a sufficient scale to supply an adequate number of degrees of freedom for error. Indiscriminate combination of non-significant mean squares can sometimes lead to absurd conclusions. In this example we could, if we wished, combine the interaction and error mean squares to give $(6,638 + 74,155)/(4 + 27) = 2,606$ based on 31 degrees of freedom. The significance of the mean squares between gaugers and between breakers could be assessed against this new error. There is no serious objection to this procedure in this particular example because the interaction was not expected, but there is no advantage in doing so.

Further applications of the Analysis of Variance

6·8   The examples already given cover a substantial proportion of the types of applications of the Analysis of Variance likely to be encountered in chemical work. More complex cases usually represent extensions and combinations of these examples. Example 6·4, for instance, is an extension of Example 6·3. It is basically a two-way rectangular classification (breakers and gaugers), with four repeats for each cell. This type of application is likely to be encountered frequently and may take a variety of different forms. When there is only one observation in each cell the analysis is the same as that of Example 6·3. When there are repeats with the same number for each cell the analysis will be similar to that of Example 6·4. The main point to remember is that in all cases, without exception, when calculating crude sums of squares, the square of any figure which is the sum of a given number of observations must be divided by the given number of observations constituting the sum.

The method used for Example 6·4 applies only when there are the same number of repeat observations in each cell.

Different numbers of observations in the cells

6·81   In the general case the number of repeat observations will not be the same in all cells. The simpler methods of the Analysis of Variance will not then apply, because the sums of squares for the sources of variation are not additive.

However, the simpler techniques apply whenever the ratios of the numbers of observations in corresponding cells of the rows, or of the columns, are the same throughout the table, since in such cases the sums of squares are additive. The analysis is carried out in a similar manner to that of Example 6·4, remembering the above rule for the divisor in the calculation of each crude sum of squares and each correction.

6·82   For the general case, in which the respective numbers in the rows are not proportional, the analysis becomes complicated and beyond the scope of this book. Frequently, however, it is possible to obtain good approximate analyses by adding dummy observations to some of the cells or assuming that the means of others are based on fewer results in order to make the respective numbers in the rows proportional. A dummy observation added must be equal in value to the mean for the cell to which it is added. The variance within cells is calculated from the original observations in the usual way, since this particular variance does not require the assumption of proportionality between the numbers of observations in the rows and columns. Where an appreciable disproportion exists reference should be made to "Design and Analysis," Chapters 6 and 11, where the general problem is dealt with.

REFERENCES

[6·1] DUNCAN, D. B. "Multiple Range and Multiple F-Tests," *Biometrics,* **11** (1955).

[6·2] PEARSON, E. S., and HARTLEY, H. O. *Biometrika Tables for Statisticians,* Vol. 1 (Cambridge University Press, 1954).

APPENDIX 6A

COMBINATION OF RESULTS FROM SEVERAL SAMPLES

SUPPOSE there are k independent unbiased estimates of a mean μ denoted by $\bar{x}_1, \bar{x}_2, \ldots, \bar{x}_k$ with variances $V_1, V_2, \ldots, V_k$. The problem is to combine these means in order to derive the best estimate of μ.

The expression $X = (w_1\bar{x}_1 + w_2\bar{x}_2 + \ldots + w_k\bar{x}_k)/W$, where $W = \Sigma w_i$, gives a weighted mean of the $\bar{x}$'s, which is a linear estimate of μ. It can be shown that the best linear combination of the $\bar{x}$'s, i.e. the one which has minimum variance, is obtained when the weights are equal (or proportional) to the inverse of the variances of the corresponding $\bar{x}_i$'s, i.e. when $w_i = 1/V_i$. The variance of the weighted mean is then:

$$V(X) = 1/W = 1 \Big/ \left(\frac{1}{V_1} + \frac{1}{V_2} + \ldots + \frac{1}{V_k}\right)$$

This result can be applied to the analyses on a number of samples taken from a batch. Suppose there are k samples whose means are $\bar{x}_1, \bar{x}_2, \ldots, \bar{x}_k$ respectively and let n_i denote the number of analyses on the ith sample. Denote the variance of sampling by σ_1^2 and the variance of analytical error by σ_0^2, then the variance of $\bar{x}_i$ is $V_i = \sigma_1^2 + \sigma_0^2/n_i$. The weight to be applied to $\bar{x}_i$ in order to obtain the best estimate for the batch mean is then $w_i = 1/(\sigma_1^2 + \sigma_0^2/n_i)$.

When estimates are available for σ_1^2 and σ_0^2, the precision of any sampling and testing scheme can be assessed. Given the costs of sampling and testing, the cost efficiency can also be assessed. Thus, if $C_1 = $ cost of one sample, $C_0 = $ cost of one analysis, the total cost of the above scheme is $kC_1 + \Sigma n_i C_0$. Its cost efficiency is $W/(kC_1 + \Sigma n_i C_0)$, where $W = \Sigma w_i = \Sigma 1/(\sigma_1{}^2 + \sigma_0{}^2/n_i)$.

The weight w_i, which is the inverse of the variance of $\bar{x}_i$, is sometimes referred to as the amount of information contributed by $\bar{x}_i$. The smaller the variance, the more precise the estimate and the greater the amount of information it contains. The sum of the weights $W = \Sigma w_i$ is the total amount of information contained in the n sample means. Since the variance of X is $1/W$, it follows there is no loss of information when the means are combined in this way.

Appendix 6B

ANALYSIS OF HIERARCHIC DATA

Hierarchic data with two sources of variation

6B·1   Hierarchic data with two sources of variation can be set out as in Table 6B·1.

Table 6B·1

DATA WITH TWO SOURCES OF VARIATION

Group No.	Observations	Group Total	Group Mean	No. of Observations in the Group
1	$x_{11}, x_{12}, x_{13}, \ldots, x_{1n_1}$	S_1	$\bar{x}_1$	n_1
2	$x_{21}, x_{22}, x_{23}, \ldots, x_{2n_2}$	S_2	$\bar{x}_2$	n_2
3	$x_{31}, x_{32}, x_{33}, \ldots, x_{3n_3}$	S_3	$\bar{x}_3$	n_3
.	. . . .	.	.	.
.	. . . .	.	.	.
.	. . . .	.	.	.
k	$x_{k1}, x_{k2}, x_{k3}, \ldots, x_{kn_k}$	S_k	$\bar{x}_k$	n_k

The numbers of observations in each group are not necessarily the same.

Grand total $= S = S_1 + S_2 + S_3 + \ldots + S_k$

Total number of observations $= N = n_1 + n_2 + n_3 + \ldots + n_k$

Grand mean $= S/N = \bar{x}$

The quantities required for the construction of the Analysis of Variance table are:

1. *Correction for the mean*

   Square the grand total and divide by the total number of observations $= S^2/N$.

2. *Total sum of squares*

Square each observation and add, then subtract the correction for the mean:

$$\text{Total sum of squares} = (x_{11}{}^2 + x_{12}{}^2 + \ldots + x^2{}_{kn_k}) - S^2/N$$

$$= \sum_{i=1}^{k} \sum_{j=1}^{n_i} x_{ij}{}^2 - S^2/N$$

The quantity $\sum\limits_{i=1}^{k} \sum\limits_{j=1}^{n_i} x^2{}_{ij}$ is called the crude total sum of squares.

3. *Sum of squares between groups*

Square each group total, divide each by the number of observations in the group, and add. This gives the crude sum of squares between groups. Subtract the correction for the mean:

$$\text{Sum of squares between groups} = (S_1{}^2/n_1 + S_2{}^2/n_2 + \ldots + S_k{}^2/n_k) - S^2/N$$

$$= \sum_{i=1}^{k} (S_i{}^2/n_i) - S^2/N$$

The total degrees of freedom is one less than the total number of observations $= (N - 1)$, and the degrees of freedom between groups is one less than the number of groups $= (k - 1)$. The Analysis of Variance table may then be constructed thus:

Source of Variation	Sum of Squares	Degrees of Freedom	Mean Square
Between Groups	$\sum\limits_{i=1}^{k} (S_i{}^2/n_i) - S^2/N$	$k - 1$	M_1
Within Groups	$\sum\limits_{i=1}^{k} \sum\limits_{j=1}^{n_i} x_{ij}{}^2 - (S_i{}^2/n_i)$	$(N - k)$	M_0
Total	$\sum\limits_{i=1}^{k} \sum\limits_{j=1}^{n_i} x_{ij}{}^2 - S^2/N$	$N - 1$	

The sum of squares and the degrees of freedom within groups are obtained by subtraction from the total.

The mean squares, M_1 and M_0, are the sums of squares divided by the degrees of freedom.

When all groups contain the same number $n = N/k$ observations, the crude sum of squares between groups is equal to $1/n$ times the sum of squares of the individual group totals.

When each group has two observations, the sum of squares within groups can be obtained directly as follows (see § **3·341** for details):

Calculate the differences of the observations within each group. Denote these by $d_1, d_2, \ldots, d_k$. The sum of squares within groups is then $\sum\limits_{i=1}^{k} d_i^2/2$, that is, one-half the sum of squares of these differences.

Quantities estimated by the mean squares

(i) *For equal numbers in the groups*
$$M_1 \to \sigma_0^2 + n\sigma_1^2$$
$$M_0 \to \sigma_0^2$$
where σ_0^2 is the true variance within groups and σ_1^2 the true variance between groups.

(ii) *For unequal numbers in the groups*
$$M_1 \to \sigma_0^2 + \bar{n}\sigma_1^2$$
$$M_0 \to \sigma_0^2$$
where $\bar{n} = (N^2 - \sum\limits_{i=1}^{k} n_i^2)/(k-1)N$.

When all n_i are equal, this expression reduces to $\bar{n} = N/k$.

Hierarchic data with three sources of variation

6B·2 Suppose there are k groups, each consisting of a number of sub-groups. Let the ith group contain r_i sub-groups, and denote the number of observations in these sub-groups by n_{i1}, n_{i2}, etc.

The totals of the observations in each sub-group, denoted by S_{ij}, may be set out as in Table 6B·2.

Table 6B·2

DATA WITH THREE SOURCES OF VARIATION

Group No.	Sub-group Totals and Numbers of Observations	Group Totals and Numbers of Observations
1	$S_{11}(n_{11}), S_{12}(n_{12}), \ldots$	$S_1(n_1)$
2	$S_{21}(n_{21}), S_{22}(n_{22}), \ldots$	$S_2(n_2)$
.	. .	.
.	. .	.
.	. .	.
k	$S_{k1}(n_{k1}), S_{k2}(n_{k2}), \ldots$	$S_k(n_k)$

$S_1, S_2, \ldots$ are the group totals obtained by summing the totals in each of the corresponding sub-groups. The numbers in brackets represent the numbers of observations involved in each total.

Grand total $= S = S_1 + S_2 + \ldots + S_k$
Total number of observations $= N = n_1 + n_2 + \ldots + n_k$
Total number of sub-groups $= R = r_1 + r_2 + \ldots + r_k$

(i) *Correction for the mean.* Square the grand total and divide by the total number of observations $= S^2/N$.

(ii) *Total sum of squares.* This is the sum of squares of all N observations minus the correction for mean. It is based on $(N-1)$ degrees of freedom.

(iii) *Sum of squares between groups.* This is derived from the group totals as follows:

$$(S_1{}^2/n_1 + S_2{}^2/n_2 + \ldots + S_k{}^2/n_k) - S^2/N$$

This is based on $(k-1)$ degrees of freedom.

(iv) *Total sum of squares between sub-groups.* This is derived from the sums of each sub-group. There are $(r_1 + r_2 + \ldots + r_k) = R$ sub-groups in all. The crude sum of squares is obtained by squaring each sub-group total, dividing by the corresponding numbers of observations, and adding.

Total sum of squares between sub-groups

$$= (S_{11}{}^2/n_{11} + S_{12}{}^2/n_{12} + \ldots + S_{k1}{}^2/n_{k1} + \ldots) - S^2/N$$

This is based on $(R-1)$ degrees of freedom.

From the above quantities we derive:

Sum of squares between sub-groups within groups $=$ (iv) $-$ (iii)

Sum of squares within sub-groups $\qquad\qquad\quad =$ (ii) $-$ (iv)

The Analysis of Variance table is:

Table 6B·3

ANALYSIS OF VARIANCE

(Based on Table 6B·2)

Source of Variation	Sum of Squares	Degrees of Freedom	Mean Square
Between Groups $\quad$ ..	$\sum\limits_{i=1}^{k} (S_i{}^2/n_i) - S^2/N$	$k-1$	M_2
Within Groups Between Sub-groups	$\sum\limits_{i=1}^{k} \sum\limits_{j=1}^{r_i} (S_{ij}{}^2/n_{ij}) - \sum\limits_{i=1}^{k} (S_i{}^2/n_i)$	$R-k$	M_1
Within Groups Within Sub-groups	$\sum\limits_{i=1}^{k} \sum\limits_{j=1}^{r_i} \sum\limits_{t=1}^{n_{ij}} x_{ijt}{}^2$ $- \sum\limits_{i=1}^{k} \sum\limits_{j=1}^{r_i} (S_{ij}{}^2/n_{ij})$	$N-R$	M_0
Total .. $\qquad$ .. $\qquad$ ..	$\sum\limits_{i=1}^{k} \sum\limits_{j=1}^{r_i} \sum\limits_{t=1}^{n_{ij}} x_{ijt}{}^2 - S^2/N$	$N-1$	

The mean squares are obtained by dividing the sums of squares by the appropriate degrees of freedom.

Quantities estimated by the mean squares

6B·21 *All groups containing the same number* r *of sub-groups and all sub-groups containing the same number* n *of observations*:

$$M_0 \text{ estimates } \sigma_0^2$$
$$M_1 \text{ estimates } \sigma_0^2 + n\sigma_1^2$$
$$M_2 \text{ estimates } \sigma_0^2 + n\sigma_1^2 + rn\sigma_2^2$$

where σ_0^2 = true variance within sub-groups = experimental error variance.

σ_1^2 = true variance between means of sub-groups independent of σ_0^2.

σ_2^2 = true variance between means of groups independent of σ_0^2 and σ_1^2.

Estimates of σ_0^2, σ_1^2 and σ_2^2 can readily be derived from M_0, M_1, and M_2.

6B·22 *Sub-group numbers and group numbers not all equal as in Table* 6B·3

$$M_0 \text{ estimates } \sigma_0^2$$
$$M_1 \text{ estimates } \sigma_0^2 + \bar{n}_1\sigma_1^2$$
$$M_2 \text{ estimates } \sigma_0^2 + \bar{n}_2\sigma_1^2 + \bar{n}_3\sigma_2^2$$

where $\bar{n}_1 = \left\{ N - \sum_{i=1}^{k} \left(\sum_{j=1}^{r_i} n_{ij}^2/n_i \right) \right\} \Big/ (R - k)$

$\bar{n}_2 = \left\{ \sum_{i=1}^{k} \left(\sum_{j=1}^{r_i} n_{ij}^2/n_i \right) - \sum_{i=1}^{k} \sum_{j=1}^{r_i} n_{ij}^2/N \right\} \Big/ (k - 1)$

$\bar{n}_3 = \left(N^2 - \sum_{i=1}^{k} n_i^2 \right) \Big/ \{(k - 1)N\}$

APPENDIX 6C

CONFIDENCE LIMITS OF THE COMPONENTS OF VARIANCE

CONSIDER the Analysis of Variance of a hierarchic classification with three sources of variation, and for convenience refer to these respectively as "between batches," "sampling error" and "analytical error"; denote their variances by σ_2^2, σ_1^2 and σ_0^2 respectively. The Analysis of Variance table will have the form:

Source of Variation	Degrees of Freedom	Mean Square	Quantities estimated by the Mean Squares
Between Batches	ϕ_2	M_2	$\sigma_0^2 + \bar{n}_2\sigma_1^2 + \bar{n}_3\sigma_2^2$
Sampling Error	ϕ_1	M_1	$\sigma_0^2 + \bar{n}_1\sigma_1^2$
Analytical Error	ϕ_0	M_0	σ_0^2

The expressions for $\bar{n}_1$, $\bar{n}_2$ and $\bar{n}_3$ are given in Appendix 6B·22. Estimates of the variances are:

$$\sigma_0{}^2 \to M_0$$

$$\sigma_1{}^2 \to \frac{1}{\bar{n}_1}(M_1 - M_0)$$

$$\sigma_2{}^2 \to \frac{1}{\bar{n}_3}\left\{(M_2 - M_1) + \frac{(\bar{n}_1 - \bar{n}_2)}{\bar{n}_1}(M_1 - M_0)\right\}$$

The expression $(\bar{n}_1 - \bar{n}_2)/\bar{n}_1$ is usually negligible, in which case the expression for the estimate of $\sigma_2{}^2$ reduces to $(M_2 - M_1)/\bar{n}_3$.

Confidence limits for σ_0

σ_0 is estimated by $\sqrt{M_0}$ based on ϕ_0 degrees of freedom. The factors for the lower and upper confidence limits are given in Table H, from which the confidence limits for σ_0 are readily calculated (see § 4·33).

Confidence limits for σ_1

In the first place we note that:

$$(\sigma_0{}^2 + \bar{n}_1\sigma_1{}^2)/\sigma_0{}^2 = \{1 + \bar{n}_1(\sigma_1/\sigma_0)^2\} \to M_1/M_0$$

M_1/M_0 is the ratio of two independent mean squares and is exactly comparable with the ratio $s_1{}^2/s_0{}^2$ of estimates of two separate variances. The corresponding confidence limits have been considered in § 4·31. The $100(1 - 2\alpha)\%$ confidence limits for the ratio of the true variances are:

$$(s_1{}^2/s_0{}^2)L_1{}^2 \quad \text{and} \quad (s_1{}^2/s_0{}^2)L_2{}^2$$

where L_1 and L_2 are the multipliers for the lower and upper confidence limits for the ratio of two standard deviations based respectively on ϕ_1 and ϕ_0 degrees of freedom, and α the probability level (Table H). These factors have to be squared to apply to the ratio of variances.

The confidence limits for $\{1 + \bar{n}_1(\sigma_1/\sigma_0)^2\}$ are thus:

$$\frac{M_1 L_1{}^2}{M_0} \quad \text{and} \quad \frac{M_1 L_2{}^2}{M_0}$$

Accordingly, the confidence limits for (σ_1/σ_0) are:

$$\sqrt{\left\{\frac{1}{\bar{n}_1}\left(\frac{M_1 L_1{}^2}{M_0} - 1\right)\right\}} \quad \text{and} \quad \sqrt{\left\{\frac{1}{\bar{n}_1}\left(\frac{M_1 L_2{}^2}{M_0} - 1\right)\right\}}$$

These confidence limits are exact. Multiplying these by σ_0 will give the exact confidence limits for σ_1. σ_0, however, is not known exactly and has to be replaced by its estimate, $\sqrt{M_0}$. Approximate confidence limits for σ_1 are therefore:

$$\sqrt{\left\{\frac{1}{\bar{n}_1}(M_1 L_1{}^2 - M_0)\right\}} \quad \text{and} \quad \sqrt{\left\{\frac{1}{\bar{n}_1}(M_1 L_2{}^2 - M_0)\right\}}$$

These limits are good approximations which can be safely applied when ϕ_0 is more than 10, but some caution must be exercised when ϕ_0 is less than 10. Situations in which ϕ_0 is so small should occur only very rarely.

When $M_1 L_1{}^2 \leqslant M_0$, the lower confidence limit must be taken to be zero. This arises when M_1 is not significantly larger than M_0.

Confidence limits for σ_2

These limits are given only for those cases in which $\bar{n}_1$ and $\bar{n}_2$ can be assumed equal. Only in very unbalanced designs, which should rarely occur, will this assumption be seriously in error.

Equating $\bar{n}_1$ to $\bar{n}_2$ in the above table we have:

$$\{1 + \bar{n}_3 \sigma_2{}^2/(\sigma_0{}^2 + \bar{n}_1 \sigma_1{}^2)\} \to M_2/M_1$$

i.e. $\qquad \sigma_2{}^2 \to (M_1/\bar{n}_3)\{(M_2/M_1) - 1\} = (M_2 - M_1)/\bar{n}_3$

Approximate confidence limits for σ_2 are then derived in exactly the same way as for σ_1, substituting M_1 for M_0 and M_2 for M_1. The confidence limits are:

$$\sqrt{\{(M_2 L_1{}^2 - M_1)/\bar{n}_3\}} \quad \text{and} \quad \sqrt{\{(M_2 L_2{}^2 - M_1)/\bar{n}_3\}}$$

where L_1 and L_2 are the appropriate multipliers for ϕ_2 and ϕ_1 degrees of freedom for the chosen value of a.

Appendix 6D*

COMPARISON OF SEVERAL VARIANCE ESTIMATES

METHODS are given in the literature for the comparison of several variance estimates. The best known of these is the Bartlett test [6D·1], which is designed to test the Null Hypothesis that all the variance estimates being compared are estimates of the same variance. This method, however, is very sensitive to departures from the assumption of Normality; indeed, it has been shown that the Bartlett test is a good one for the purpose of testing departures from Normality ([6D·2] and ["Design and Analysis," App. 2A]). Unless there is sufficient evidence to assume that the distributions are at least approximately Normal, the result of the Bartlett test should be interpreted with caution.

In § 4·511 a method is given for the comparison of two variance estimates. This method is insensitive to departures from Normality and may be safely used in all practical situations when a sufficient number of observations are available to justify a comparison of two variance estimates. This method may be readily extended to the comparison of several variance estimates [6D·2].

* This appendix assumes a knowledge of the method of the analysis of variance given in the chapter, and should therefore be read last.

Suppose we wish to compare the variations in two or more sets of observations. The method is simply to divide each group of observations into sub-groups of equal size, using a suitable process of randomisation. Calculate the variance of each sub-group and the logarithms of these variances. These logarithms then supply the "observations" to which we apply the usual method of the Analysis of Variance. The result of this analysis will be an Analysis of Variance table giving a "Mean Square" between groups and a "Mean Square" within groups. A comparison of these two mean squares by the F-test will test the Null Hypothesis that all the variances of the original groups of observations are equal. We may also use the "Mean Square" within groups referred to above as an error variance to compare any two groups.

At a slight sacrifice of information we may use the logarithms of the ranges of the sub-groups in place of the logarithms of the variances.

The method just described for comparing a number of variance estimates is seen to be simply a straightforward example of the application of the Analysis of Variance. The method may also be used when the groups belong to a cross-classification (e.g. see § 6·21), provided a sufficient number of observations exist in each cell of the table. The observations in each cell of the table are divided into sub-groups as explained above, and the variances of these sub-groups are calculated. A new two-way table is formed, the entries in each cell now being the logarithms of the variances of the sub-groups of the observations of the corresponding cell of the original table.

An Analysis of Variance of these log variances is carried out in exactly the same way as the analysis of Example 6·4, and the resulting Analysis of Variance table will enable one to decide whether the variability differs "between breakers" or "between gaugers" in just the same way as the Analysis of Variance of the original observations will enable the corresponding *means* to be compared.

REFERENCES

[6D·1] BARTLETT, M. S. "Properties of Sufficiency and Statistical Tests," *Proc. Royal Soc. A*, **160** (1937), 268.

[6D·2] BOX, G. E. P. "Non-Normality and Tests on Variances," *Biometrika*, **40** (1953), 318–35.

APPENDIX 6E

ANALYSIS OF VARIANCE OF TWO-WAY CROSS-CLASSIFICATION

THE data are arranged in a two-way table as follows:

Table 6E·1
TWO-WAY CLASSIFICATION

Row	Column					Row Totals
	1	2	3	$\ldots$	c	
1	x_{11}	x_{12}	x_{13}	$\ldots$	x_{1c}	R_1
2	x_{21}	x_{22}	x_{23}	$\ldots$	x_{2c}	R_2
3	x_{31}	x_{32}	x_{33}	$\ldots$	x_{3c}	R_3
.	.	.	.		.	.
.	.	.	.		.	.
.	.	.	.		.	.
r	x_{r1}	x_{r2}	x_{r3}	$\ldots$	x_{rc}	R_r
Column totals	C_1	C_2	C_3	$\ldots$	C_c	S

There are r rows and c columns.

Each cell contains one observation, x_{ij}. S is the grand total $= \sum\limits_{i=1}^{r} R_i = \sum\limits_{j=1}^{c} C_j$.
Total number of observations $= rc = n$.

The successive steps in the Analysis of Variance are as follows:

1. Correction for the mean $= S^2/n$.

2. Total sum of squares $=$ sum of squares of all n individual observations minus the correction for the mean $= \sum\limits_{i=1}^{r} \sum\limits_{j=1}^{c} x_{ij}^2 - S^2/n$.

3. Sum of squares between rows $= \sum\limits_{i=1}^{r} R_i^2/c - S^2/n$.

4. Sum of squares between columns $= \sum\limits_{j=1}^{c} C_j^2/r - S^2/n$.

The Analysis of Variance table may now be constructed as in Table 6E·2, where the "remainder" is derived by subtraction from the "total."

The mean squares M_0, M_R and M_C are the sums of squares divided by the appropriate degrees of freedom. σ_0^2, σ_R^2 and σ_C^2 are the true variances of the three sources of variation.

Interpretation of the remainder sum of squares

Let $\bar{x}_j$ represent the mean of the jth column, $\bar{x}_i$ the mean of the ith row and $\bar{x}$ the grand mean.

The deviation of x_{ij} from the grand mean $\bar{x}$ may be represented as:

$$(x_{ij} - \bar{x}) = (\bar{x}_j - \bar{x}) + (\bar{x}_i - \bar{x}) + (x_{ij} - \bar{x}_j - \bar{x}_i + \bar{x})\ldots(6E\cdot1)$$

Now, $(\bar{x}_j - \bar{x})$ and $(\bar{x}_i - \bar{x})$ are simply the deviations of the column and row means from the grand mean, in other words the "column effect" and the

Table 6E·2

ANALYSIS OF VARIANCE

Source of Variation	Sum of Squares	Degrees of Freedom	Mean Square	Quantity estimated by the Mean Squares
Between Rows	$\sum\limits_{i=1}^{r} R_i{}^2/c - S^2/n$	$r - 1$	M_R	$\sigma_0{}^2 + c\sigma_R{}^2$
Between Columns	$\sum\limits_{j=1}^{c} C_j{}^2/r - S^2/n$	$c - 1$	M_C	$\sigma_0{}^2 + r\sigma_C{}^2$
Remainder	$\sum\limits_{i=1}^{r} \sum\limits_{j=1}^{c} x_{ij}{}^2 + (S^2/n)$ $\quad - (\sum\limits_{i=1}^{r} R_i{}^2/c) - (\sum\limits_{j=1}^{c} C_j{}^2/r)$	$(c - 1)(r - 1)$	M_0	$\sigma_0{}^2$
Total ..	$\sum\limits_{i=1}^{r} \sum\limits_{j=1}^{c} x_{ij}{}^2 - S^2/n$	$n - 1$		

"row effect" respectively. If the row and column effects are assumed purely additive, the expected value of x_{ij} would be:

$$\bar{x} + (\bar{x}_i - \bar{x}) + (\bar{x}_j - \bar{x}) \quad \ldots\ldots\ldots\ldots\ldots\ldots(6E\cdot2)$$

The deviation of the observation from its expected value is therefore:

$$x_{ij} - \{\bar{x} + (\bar{x}_j - \bar{x}) + (\bar{x}_i - \bar{x})\} = (x_{ij} - \bar{x}_j - \bar{x}_i + \bar{x}) \ldots(6E\cdot3)$$

which is precisely the third term on the right-hand side of the identity $(6E\cdot1)$,

Squaring both sides of the identity and summing over all observations. the following identity for the sum of squares may readily be proved:

$$\sum\limits_{i=1}^{r} \sum\limits_{j=1}^{c} (x_{ij} - \bar{x})^2 = \sum\limits_{j=1}^{c} r(\bar{x}_j - \bar{x})^2 + \sum\limits_{i=1}^{r} c(\bar{x}_i - \bar{x})^2 +$$

$$\sum\limits_{i=1}^{r} \sum\limits_{j=1}^{c} (x_{ij} - \bar{x}_j - \bar{x}_i + \bar{x})^2 \ldots\ldots(6E\cdot4)$$

$\sum\limits_{i=1}^{r} \sum\limits_{j=1}^{c} (x_{ij} - \bar{x})^2$ is the total sum of squares, $\sum\limits_{j=1}^{c} r(\bar{x}_j - \bar{x})^2$ is the sum of squares between columns, $\sum\limits_{i=1}^{r} c(\bar{x}_i - x)^2$ is the sum of squares between rows.

Rearranging Equation $(6E\cdot4)$, we see that the "Remainder sum of squares" of Table 6E·2 is the sum of squares of the deviations of the actual observations from their expected values.

If we set up the Null Hypothesis that there are no real differences in row means or column means, then each of the mean squares of Table 6E·2 supplies an unbiased estimate of the experimental error variance $\sigma_0{}^2$.

Appendix 6F

ESTIMATION OF MISSING VALUES IN A TWO-WAY CROSS-CLASSIFICATION

It sometimes happens in an experiment of the type considered in Example 6·3, i.e. with data which can be classified independently in two ways, that one or more of the results is unreliable or missing, due to some abnormal cause or due to accident. For example, in penicillin testing a pot may be accidentally disturbed, causing the penicillin solution to leak on the surface.

When only one result in the set is missing or abnormal it may be estimated by the following formula:

$$K(r-1)(c-1) = (r+c-1)S - rS_R - cS_C \quad \ldots\ldots(6F\cdot1)$$

where　K = estimate of missing value,

r = number of rows,

c = number of columns,

S = sum of all known $(rc-1)$ observations,

S_R = sum of row totals, excluding the row from which the result is missing,

S_C = sum of column totals, excluding the column from which the result is missing.

For example, suppose that in Table 6·6 the result on sample 1 of plate 1 is missing. We have:

$$r = 24, \quad c = 6, \quad S = 428 - 7 = 421$$
$$S_R = 428 - 23 = 405, \quad S_C = 428 - 124 = 304$$

Therefore, substituting in the formula:

$$K \times 23 \times 5 = 29 \times 421 - 24 \times 405 - 6 \times 304$$

or
$$115K = 665$$

i.e.
$$K = 665/115 = 5\cdot8$$

This differs from the observed value, owing to experimental error.

Appendix 6G

COMPARISONS OF THE EFFICIENCIES OF DESIGNS BASED ON APPROXIMATELY THE SAME NUMBER OF ANALYSES

There is no single measure for the efficiency of a hierarchic design, but since the efficiency will obviously depend on the precisions of the estimates made of the separate variances, the latter may be used for comparing the efficiencies of two or more designs. We use the following expression as a convenient measure of the precision of an estimate of component of variance:

$$Q = \frac{\text{Upper confidence limit for the estimate}}{\text{Estimated value}}$$

For experiments consisting of the analysis of samples drawn from batches of material let σ_0^2 denote the analytical error, σ_1^2 the sampling error, and σ_2^2

the variance between batches. The Analysis of Variance table will be of the form shown in Appendix 6C, and we shall use the same notation.

$Q(\sigma_0^2)$, the precision of the estimate M_0 of the analytical error, depends only on the number of degrees of freedom available for the estimate, and its value is given by $[L_2(a)]^2$, where $L_2(a)$ is the entry in Table H for the upper confidence limit corresponding to degrees of freedom of ϕ_0 and ∞ and the chosen probability level a.

Using the expression obtained in Appendix 6C for the upper confidence limit of the estimate of σ_1^2, the precision of the estimate of the sampling error is approximately:

$$Q(\sigma_1^2) = \frac{M_1 L_2^2 - M_0}{M_1 - M_0} = L_2^2 + \frac{L_2^2 - 1}{\bar{n}_1 R_1} \quad \dots\dots\dots(6G\cdot1)$$

where $R_1 = \sigma_1^2/\sigma_0^2$, L_2 is the value of $L_2(a, \phi_1, \phi_0)$ in Table H and $\bar{n}_1$ is as defined in Appendix 6B·22.

The precision of the estimate of the variance between batches is more complicated, but provided the design is balanced (i.e. $\bar{n}_1 = \bar{n}_2$) or nearly so, the following formula is a good approximation:

$$Q(\sigma_2^2) = \frac{M_2 {L'}_2^2 - M_1}{M_2 - M_1} = {L'}_2^2 + \frac{{L'}_2^2 - 1}{\bar{n}_3 R_2} \quad \dots\dots\dots(6G\cdot2)$$

where $R_2 = \sigma_2^2/(\sigma_0^2 + \bar{n}_1 \sigma_1^2)$, L'_2 is the value of $L_2(a, \phi_2, \phi_1)$ in Table H and $\bar{n}_3$ is as defined in Appendix 6B·22.

Example

Suppose it is required to determine the most efficient arrangement of sampling and analysing a number of batches subject to the condition that the same number of samples (not exceeding 3) are taken from each batch, the same number of analyses are carried out on each batch and the total number of analyses made are roughly 48. The five designs possible under these conditions are considered below, the precisions of the variance estimates being calculated using the upper limit of the 95% confidence interval (i.e., $a = 0\cdot025$) in the formula for Q.

Design 1

Two samples from each of 12 batches, each sample analysed twice. For this design, which is a balanced one, i.e. the same number of analyses in each sample, we have:

$N = $ total number of analyses $\qquad\qquad\qquad\qquad = 48$

$n_{ij} = $ number of analyses on the jth sample from the ith
$\qquad$ batch $\qquad\qquad\qquad\qquad\qquad\qquad\qquad = 2$ for all i, j

$n_i = \overset{r_i}{\underset{j=1}{\Sigma}} n_{ij} = $ number of analyses on the ith batch $\quad = 4$ for all i

$k = $ number of batches $\qquad\qquad\qquad\qquad\qquad = 12$

$T = $ total number of samples $\qquad\qquad\qquad\qquad = 24$

L

Using the formulae given in App. 6B·22:

$$\bar{n}_1 = (48 - 12 \times 2 \times 4/4)/(24 - 12) \qquad\qquad = 2$$
$$\bar{n}_2 = (12 \times 2 \times 4/4 - 24 \times 4/48)/(12 - 1) \qquad = 2$$
$$\bar{n}_3 = (48^2 - 12 \times 16)/(11 \times 48) \qquad\qquad = 4$$

Since the design is balanced these values can be obtained directly (see App. 6B·21).

We also require the degrees of freedom for the three sources of variation. These are:

$$\phi_2 = \text{degrees of freedom for batches} \qquad = 11$$
$$\phi_1 = \text{degrees of freedom for sampling error} = 12$$
$$\phi_0 = \text{degrees of freedom for analytical error} = 24$$

From Table H we find, using linear interpolation where necessary:

$$L_2(a) = L_2(0·025, \ 24, \ \infty \ = 1·39$$
$$L_2 \quad = L_2(0·025, \ 12, \ 24) = 1·74$$
$$L'_2 \quad = L_2(0·025, \ 11, \ 12) = 1·85$$

Whence
$$Q(\sigma_0{}^2) = 1·39^2 = 1·93$$
$$Q(\sigma_1{}^2) = 1·74^2 + (1·74^2 - 1)/2R_1 = 3·03 + 1·01/R_1$$
$$Q(\sigma_2{}^2) = 1·85^2 + (1·85^2 - 1)/4R_2 = 3·42 + 0·61/R_2$$

Design 2

Three samples from each of 8 batches, each sample analysed twice. This design is also balanced.

The following results are obtained as in design 1:

From App. 6B·21

$$N = 48 \quad n_{ij} = 2 \quad n_i = 6 \quad k = 8 \quad T = 24$$
$$\bar{n}_1 = 2 \quad \bar{n}_2 = 2 \quad \bar{n}_3 = 6$$
$$\phi_2 = 7 \quad \phi_1 = 16 \quad \phi_0 = 24$$

$$L_2(a) = L_2(0·025, \ 24, \ \infty) \qquad = 1·39$$
$$L_2 \quad = L_2(0·025, \ 16, \ 24) \qquad = 1·62$$
$$L'_2 \quad = L_2(0·025, \ 7, \quad 16) \qquad = 2·13$$
$$Q(\sigma_0{}^2) = 1·39^2 \qquad\qquad\qquad = 1·93$$
$$Q(\sigma_1{}^2) = 1·62^2 + (1·62^2 - 1)/2R_1 = 2·62 + 0·81/R_1$$
$$Q(\sigma_2{}^2) = 2·13^2 + (2·13^2 - 1)/6R_2 = 4·54 + 0·59/R_2$$

Design 3

Two samples from each of 16 batches, one sample analysed once and the other twice.

Here: $\qquad N = 48 \quad n_{ij} = 1, 2 \quad n_i = 3 \quad k = 16 \quad T = 32$

From App. 6B·22

$$\bar{n}_1 = \{48 - 16(1^2 + 2^2)/3\}/16 = 4/3 \qquad\qquad\qquad = 1\cdot33$$
$$\bar{n}_2 = \{16(1^2 + 2^2)/3 - 16(1^2 + 2^2)/48\}/15 = 5/3 = 1\cdot67$$
$$\bar{n}_3 = (48^2 - 16 \times 3^2)/(15 \times 48) \qquad\qquad\qquad = 3$$

$$\phi_2 = 15 \qquad \phi_1 = 16 \qquad \phi_0 = 16$$

$$L_2(a) = L_2(0\cdot025, 16, \infty) \qquad\qquad\qquad\qquad = 1\cdot53$$
$$L_2 \;\;= L_2(0\cdot025, 16, 16) \qquad\qquad\qquad\qquad = 1\cdot67$$
$$L'_2 \;\;= L_2(0\cdot025, 15, 16) \qquad\qquad\qquad\qquad = 1\cdot68$$

Therefore $\quad Q(\sigma_0^2) = 2\cdot34$

$$Q(\sigma_1^2) = 1\cdot67^2 + (1\cdot67^2 - 1)/1\cdot33R_1 = 2\cdot79 + 1\cdot34/R_1$$

Since $\bar{n}_1$ and $\bar{n}_2$ do not differ appreciably we may assume them to be equal, and it follows from (6G·2) that:

$$Q(\sigma_2^2) = 1\cdot68^2 + (1\cdot68^2 - 1)/3R_2 = 2\cdot82 + 0\cdot61/R_2$$

Design 4

Three samples from each of 12 batches, two samples analysed once and the other twice.

$$N = 48 \qquad n_{ij} = 1, 1, 2 \qquad n_i = 4 \qquad k = 12 \qquad T = 36$$

$$\bar{n}_1 = \{48 - 12(1^2 + 1^2 + 2^2)/4\}/24 = 5/4 \qquad = 1\cdot25$$
$$\bar{n}_2 = \{12(1^2 + 1^2 + 2^2)/4$$
$$\qquad\qquad - 12(1^2 + 1^2 + 2^2)/48\}/11 = 3/2 = 1\cdot50$$
$$\bar{n}_3 = (48^2 - 12 \times 16)/(11 \times 48) \qquad\qquad = 4$$

$$\phi_2 = 11 \qquad \phi_1 = 24 \qquad \phi_0 = 12$$

$$L_2(a) = L_2(0\cdot025, 12, \infty) \qquad\qquad\qquad = 1\cdot65$$
$$L_2 \;\;= L_2(0\cdot025, 24, 12) \qquad\qquad\qquad = 1\cdot60$$
$$L'_2 \;\;= L_2(0\cdot025, 11, 24) \qquad\qquad\qquad = 1\cdot79$$
$$Q(\sigma_0^2) \qquad\qquad\qquad\qquad\qquad\qquad\qquad = 2\cdot72$$
$$Q(\sigma_1^2) = 1\cdot60^2 + (1\cdot60^2 - 1)/1\cdot25R_1 \qquad = 2\cdot56 + 1\cdot25/R_1$$

and since $\bar{n}_1$ and $\bar{n}_2$ do not differ appreciably we have approximately:

$$Q(\sigma_2^2) = 1\cdot79^2 + (1\cdot79^2 - 1)/4R_2 = 3\cdot20 + 0\cdot55/R_2$$

Design 5

Three samples from each of 10 batches, two samples analysed twice and the third once.

(Note that in this design there are 50 analyses altogether as opposed to 48 in the previous designs.)

$$N = 50 \qquad n_{ij} = 2, 2, 1 \qquad n_i = 5 \qquad k = 10 \qquad T = 30$$

$$\bar{n}_1 = \{50 - 10(2^2 + 2^2 + 1^2)/5\}/20 = 8/5 \qquad\qquad = 1\cdot60$$

$$\bar{n}_2 = \{10(2^2 + 2^2 + 1^2)/5 - 10(2^2 + 2^2 + 1^2)/50\}/9 = 1\cdot80$$

$$\bar{n}_3 = (50^2 - 10 \times 5^2)/(9 \times 50) \qquad\qquad = 5$$

$$\phi_2 = 9 \qquad \phi_1 = 20 \qquad \phi_0 = 20$$

$$L_2(a) = L_2(0\cdot025, 20, \infty) \qquad\qquad\qquad = 1\cdot45$$

$$L_2 \quad = L_2(0\cdot025, 20, 20) \qquad\qquad\qquad = 1\cdot57$$

$$L'_2 \quad = L_2(0\cdot025, 9, \ 20) \qquad\qquad\qquad = 1\cdot92$$

$$Q(\sigma_0^2) \qquad\qquad\qquad\qquad\qquad\qquad\qquad = 2\cdot10$$

$$Q(\sigma_1^2) = 1\cdot57^2 + (1\cdot57^2 - 1)/1\cdot6R_1 \qquad\qquad = 2\cdot46 + 0\cdot91/R_1$$

and the approximate result:

$$Q(\sigma_2^2) = 1\cdot92^2 + (1\cdot92^2 - 1)/5R_2 \qquad\qquad = 3\cdot69 + 0\cdot54/R_2$$

These results are conveniently summarised in the following table:

Design	1	2	3	4	5
No. of batches ..	12	8	16	12	10
No. of analyses per batch	4	6	3	4	5
No. of samples per batch	2	3	2	3	3
Total No. of analyses (d.f. for analytical error)	48 (24)	48 (24)	48 (16)	48 (12)	50 (20)
Total No. of samples (d.f. for sampling error)	24 (12)	24 (16)	32 (16)	36 (24)	30 (20)
d.f. for batches ..	11	7	15	11	9
$Q(\sigma_0^2)$	1·93	1·93	2·34	2·72	2·10
$Q(\sigma_1^2)$	3·03 + 1·01/R_1	2·62 + 0·81/R_1	2·79 + 1·34/R_1	2·56 + 1·25/R_1	2·46 + 0·91/R_1
$Q(\sigma_2^2)$	3·42 + 0·61/R_2	4·54 + 0·59/R_2	2·82 + 0·61/R_2	3·20 + 0·55/R_2	3·69 + 0·54/R_2

It is evident from the results that no design emerges as the best with respect to all three sources of variation. Consequently the ultimate choice will have to be decided by other considerations, such as the economics of sampling and analysing, an account of which will be found in Chapter 4 of "Design and Analysis."

If a balanced design is preferred, then we note that whereas the first design gives the more precise estimate of σ_2^2 it gives the less precise estimate of σ_1^2. The difference, however, is more marked between the precisions of σ_2^2 than those of σ_1^2, particularly when R_1 is greater than unity, as is usually the case; this may be sufficient to favour the first of the balanced designs in these circumstances.

Design 3 has the largest number of batches and, as expected, gives the most precise estimate of σ_2^2. The precisions of σ_0^2 and σ_1^2 are not much inferior to the other designs. This design in which each batch is sampled twice, one sample analysed once and the other twice, is a good compromise.

The above expressions for Q may be simplified for comparisons of the precisions of the estimates of σ_1^2 and σ_2^2. For if we assume that R_1 and R_2 are greater than unity, it is evident that for comparison purposes the values of $Q(\sigma_1^2)$ and $Q(\sigma_2^2)$ may be fairly accurately replaced by L_2^2 and $L'_2{}^2$ respectively, so that we need only consider the terms independent of R_1 and R_2.

CHAPTER 7

LINEAR RELATIONSHIPS BETWEEN TWO VARIABLES

In experimental work we often wish to find out whether, and by how much, the level of one quantity changes with changes in the level of some other quantity. In this chapter a number of problems of this sort are considered, in which the relationship can be represented approximately by a straight line graph.

Introduction

7·1 Physical and chemical laws can usually be expressed in mathematical form. A simple example is Boyle's Law relating volume and pressure of a perfect gas under constant temperature. Some of these laws have been derived empirically and others, for example the sedimentation laws of suspensions of particles in a viscous medium, have been derived mathematically. Each law expresses a relationship between a number of variables and can be used to estimate the value of any one variable given values of all the others. This is the principle used in instruments for measuring temperatures, pressures, flow rates of liquids and gases, etc.

This chapter deals mainly with the problem of estimating empirically a relation between variables. The problem is frequently encountered throughout industry, as for instance in the calibration of instruments. It also arises in laboratory testing when the property of main interest can be determined only by destroying the article, as in tests for breakage strength, or by uneconomical means, as in most service tests on finished materials. It is then desirable to find more economical tests by measuring some other properties which can be related to the required property.

There are many other applications, one of particular importance in the chemical industry being to estimate the dependence of yield and quality of products on reaction conditions such as temperature, pressure, concentration time of reaction, etc. This is required for determining the best operating conditions of the process and for assessing what latitude can be tolerated in the reaction conditions. In chemical processes a further advantage of estimating empirically the relation between variables is that it may increase one's understanding of the chemistry and the kinetics of the reaction.

Functional relationship

7·11 When a unique relationship between the variables exists or can be postulated, then the variables are said to be Functionally Related. As will be shown later, not all related variables are functionally related. If, however, it is known that a variable y and another variable x are functionally related, then an approximation to the form of this relationship over given ranges of the variables can be estimated empirically from measurements of the corresponding values of y and x when these are varied over the given ranges. An example is the calibration of a platinum resistance thermometer, where the resistance is measured at a number of fixed reference points of temperature—such as the boiling points and freezing points of certain liquids—which, under specified conditions, are known not to vary and have been determined with a high degree of accuracy in relation to the absolute temperature scale. For simplicity we shall assume that the resistance and temperature are linearly related, although in practice this is only a rough approximation.

Measurements of resistance are subject to error, and the temperature reference points depend on having exact conditions which may not be experimentally attainable. The plotted points will not therefore fall exactly on a straight line but will vary randomly about one, that is, about the graph of the functional relation. If the determinations are repeated again and again and the average values plotted, then in the limit the points will, if there are no systematic errors, fall exactly on the graph of the functional relation.

The example illustrates the situation in which a unique functional relationship exists and independent repeat determinations on the same sample or on the same reference points vary randomly about it; in other words, the variation of the experimentally determined points about the graph of the functional relationship is due entirely to random experimental errors. The functional relationship describes the relationship between the true values of the variables, and is the one to use when estimating the true value of one variable from an experimentally determined value of the other, even though the latter may be subject to random error. The more precisely the one variable is measured the more precise will be the estimate of the other variable.

Regression

7·12 Relationships between variables are not always unique in the sense that, apart from experimental errors, a particular value of one variable always corresponds to the same value of the other variable. An example is the relation between the weight and height of adult males for a given population. If the weight of each individual is plotted against his height, a diagram such as that given in Figure 7·1 results.

This method of graphical presentation is called a Dot or Scatter Diagram. For any given height there is a wide range of observed weights, and *vice versa*. Some of this variation will be due to errors of measurement of weight and height, but most of it will be due to real variation between individuals. There is thus no unique relationship between true weight and true height. However, the average observed weight for a given observed height increases with increasing height, and the average observed height for a given observed weight increases with increasing weight. The graph of the mean value of one variable for given values of the other variable, when referred to the whole population, is called a Regression. The graph, or in other words, the *locus* of the mean weight of all individuals of given height, is called the Regression of Weight on Height, and the locus of mean height of all individuals of given

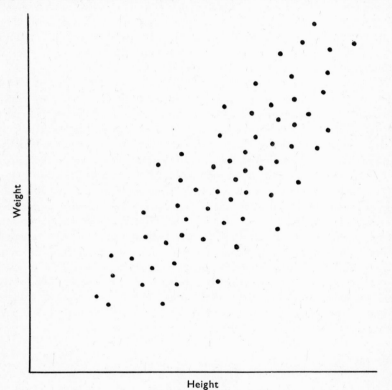

Fig. 7·1. Scatter diagram

weight is called the Regression of Height on Weight. *These two regression lines are generally different.* This is seen by referring to Figure 7·2.

The ellipse is intended to depict the distribution of weight and height. The mid-points of the vertical lines depict the mean weights for given heights, and these fall in a straight line. The mid-points of the horizontal lines depict the mean heights for given weights, and these also fall on a straight line, but this line is different from the other. Both pass through the centre of the ellipse. The two lines are closer together for more elongated ellipses.

An example is also given in Figure 7·32. If the two variables in this figure were functionally related and the scatter arose because of errors of measurement, the two regression lines would still exist and a third line could be drawn representing the functional relationship. All three lines are different; that representing the functional relationship lies between the two regression lines and passes through their point of intersection when the relationship is linear.

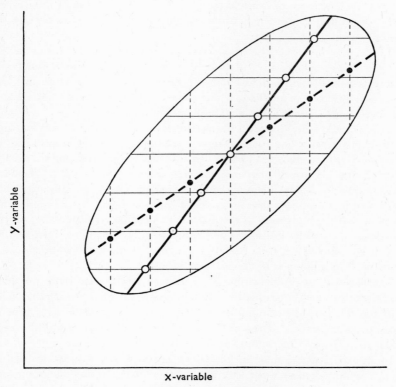

Fig. 7·2. The two regression lines

The possible existence of all three lines may appear a little confusing.* It is emphasised that a functional relationship exists only in those situations where the variation about the line is due entirely to experimental errors, and it represents the relationship between the "true" values of the variables which

---

* Usually, a functional relationship is determined from a planned experiment carried out under carefully controlled conditions. Under these circumstances the variation about the line is small and all three lines are practically identical.

need not refer to any given Universe. On the other hand, regression lines must refer to a given Universe and they represent the relationships between the *means* of the values of one variable and any specified values of the other. They are used in those situations where we are interested in mean values. The following is an illustration based on the example of Figure 7·1. Suppose we had observed the height of an individual from this population but not his weight, and we required to estimate the latter. For the given observed height there is a whole range of possible observed weights; the mean of these gives, however, an unbiased estimate of the weight we might expect to observe for the individual.

There are other situations where we may require the use of mean values, but the above remarks are sufficient to indicate the existence of functional and regression relationships and some of the distinctions between them. The situations have been simplified for this purpose, but more detailed discussions are given in later sections in relation to specific examples.

This chapter deals only with linear regression and functional relationships between two variables, more complex relationships being considered in Chapter 8. Regressions are treated first, because the calculations are usually simpler, and because in most experiments designed to estimate functional relationships the independent variables (e.g. temperature, pressure and concentration in a chemical process) are usually determined without appreciable error so that the regression of the dependent variable (yield, quality) on the independent variables is also the best estimate of the functional relationship. It will be appreciated, however, that it is usually a functional relationship which is of most interest in the chemical industry.

Another class of problems involving related variables are those in which we are not so much interested in estimating one variable from another as in studying the joint distribution of the variables and in obtaining a general measure of the extent of association between them. Such problems come under the title of "Correlation," and are dealt with in § 7·9.

In an experiment comparing the effectiveness of two drug treatments on groups of individuals in a clinical trial, the individuals within each group vary in a number of characteristics, such as weight, age, etc., which may influence the effectiveness of the drug. These unavoidable variations will increase the variation of the response to the drugs within the groups, and if they are not allowed for may seriously reduce the precision of the comparison between the two groups. Methods exist to eliminate the effect of these variations between the individuals, and thus increase the sensitivity of the experiment. These methods come under the title of "Allowance for Concomitant Variation," usually known as "Analysis of Covariance," and are considered in § 7·8 for one "nuisance" factor. More complicated cases are dealt with in Chapter 8.

LINEAR REGRESSION

7·2 An example will first of all be described which requires the use of linear regression. This will be followed by an exposition of the methods involved in deriving the equation of the regression in the general case, and in deriving the confidence limits for the equation and for predictions obtained from it.

Table 7·1

PHYSICAL PROPERTIES OF RUBBER SAMPLES

Specimen No.	Abrasion Loss (g./h.p. hour)	Hardness (degrees Shore)
1	372	45
2	206	55
3	175	61
4	154	66
5	136	71
6	112	71
7	55	81
8	45	86
9	221	53
10	166	60
11	164	64
12	113	68
13	82	79
14	32	81
15	228	56
16	196	68
17	128	75
18	97	83
19	64	88
20	249	59
21	219	71
22	186	80
23	155	82
24	114	89
25	341	51
26	340	59
27	283	65
28	267	74
29	215	81
30	148	86

These methods will then be applied to the particular example, and at the end of the section a more detailed discussion will be given of the meaning and the uses of regression equations.

Example 7·1: Hardness and abrasion resistance of rubber

7·21 An investigation had been carried out on the properties of a synthetic rubber. Varying amounts and types of compounding material were used in the preparation of a number of specimens of this rubber and a wide range in the physical properties was obtained. Table 7·1 gives the abrasion loss and hardness of thirty different specimens. These results are shown graphically in Figure 7·3.

An inspection of these figures shows that high values of abrasion loss tend to coincide with low values of hardness. This is brought out more clearly in the scatter diagram of Figure 7·3, in which the two properties are plotted against each other.

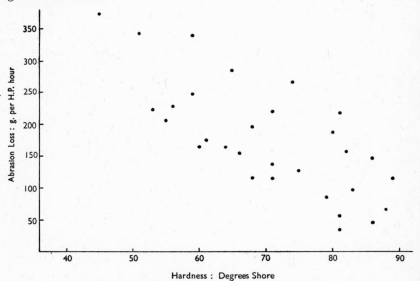

Fig. 7·3. Scatter diagram of abrasion loss and hardness

The errors in measuring the abrasion loss and hardness are small compared with the scatter of the points about any vertical or horizontal line; hence repeat measurements on the same samples will give substantially the same results. Different samples may have the same hardness but different abrasion losses and *vice versa*, these differences being mainly due to real variations between the samples. There is no question, therefore, of a unique functional relationship between these two properties.

The determinations of hardness can be carried out quickly and simply, but the determinations of abrasion loss require an elaborate apparatus and are much more difficult to carry out. It would therefore be a considerable advantage if abrasion loss could be predicted with sufficient accuracy from the measurements of hardness. We require an equation expressing abrasion loss in terms of hardness which in the long run will give the best estimates of abrasion losses on future samples for which only hardness measurements will be carried out. Let y denote abrasion loss and x hardness.

Figure 7·3 represents observed values on 30 specimens; suppose observations were available on an indefinitely large number of specimens. For any given observed value of hardness there would be a distribution of observed values of abrasion loss. This distribution will be assumed to have the same standard deviation, σ, throughout the range of hardness. This assumption may seem a very restrictive one, but in practice it is usually sufficiently closely satisfied, and where it is not, the data can usually be transformed to make it valid. Let $Y(x)$ be the mean abrasion loss for the given hardness, then the distribution of the possible values that the abrasion loss can take for a future specimen with a hardness of x can be expressed in terms of $Y(x)$ and σ. $Y(x)$, considered as a function of x, is the regression of abrasion loss on hardness, and it is clear from an inspection of Figure 7·3 that the regression can be assumed to be linear. Neither $Y(x)$ nor σ is known, and these have to be estimated from the data. Even in a fairly large sample from a Universe in which the regression is linear, the plot of the means of the actual observations of one variable for given values of the other will not usually fall exactly on a straight line, owing to random sampling errors. The regression calculated from a sample will be an *estimate* of the Universe regression, and will be subject to the usual random sampling errors. The estimated regression equation of the abrasion loss on hardness gives the predicted value of abrasion loss for any given value of hardness. The confidence limits of the predicted value can be calculated, and the methods for doing this are considered in later sections.

Estimation of regression lines

7·22   The actual method of estimating a linear regression, usually referred to as fitting a straight line to the data, is straightforward. Denoting abrasion loss by y and hardness by x, we require to estimate the values of the constants a and b in the equation

$$Y = a + bx \quad \dots\dots\dots\dots\dots\dots\dots\dots(7\cdot1)$$

The capital letter is introduced to denote the "predicted" or mean value of the dependent variable, and the small letter is used to denote an observed value.

There are several possible methods of estimating a and b in Equation ($7·1$), but the one of most interest is that which uses what is called the "Method of Least Squares," and which consists in finding the values of the constants a and b that make the sum of squares of the deviations of the observed values (in this case the abrasion loss) from the line a minimum. The line which satisfies these requirements passes through the mean of all the observations. The details of the method are given in Appendix 7A, where it is shown that if we denote the observations by

$$(x_1, y_1), (x_2, y_2), \ldots, (x_n, y_n)$$

the equation of the line is

$$Y = \bar{y} + b(x - \bar{x}) \quad \ldots\ldots\ldots\ldots\ldots\ldots(7·11)$$

where

$$\bar{y} = \text{mean of } y_1, y_2, \ldots, y_n$$
$$\bar{x} = \text{mean of } x_1, x_2, \ldots, x_n$$
$$b = \frac{\Sigma(x - \bar{x})(y - \bar{y})}{\Sigma(x - \bar{x})^2} \quad \ldots\ldots\ldots\ldots\ldots\ldots(7·12)$$

Equation ($7·11$) is the regression of y upon x, and b is termed the Regression Coefficient of y upon x. The numerator of b is the sum of products of the deviations of the observed x's and y's from their respective means; the expression expanded is

$$\Sigma(x - \bar{x})(y - \bar{y}) = (x_1 - \bar{x})(y_1 - \bar{y})$$
$$+ (x_2 - \bar{x})(y_2 - \bar{y}) + \ldots + (x_n - \bar{x})(y_n - \bar{y})$$

and its denominator is the sum of squares of the deviations of the observed x's from their mean—a quantity which has been encountered frequently in the previous chapters in calculating a variance.

A simplified formula, similar to that used for sums of squares, exists for calculating $\Sigma(x - \bar{x})(y - \bar{y})$. The formula is

$$\Sigma(x - \bar{x})(y - \bar{y}) = \Sigma(x - \bar{x})y = \Sigma xy - (\Sigma x \Sigma y)/n \quad \ldots(7·13)$$

The quantity Σxy is called the crude sum of products of the observations, and $(\Sigma x \Sigma y)/n$ is the "correction for the means."

In order to simplify the arithmetical computations, a constant quantity may be substracted from each x and similarly from each y; the constant subtracted from the x's need not be the same as that subtracted from the y's.

Variation about the regression

7·23 The estimated regression equation of y on x based on a sample of n observations is

$$Y = \bar{y} + b(x - \bar{x})$$

where b is given by Equation ($7·12$). The precision of this regression equation will depend on n, on the extent of scatter about the regression and on the range of values of the x variable. The variation about the regression, represented by the deviations of the y observations from the line, must be less than the total variation of the y observations about their mean, and the extent by which it is less represents the amount of variation accounted for by the regression.

Consider any one observation (x_1, y_1) of the sample. The point on the regression corresponding to x_1, given by substituting x_1 in the regression equation, is $Y_1 = \bar{y} + b(x_1 - \bar{x})$. The deviation of the actual observation y_1 from the regression can be expressed as the algebraic difference between two deviations, that of the deviation of the observation from the average, $y_1 - \bar{y}$, and that of the deviation of the corresponding point on the regression from the average, $Y_1 - \bar{y}$; thus:

$$y_1 - Y_1 = (y_1 - \bar{y}) - (Y_1 - \bar{y})$$

This is seen to be an algebraic identity. The deviation $(Y_1 - \bar{y})$ is seen from the regression equation to be equal to $b(x_1 - \bar{x})$.

We can determine $(y_1 - Y_1)$ individually for all observations, square, and add to obtain the sum of squares of the deviations from the regression, but it can be shown algebraically (Appendix 7A) that the sum of squares about the regression is given by

$$\Sigma(y - Y)^2 = \Sigma(y - \bar{y})^2 - \Sigma(Y - \bar{y})^2 \quad \ldots\ldots\ldots(7\cdot2)$$

Now, in Equation (7·2), $\Sigma(y - \bar{y})^2$ is the sum of squares of the observations about their mean $\bar{y}$, and $\Sigma(Y - \bar{y})^2$, called the sum of squares due to the regression, is the sum of squares of the deviations of the corresponding points on the regression from the mean. We thus have the identity:

$$\begin{array}{ccc} \text{Sum of squares of } y & = & \text{sum of squares} & - & \text{sum of squares due} \\ \text{about regression} & & \text{of } y \text{ about mean} & & \text{to the regression} \end{array} \quad ..(7\cdot21)$$

This is equivalent to:

$$\begin{array}{ccc} \text{Sum of squares} & = & \text{sum of squares} & + & \text{sum of squares due} \\ \text{of } y \text{ about mean} & & \text{about regression} & & \text{to the regression} \end{array} \quad ..(7\cdot22)$$

The sum of squares due to the regression represents the amount by which the total sum of squares of one variable is reduced when allowance is made for variations in the other variable. The alternative expression for $\Sigma(Y - \bar{y})^2$ is $b^2\Sigma(x - \bar{x})^2$; the variations in x are thus responsible for a component $b^2\Sigma(x - \bar{x})^2$ of the total variation in y.

The sum of squares about the regression is based on $n - 2$ degrees of freedom, since two degrees of freedom have been used up in calculating the regression, one for the mean $\bar{y}$ and one for the regression coefficient b. Dividing the sum of squares about the regression by the degrees of freedom gives an estimate of σ^2, the Variance About the Regression.

If the regression equation were known exactly, or estimated from an indefinitely large number of observations, the variance about the regression would represent the error with which any observed value of y could be predicted from a given value of x. This variance is often referred to as the error variance, and an estimate of it based on $(n-2)$ degrees of freedom is given by the variance about the regression for the sample. This variance is of fundamental importance because the accuracy of the estimate of the regression equation from a sample depends upon it.

Standard error of the regression coefficient

7·24   It is shown in Appendix 7B that the variance of the regression coefficient is given by the formula:

$$V(b) = \frac{\sigma^2}{\Sigma(x - \bar{x})^2} \quad\ldots\ldots\ldots\ldots\ldots\ldots(7\cdot3)$$

and its standard error by

$$S.E.(b) = \frac{\sigma}{\sqrt{\{\Sigma(x - \bar{x})^2\}}} \quad\ldots\ldots\ldots\ldots\ldots(7\cdot31)$$

where σ^2 is the variance about the regression.

We have to substitute for σ its estimated value, s, based on $(n-2)$ degrees of freedom. If we assume that the variation about the line is Normal,* the $100(1-2a)\%$ confidence limits for b are $b \pm t_a s/\sqrt{\{\Sigma(x - \bar{x})^2\}}$, where t_a is the value of t from Table C corresponding to probability a for $n-2$ degrees of freedom. It will be seen that the precision with which the regression coefficient is estimated depends upon the variance about the regression, the range of the values of the x-variable and the size of the sample. To test whether b differs from zero we calculate the expression

$$t = b/S.E.(b) = b\sqrt{\{\Sigma(x - \bar{x})^2\}}/s \quad\ldots\ldots\ldots\ldots(7\cdot32)$$

and refer the value to the t-tables. t_a and t have the same number of degrees of freedom as s^2, in this case $n-2$.

Standard error of the regression estimate

7·25   Both constants in the regression equation are subject to error because they are estimated from a limited number of observations. An error in the mean gives rise to a constant error for any point on the line, since a change in this constant moves the line up or down without changing its slope. An error in the slope of the line gives rise to an error which is zero at the point $(\bar{x}, \bar{y})$ and increases as x departs from $\bar{x}$.

The regression estimate at a given value x_k of x is

$$Y_k = \bar{y} + b(x_k - \bar{x})$$

It can be shown that $\bar{y}$ and b are independent, whence it follows from § **3·71**, that for any given value of x, say x_k, the variance of the regression estimate is given by

$$V(Y_k) = V(\bar{y}) + (x_k - \bar{x})^2 V(b)$$

* The confidence limits are not sensitive to departures from the assumption of Normality, and may be assumed to be "correct" in most practical situations.

Now $V(\bar{y}) = \sigma^2/n$ and $V(b)$ is given by Formula (7·3),

therefore $$V(Y_k) = \frac{\sigma^2}{n} + \frac{(x_k - \bar{x})^2\sigma^2}{\Sigma(x - \bar{x})^2} \quad \dots\dots\dots\dots(7\cdot33)$$

and $$S.E.(Y_k) = \sigma \sqrt{\left\{\frac{1}{n} + \frac{(x_k - \bar{x})^2}{\Sigma(x - \bar{x})^2}\right\}} \quad \dots\dots\dots(7\cdot331)$$

We substitute for σ the estimate s of the standard error about the regression. The error in the regression estimate is thus a minimum at $x_k = \bar{x}$ and increases as x_k deviates farther from $\bar{x}$.

Standard error of a prediction of a further observation
7·26 Formula (7·331) is the standard error, due to random sampling variation, of a point on the regression, i.e. it is the standard error of the mean value of y for a given x. The observed value of y may vary about the mean value with a standard deviation of σ. These two variations are independent; therefore, when Y_k is used as an estimate of y for a future observation for which the value of x is x_k, the variance of this estimate is the sum of the variance of the mean value (Formula (7·33)) and the variance about this value (σ^2). Thus $V(Y_k)$ becomes

$$\sigma^2 \left\{1 + \frac{1}{n} + \frac{(x_k - \bar{x})^2}{\Sigma(x - \bar{x})^2}\right\} \quad \dots\dots\dots\dots(7\cdot34)$$

and $S.E.(Y_k)$ becomes

$$\sigma \sqrt{\left\{\left(1 + \frac{1}{n}\right) + \frac{(x_k - \bar{x})^2}{\Sigma(x - \bar{x})^2}\right\}} \quad \dots\dots\dots(7\cdot341)$$

95% confidence limits for a predicted value are thus:

$$Y_k \pm ts \sqrt{\left\{\left(1 + \frac{1}{n}\right) + \frac{(x_k - \bar{x})^2}{\Sigma(x - \bar{x})^2}\right\}} \quad \dots\dots\dots(7\cdot35)$$

where s is the estimated value of σ and t is the value obtained from Table C for $(n - 2)$ degrees of freedom corresponding to $P = 0\cdot025$.

Application to example on abrasion loss and hardness of rubber
7·27 *Estimation of the regression of abrasion loss on hardness.* Denote the hardness observations by $x_1, x_2, \dots, x_n$, and the corresponding abrasion losses by $y_1, y_2, \dots, y_n$. Then

n = number of observations = 30

$\Sigma x = 2,108; \quad \bar{x} = 70\cdot27$

$\Sigma(x - \bar{x})^2 = \Sigma x^2 - (\Sigma x)^2/n = 152,422 - 148,122 = 4,300$

$\Sigma y = 5,263; \quad \bar{y} = 175\cdot4$

$\Sigma(y - \bar{y})^2 = \Sigma y^2 - (\Sigma y)^2/n = 1,148,317 - 923,306 = 225,011$

$\Sigma(x - \bar{x})(y - \bar{y}) = \Sigma xy - \Sigma x\Sigma y/n = 346,867 - 369,813 = -22,946$

M

From Equation (7·12), the regression coefficient is
$$b = -\,22{,}946/4{,}300 = -\,5{\cdot}336$$
The regression equation of abrasion loss on hardness is then
$$Y = 175{\cdot}4 - 5{\cdot}336(x - 70{\cdot}27)$$
or
$$Y = 550{\cdot}4 - 5{\cdot}336x \ \dots\dots\dots\dots\dots\dots\dots(7{\cdot}4)$$

Variance about the regression and standard error of regression coefficient

7·271 Sum of squares due to the regression of abrasion loss on hardness
$$= b^2 \Sigma(x - \bar{x})^2 = [\Sigma(x - \bar{x})(y - \bar{y})]^2 / \Sigma(x - \bar{x})^2$$
$$= (-\,22{,}946)^2 / 4{,}300 = 122{,}446$$

Sum of squares about the regression $= 225{,}011 - 122{,}446 = 102{,}565$

This is based on $30 - 2 = 28$ degrees of freedom; hence the variance about the regression $= 102{,}565/28 = 3{,}663$.

Variance of the regression coefficient $= 3{,}663/4{,}300 = 0{\cdot}8519$

Standard error of the regression coefficient $= 0{\cdot}923$

The t factor for $P = 0{\cdot}025$ and 28 degrees of freedom is $2{\cdot}05$, and therefore the 95% confidence limits for the regression coefficient are
$$-\,5{\cdot}336 \pm 2{\cdot}05 \times 0{\cdot}923 = -\,3{\cdot}444 \text{ to } -\,7{\cdot}228$$

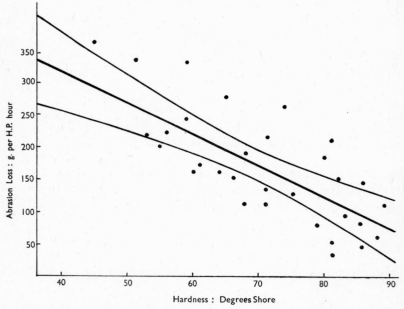

Fig. 7·31. Regression of abrasion loss on hardness and its 95% confidence limits

These limits show the precision with which the regression coefficient is estimated. Since the confidence limits do not include zero, the regression coefficient is statistically significant.

Variance of regression estimate

7·272   The variance of the regression estimate, i.e. the variance of the mean value of abrasion loss for a given value x_k of hardness, is

$$s^2[1/n + (x_k - \bar{x})^2/\Sigma(x - \bar{x})^2]$$
$$= 3,663[1/30 + (x_k - \bar{x})^2/4,300]$$
$$= 122 \cdot 1 + 0 \cdot 852(x_k - \bar{x})^2 \quad \ldots\ldots\ldots\ldots\ldots\ldots(7 \cdot 41)$$

where $\bar{x} = 70 \cdot 27$. The standard error is the square root of this quantity and the 95% confidence limits are plotted on Figure 7·31.

The variance of an estimate of the abrasion loss from a value x_k of hardness is the Expression (7·41) plus the variance about the regression, i.e.

$$\text{Variance} = 3,785 + 0 \cdot 852 \, (x_k - \bar{x})^2$$

The second part of this expression becomes appreciable only when x_k deviates by more than 20 units from the mean value of 70·27. The 95% confidence limits are

$$Y_k \pm 2 \cdot 05\sqrt{\{3,785 + 0 \cdot 852 \, (x_k - \bar{x})^2\}}$$

Predictions of hardness from abrasion loss

7·28   If the problem was one of estimating hardness from abrasion loss we should be interested in the locus of the means of the hardness measurements for given values of the abrasion loss, i.e. the regression of hardness on abrasion loss. Keeping the same notation as above, $y =$ abrasion loss and $x =$ hardness, the regression of x on y is

$$X = \bar{x} + b'(y - \bar{y}) \quad \ldots\ldots\ldots\ldots\ldots\ldots(7 \cdot 5)$$

where
$$b' = \Sigma(x - \bar{x})(y - \bar{y})/\Sigma(y - \bar{y})^2$$

This is obtained by minimising the sum of squares of the x deviations, i.e. the *horizontal* distances from the regression line. The means $\bar{x}$ and $\bar{y}$ and the quantities to derive b' have already been calculated in § **7·27**. These give

$$X = 70 \cdot 3 - 0 \cdot 102(y - 175 \cdot 4)$$

i.e. $$X = 88 \cdot 2 - 0 \cdot 102y \quad \ldots\ldots\ldots\ldots\ldots\ldots(7 \cdot 51)$$

The variance about the regression is now estimated by

$$s^2 = \frac{\Sigma(x - \bar{x})^2 - b'^2\Sigma(y - \bar{y})^2}{n - 2} \quad \text{(Compare with § \textbf{7·23}.)}$$

$$= \frac{1}{n - 2}\left\{\Sigma(x - \bar{x})^2 - \frac{[\Sigma(x - \bar{x})(y - \bar{y})]^2}{\Sigma(y - \bar{y})^2}\right\} = 70 \cdot 0011$$

The standard error of the regression coefficient b' is given by

$$\sqrt{\{s^2/\Sigma(y - \bar{y})^2\}} = \sqrt{(70 \cdot 0011/225,011)} = 0 \cdot 0176$$

[Compare with Formula (7·31).]

The 95% confidence limits for b' are

$$- 0{\cdot}102 \pm 2{\cdot}05 \times 0{\cdot}0176 = - 0{\cdot}066 \text{ to } - 0{\cdot}138$$

The two regression lines have been plotted in Figure 7·32, where it is seen that the two regressions are different. We should note that the problems represented by the two regression lines are different, the actual regressions having been obtained by different processes. The two regressions coincide only when all the points fall exactly on a straight line, which is the case when a linear functional relationship exists between variables both of which can be measured without error.

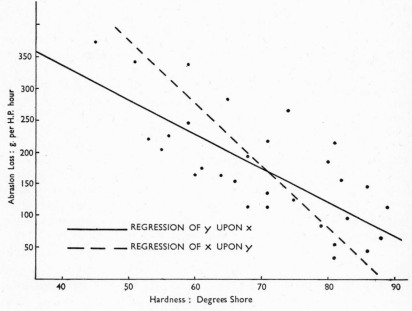

Fig. 7·32. Regression lines

The difference between two regression coefficients

7·29 When two estimates of a regression coefficient are available, for example coefficients estimated from two sets of experiments, it is usually required to compare their values. Let the two regression coefficients be b_1 and b_2 and let σ^2 be the error variance, which is usually estimated by combining the mean squares about the two regressions, i.e.

if $s_1{}^2 =$ variance about the first regression (slope b_1)

with ϕ_1 degrees of freedom

and $s_2{}^2 =$ variance about the second regression (slope b_2)

with ϕ_2 degrees of freedom

then σ^2 is estimated by

$$s^2 = (\phi_1 s_1^2 + \phi_2 s_2^2)/(\phi_1 + \phi_2)$$

From Equation (7·3) and substituting s for σ,

$$V(b_1) = s^2/\Sigma_1(x - \bar{x})^2 \qquad V(b_2) = s^2/\Sigma_2(x - \bar{x})^2$$

where $\Sigma_1(x - \bar{x})^2$ is based on the observations from which b_1 was calculated and similarly for $\Sigma_2(x - \bar{x})^2$. Therefore, since b_1 and b_2 are independent estimates [§ **3·71**]:

$$V(b_1 - b_2) = s^2 \left[\frac{1}{\Sigma_1(x - \bar{x})^2} + \frac{1}{\Sigma_2(x - \bar{x})^2} \right]$$

and

$$S.E.(b_1 - b_2) = s \sqrt{\left[\frac{1}{\Sigma_1(x - \bar{x})^2} + \frac{1}{\Sigma_2(x - \bar{x})^2} \right]}$$

These enable confidence limits for the difference to be calculated, using the value of t with $(\phi_1 + \phi_2)$ degrees of freedom. If the variances about the two regressions cannot be assumed equal, then the confidence limits are calculated using a method similar to that of § **4·232**.

Conditions for valid estimation of the regression equations

7·3 Regression equations refer to a given Universe. For the example of abrasion loss and hardness, the Universe is the totality of samples of the given synthetic rubber produced by varying the qualities and amounts of the given compounding materials within specified practical limits. The regression equations may well be different if we change to another medium, such as natural rubber or another type of synthetic rubber. The predictions of abrasion loss from hardness therefore apply only to samples of rubber from the specified Universe.

When both regression equations are required, the observations from which the regression equations are estimated should be completely random with respect to the Universe. A laboratory research programme cannot always be carried out on the basis of strict randomness, particularly when the question of relating variables is only a part of the programme. In the programme from which this example was drawn, the variations in the amounts of compounding ingredients were made to cover the ranges of interest, and in this respect the samples of rubber were not strictly random. However, no selection was made in relation to the results of the tests obtained on abrasion loss and hardness, and in this respect the results could be considered random.

Because the regression of y on x is the locus of the mean of the y observations for given values of x, then we can select the values of x. Thus, an unbiased estimate of the regression of abrasion loss on hardness can be obtained using only those results having preselected values of hardness. This is illustrated by Figure 7·4.

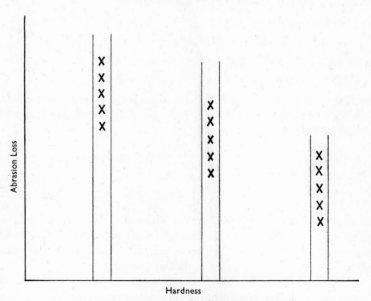

Fig. 7·4. Array distributions (schematic)

The mean of each of the arrays gives an unbiased estimate of the regression value for the appropriate hardness, and therefore the calculated regression of abrasion loss on hardness from these restricted results will be unbiased. It will naturally not be as precise in this case as an estimate based on all the tests. In some situations, however, it may be practicable to select values of the independent variable and to concentrate effort on these points. An estimate of the regression obtained from such results will usually be considerably more precise than one obtained from the same number of points scattered over the same range of the independent variable. This principle is used more extensively in planned experiments to estimate the functional relationship, and will be considered later.

Although selection of results with respect to hardness will not bias the regression of abrasion loss on hardness, such results will be useless for estimating the regression of hardness on abrasion loss.

Effect of errors of measurement
7·31 The effect of errors of measurement on the regression equation will be more clearly understood after reading §7·4 and §7·5 dealing with linear functional relations, and the reader may require to return later to this present section.

In the discussion of the regression of abrasion loss on hardness it has been repeatedly emphasised that we are dealing with *observed* values. The regression equation estimates the mean value of the abrasion loss which would be expected on specimens for which the observed hardness is x_k. When the testing errors are negligible compared with the variation about the regression, then in effect we are dealing with "true" values of the variables.

Consider a vertical array in a scatter diagram for two variables x and y, y being the dependent variable, and suppose that the points are determined without error. The mean of this array will be an unbiased estimate of the mean of the Universe of values of y for the given x, and therefore varies around the regression of y upon x. If now the values of y are subject to error but x is free from error, no bias will be introduced in the mean, though it will have a greater variance due to the errors in the determination of y. The calculated regression of the observed values of y on x is then an unbiased estimate of the regression of the true values of y on x. The only effect of the errors in the measurement of y is to increase the variability about the regression and to render the estimate of the latter less reliable. In addition to estimating the locus of the means of the observed values of y for given values of x, the regression also estimates the locus of the means of the "true" values of y.

In this situation the variance of a regression estimate remains the same (Formula 7·33) and the variance of a prediction of an *observation* of abrasion loss also remains the same (Formula 7·34), but the variance of the prediction of the *true* value of the abrasion loss will be less to the extent of the testing error variance of y.

When the independent variable is subject to appreciable error the situation is a little more complicated. The regression of observed values on observed values and the regression of true values on true values will be different, the regression of the true values being steeper than the regression of the observed values, but an estimate of either will pass through the mean of the observations. The full treatment is beyond the scope of this book, but we can always estimate the regression of the observed values of one variable on the observed values of the other, and although this may not be the best possible equation for estimating one variable from the other it will often be found adequate. When the testing errors are predominant, the variations of the true values about the regression can sometimes be ignored and the variables can be assumed to be functionally related.

LINEAR FUNCTIONAL RELATIONSHIPS

7·4 When the true values of two variables (i.e. the limits to which mean values tend on repetition of the determinations) fall on a straight line, the two variables are said to be linearly functionally related. In practice a linear functional relationship exists between two variables when the variation about a suitably drawn straight line is due, or can be assumed to be due, entirely to experimental errors.

Chemists and physicists are usually interested in functional relationships, but it is not always possible to estimate them from observed results. However, we can always estimate the locus of the mean of the y variable for given values of the x variable, and also the locus of the mean of the x variable for given values of the y variable. Although, as shown earlier in Figure 7·2, these lines are not the same, they will often serve satisfactorily for prediction purposes. There are, however, a number of situations in which the functional relationships can be readily estimated.

Functional relations are usually estimated from the results of a controlled experiment in which one variable is set at certain chosen values, and the other variable is then measured at these conditions. An example which has already been considered in the introduction is the calibration of a platinum resistance thermometer, where the resistance is measured at given temperature reference points. Other examples arise in the development of chemical processes when the dependence of yield and quality of the product on such factors as temperature, concentration, time of reaction, etc., has to be determined. A simple illustration involving one factor would be an investigation into the dependence of yield on temperature; in such an investigation the process would usually be carried out at certain chosen values of the temperature and the resulting yields of product measured.

The controlled variable is the independent variable, and the other is the dependent variable. Usually the former can be set with negligible error compared with the latter; for example the temperature in a chemical reaction can usually be controlled fairly precisely, and practically all the experimental error arises in the assessment of the yield.

Linear functional relationships when one variable has negligible error

7·5 When the independent variable can be set or determined with negligible error, the functional relationship is estimated directly by the regression equation of the dependent variable on the controlled independent variable. The reason for this will be apparent from the following considerations. Let x_k be one of the values chosen for the independent variable and let $y_1, y_2, \ldots, y_n$ be repeat values of the other variable determined at the chosen value x_k of x. The value x_k of x is assumed free from error, and it therefore represents a "true" value. The corresponding point on the functional relation must then be on the vertical through x_k. The values $y_1, y_2, \ldots, y_n$ vary, but their mean will be an unbiased estimate of the true value which will become more precise as n increases; in other words, the mean value of y for the given x is an unbiased estimate of a point on the functional relationship, but by definition it is also an estimate of a point on the regression line. The same applies for all other values of x, and therefore the regression of y on x is also an estimate of the functional relationship.

The calculations are exactly as those given previously in §§ **7·22–7·26**; thus the estimate of the linear functional relation is

$$Y - \bar{y} = b(x - \bar{x}) \quad \dots\dots\dots\dots\dots(7·6)$$

where
$$b = \Sigma(x - \bar{x})(y - \bar{y})/\Sigma(x - \bar{x})^2 \quad \dots\dots\dots(7·61)$$

The variance about the line is estimated by

$$s^2 = \Sigma(y - Y)^2/(n - 2) \quad \dots\dots\dots\dots(7·62)$$

Corresponding to Formula (*7·31*), the standard error of the slope *b* is

$$S.E.(b) = s/\sqrt{\Sigma(x - \bar{x})^2} \quad \dots\dots\dots\dots(7·63)$$

and corresponding to Formula (*7·331*), the standard error of the estimate obtained from the functional relation for a given value $x = x_k$ is

$$S.E.(Y_k) = s\sqrt{\{1/n + (x_k - \bar{x})^2/\Sigma(x - \bar{x})^2\}} \dots\dots(7·64)$$

Here we are not interested in the values of *y* which would be observed, but only in the estimate of the true value. Consequently Formula (*7·341*), which gives the standard error of the value of *y* which would be observed, is not required. The functional relationship represents the relationship between "true" values, and since it is required to estimate the true value of *y* for a given value x_k of *x*, this is obtained directly from Equation (*7·6*). Formula (*7·64*) thus gives the standard error of the estimate of *y*. This standard error is seen to be less than that for an experimentally determined *y*, since in the process of fitting the line the errors in the individual observations y_1, y_2, ..., y_n are "averaged out."

Since the variation about the functional relationship is assumed to be due entirely to experimental errors in the observations *y*, the variance about the functional relationship is an estimate of the error variance of *y*. If an independent estimate of the latter is available it is then possible to test the hypothesis that the variation about the functional relationship is due entirely to experimental errors in *y*.

7·51   In a calibration problem it can usually be assumed that one variable has negligible error; for example, in the calibration of a platinum resistance thermometer referred to earlier it can be assumed that the errors in setting the chosen values of the temperature are negligible, so that the regression equation

$$Y = \bar{y} + b(x - \bar{x})$$

where *Y* is the resistance and *x* the temperature, estimates the functional relationship. The latter is often referred to as the standard curve.

The temperature is estimated from a measurement of the resistance. If this were a regression problem we should use the regression of temperature upon resistance, i.e. *x* upon *y*, for this purpose, but since we are interested in estimating true values, and since the functional relation is unique, the same equation should be used for estimating both *x* from *y* and

y from x. Herein lies an important difference between regression equations and functional relationships.

The estimate of x from a given value y_k of y is, from Equation (7·6):

$$X_k = (y_k - \bar{y})/b + \bar{x}\dots\dots\dots\dots\dots(7\cdot65)$$

Standard error of estimate

7·52 It is now required to determine the confidence limits for the value of x corresponding to an observation y_k of y. An approximate formula will be given in this section, and the exact formula, which is more complicated, is given in Appendix 7D. The approximate formula will be found to be sufficiently accurate for most practical purposes.

The estimate of x for a given value y_k of y is given by Equation (7·65). Since $V(\bar{x})$ is zero, the variance of the estimate is

$$V(X_k) = \frac{V(y_k - \bar{y})}{b^2} + \left(\frac{y_k - \bar{y}}{b}\right)^2 \frac{V(b)}{b^2}$$

This is derived using the method of § **3·72**. Now,

$$V(b) = \sigma^2/\Sigma(x - \bar{x})^2$$

where σ^2 is the variance about the line, and

$$V(y_k - \bar{y}) = \left(1 + \frac{1}{n}\right)\sigma^2$$

If the experiment had been arranged so that y_k was the mean of m determinations of the resistance, we should have had

$$V(y_k - \bar{y}) = \left(\frac{1}{m} + \frac{1}{n}\right)\sigma^2$$

In this general case, therefore:

$$V(X_k) = \left(\frac{1}{m} + \frac{1}{n}\right)\frac{\sigma^2}{b^2} + \frac{(y_k - \bar{y})^2}{b^2}\frac{\sigma^2}{b^2\Sigma(x - \bar{x})^2}$$

$$= \frac{\sigma^2}{b^2}\left\{\frac{1}{m} + \frac{1}{n} + \frac{(y_k - \bar{y})^2}{b^2\Sigma(x - \bar{x})^2}\right\} \quad\dots\dots\dots\dots(7\cdot651)$$

$$S.E.(X_k) = \frac{\sigma}{b}\sqrt{\left\{\left(\frac{1}{m} + \frac{1}{n}\right) + \frac{(y_k - \bar{y})^2}{b^2\Sigma(x - \bar{x})^2}\right\}} \quad\dots\dots\dots(7\cdot652)$$

The estimate s of the standard deviation about the regression based on $n-2$ degrees of freedom has to be used for σ; the confidence limits for X_k can then be derived using the appropriate value of t.

We note that $S.E.(X_k)$ decreases as m increases, i.e. the accuracy of the predicted value X_k increases with the number of replications for the determination of y. The reason for this is that the effect of experimental errors is reduced by replicating, but for a given estimate of the functional relationship the standard error cannot be reduced below the value given by Expression (7·652) with the term $1/m$ omitted.

7·53   The independent variable need not be controlled to apply the above methods of calculation—the only necessary condition is that the independent variable is determined with negligible error. The functional relation is still given by the regression of y upon x.

Although the independent variable is the one that is most likely to be accurately determined, it is possible in some instances that the reverse is the case, that y is accurately determined and the independent variable x is not. For this situation the regression of x upon y then gives an unbiased estimate of the functional relationship. This is true even when the x variable is the one that is controlled—the criterion is simply which variable is free from error.

The functional relationship in the more general case, where both x and y are subject to appreciable error, is considered later in the chapter, where also further discussion is given on the uses of regression equations and functional relationships. When the ranges of the x and y variables used to determine the relationships are very much larger than the errors of measurement, the two regressions and the functional relationship will be very close to one another and for practical purposes may be assumed to be coincident.

Example 7·2

7·54   The following example used to illustrate functional relationship with one variable controlled is in effect a calibration problem and refers to the assay of samples of penicillin. The data are given in Table 7·2, and are to be used to determine a standard curve.

Six concentrations of pure penicillin differing in twofold steps from 1 unit to 32 units per ml. are set up on a plate (see § **6·6** for details of technique). Table 7·2 gives the circle diameters of the zones of inhibition in millimetres for each concentration.

Table 7·2

PENICILLIN CONCENTRATIONS

Concentration of penicillin solution	1	2	4	8	16	32
$x = \log_2$ concentration	0	1	2	3	4	5
Circle diameter (mm.) $= y$	15·87	17·78	19·52	21·35	23·13	24·77

In this example the x-variable (i.e. concentration of penicillin) has been set without appreciable error at certain fixed values. However, errors arise in the determination of the circle diameter.

The results of Table 7·2 are plotted in Figure 7·5. A logarithmic scale to the base 2 is taken for the concentration of penicillin, since on this scale, the

relation appears linear. Moreover, the series of concentrations 1, 2, 4, 8, . . .
become equally spaced, twofold increases being represented by unit displace-
ments along the concentration axis.

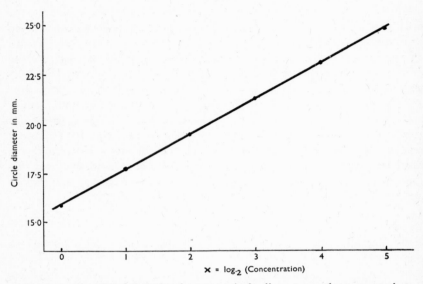

Fig. 7·5. Penicillin. Relation between circle diameter and concentration

The calculation of the regression of y upon x for this example is identical
with that for Example 7·1. The details are:

$$n = 6 \qquad \Sigma x = 15 \qquad\qquad\qquad \Sigma y = 122\cdot42$$
$$\bar{x} = 2\cdot50 \qquad\qquad\qquad \bar{y} = 20\cdot40$$
$$\Sigma x^2 = 55 \qquad\qquad\qquad \Sigma xy = 337\cdot24$$
$$(\Sigma x)^2/n = 37\cdot5 \qquad\qquad (\Sigma x)(\Sigma y)/n = 306\cdot05$$
$$\Sigma(x - \bar{x})^2 = 17\cdot5 \qquad \Sigma(x - \bar{x})(y - \bar{y}) = 31\cdot19$$
$$\therefore\; b = 31\cdot19/17\cdot5 = 1\cdot782$$

The regression of y on x is therefore given by

$$Y = 20\cdot40 + 1\cdot782(x - 2\cdot50)$$
$$\text{i.e. } Y = 15\cdot94 + 1\cdot782x$$

This equation is an estimate of the functional relationship, and is therefore
the one to use for estimating y from a given x and also for estimating x from
a given y. In practice the equation is required for the purpose of estimating
the concentration of an unknown sample from an observed value of the circle
diameter. We therefore write it in the form

$$X = (y - 15\cdot94)/1\cdot782$$

where x, Y have been replaced by X, y respectively, in accordance with our notation of capital letters for predicted values and small letters for observed values.

Standard error of the estimate of x

7·55   The standard error of an estimate of x is given by Formula (7·652) with $m = 1$.

For the data of Table 7·2:

$$\Sigma y^2 = 2{,}553\cdot3880$$
$$(\Sigma y)^2/n = 2{,}497\cdot7761$$
$$\therefore \; \Sigma(y - \bar{y})^2 = 55\cdot6119$$

Thus, from (7·21) and the results obtained above:

Sum of squares
about the regression $= \Sigma(y - \bar{y})^2 - b^2 \Sigma(x - \bar{x})^2$

$$= \Sigma(y - \bar{y})^2 - \frac{[\Sigma(x - \bar{x})(y - \bar{y})]^2}{\Sigma(x - \bar{x})^2}$$

$$= 55\cdot6119 - (31\cdot19)^2/17\cdot5 = 0\cdot0224$$

Whence the estimated variance about the regression is

$$s^2 = 0\cdot0224/4 = 0\cdot0056$$

Substituting in Formula (7·652) the standard error of the estimated value of x corresponding to an observed circle diameter y is

$$\frac{\sqrt{0\cdot0056}}{1\cdot782} \sqrt{\left\{ \left(1 + \frac{1}{6}\right) + \frac{(y - 20\cdot40)^2}{55\cdot59} \right\}}$$

$$= 0\cdot042 \sqrt{\left\{ 1\cdot1667 + \frac{(y - 20\cdot40)^2}{55\cdot59} \right\}}$$

Determination of the functional relationship when both variables are subject to error

7·6   The assumptions are that a linear functional relationship exists between y and x and that the only reason why the observations depart from this is the errors in the measurement of y and x. These errors are assumed to be independent—they usually are in practice.

Let the error variance of y be σ_y^2 and that of x be σ_x^2. A separate experiment may be necessary to determine these, but usually, when obtaining the initial data, repeat measurements will be made on each sample in order to supply estimates of σ_x^2 and σ_y^2.

The line must pass through the mean of the observations, and must therefore have the form

$$y = \bar{y} + b(x - \bar{x})$$

where the slope b has to be determined. This is given by [7·1]

$$b = m + \sqrt{(m^2 + k^2)}$$

where $k^2 = \sigma_y^2/\sigma_x^2$:

and $\quad m = \{\Sigma(y - \bar{y})^2 - k^2\Sigma(x - \bar{x})^2\}/2\Sigma(x - \bar{x})(y - \bar{y})$.

The error variances of x and y are then estimated from the formula

$$\sigma_y^2 = k^2\sigma_x^2 = \frac{\Sigma(y - \bar{y})^2 - b\Sigma(x - \bar{x})(y - \bar{y})}{(n - 2)}$$

To apply the above formulae it is not necessary to know the values of both σ_x^2 and σ_y^2 but simply the ratio of the two. Even when one variance only is known, b can still be estimated; the formula is then

$$b = \frac{\Sigma(y - \bar{y})^2 - n\sigma_y^2}{\Sigma(x - \bar{x})(y - \bar{y})}$$

in which we have assumed σ_y^2 to be the known and σ_x^2 the unknown variance. An estimate of σ_x^2 can then be obtained from the formula

$$\sigma_x^2 = \frac{\Sigma(x - \bar{x})^2}{(n - 2)} - \frac{\Sigma(x - \bar{x})(y - \bar{y})}{(n - 2)b}$$

where n is the number of pairs of observations (x, y). The above formula for σ_y^2 applies when σ_y^2 is the unknown variance.

Standard errors of the constants of the linear functional relation

7·61 If the estimated functional relation is written in the form

$$y = \bar{y} + b(x - \bar{x}) \dots\dots\dots\dots\dots\dots\dots(7\cdot66)$$

it can be shown that the variance of b is

$$V(b) = \frac{(k^2 + b^2)^2[\Sigma(y - \bar{y})^2 - b\Sigma(x - \bar{x})(y - \bar{y})]}{k^2(n - 2)[k^2\Sigma(x - \bar{x})^2 + b\Sigma(x - \bar{x})(y - \bar{y})]} \dots(7\cdot661)$$

When both σ_x^2 and σ_y^2 are known:

$$V(b) = \frac{\sigma_x^2(k^2 + b^2)^2}{k^2\Sigma(x - \bar{x})^2 + b\Sigma(x - \bar{x})(y - \bar{y})} \dots\dots\dots(7\cdot662)$$

where k is the ratio of the standard error of measurement of the y observations to the standard error of measurement of the x observations, i.e. $k = \sigma_y/\sigma_x$.

The variance of a predicted value of y for a given value x_0 of x is

$$V(y_0) = V(\bar{y}) + (x_0 - \bar{x})^2V(b) + b^2V(x_0 - \bar{x})$$

$$= k^2\sigma_x^2/n + (x_0 - \bar{x})^2V(b) + b^2\sigma_x^2\left(1 + \frac{1}{n}\right)$$

where $V(b)$ is given by Equation (7·661), or by Equation (7·662) when both σ_x and σ_y are known. σ_x has to be taken into account in the last term because x_0 may be in error and a repeat determination may give a different value for x.

Fitting of linear functional relationship when the error variances of x and y are unknown

7·62   A simple method for obtaining a good estimate of a linear functional relationship for certain situations when the errors in the variables are unknown is given by M. S. Bartlett [7·2].

Since it is known that the linear functional relation must pass through the mean, one point on the line is readily determined, and all that remains is to estimate the slope. The procedure is to plot the points on a graph and divide the n plotted points into three groups, the two end groups having the same number, p, of points chosen to be as near to $n/3$ as possible. The three groups must be non-overlapping when considered in a given direction, e.g. in the x-direction. It is assumed that the errors in the observations do not interfere with the division made. This condition is usually satisfied in a planned experiment because the intervals between adjacent values of the dependent (or the independent) variable are much larger than the errors in their measurement. This is particularly so for the x-variable, with respect to which the division should therefore be made. The slope is determined as follows. Compute the means of each of the two end groups and denote them by $(\bar{x}_1, \bar{y}_1)$, $(\bar{x}_3, \bar{y}_3)$. The line joining these two points gives the estimate of the slope, i.e.

$$b = (\bar{y}_3 - \bar{y}_1)/(\bar{x}_3 - \bar{x}_1)$$

The functional relation is then a line, with this slope, passing through the grand mean.

The confidence limits β_1 and β_2 of the true value of the regression coefficient are given by the roots of the quadratic equation with respect to β:

$$\tfrac{1}{2}p(n-3)(\bar{x}_3 - \bar{x}_1)^2(b-\beta)^2 = t^2(C_{yy} - 2\beta C_{xy} + \beta^2 C_{xx})\ldots.(7\cdot67)$$

where n = number of pairs of observations,

       p = number of pairs of observations in each end group,

       b = estimate of the regression coefficient given above,

$\bar{x}_1, \bar{x}_3$ = means of the two outer groups,

   C_{xx} = sum of squares of x *within* the three groups,

   C_{xy} = sum of products of x and y *within* the three groups,

   C_{yy} = sum of squares of y *within* the three groups,

     t = the value of t for the confidence interval required for the $(n-3)$ degrees of freedom available within the groups.

The method of calculating these quantities is detailed in Appendix 7E, where a numerical illustration is also given.

Controlled and uncontrolled experiments

7·63   There are in general two ways of estimating the relation between two variables: one is a controlled experiment in which one variable is held at certain preset values, and the other an uncontrolled experiment in which the variations occur by chance. Consider a chemical process in which variations occur in the yield of product from batch to batch and it is necessary to investigate the causes of this variation. It is found on examination of the batch records that there are variations in temperature of the reaction from batch to batch. It is required to find whether temperature variations are the cause or a contributory cause of the yield variation. There are two ways of investigating this:

(a) To carry out a controlled experiment in which the temperature is carefully maintained at certain chosen values for a number of batches; for example, two or more batches may be made at each of four different temperatures covering a range larger than that found in normal manufacture.

(b) To use the actual process records of yield and temperature and examine the relation between them.

In the controlled experiment it is clear that, both for estimating the slope of the relationship and for predicting the yield at any given temperature, the relation of interest is the functional one and not that given by either of the regression lines. Usually, however, the controlled variable, which is considered as the independent variable and is denoted by x, can be set with a high degree of accuracy in relation to the error in the other variable, in which case the regression of y on x provides an estimate of the functional relationship. As an added safeguard, the range of the independent variable can be made very large compared with the error in its determination, in which case both regression equations and the functional relationship, for practical purposes, coincide.

In the uncontrolled experiment the batches must be considered as a sample from the Universe of batches. Many factors other than variation in temperature and errors in measurement will contribute to the variation in yield. Errors in estimation of yield and temperature may, in fact, account for only a small proportion of the variation. Although we may be interested in the functional relationship, we cannot estimate it from the data, and must then use the regression lines to assess the association between the two variables. Predictions from these regression lines apply only to the given process operated in the same way as before, on the assumption that the process is stable.

The second method is rarely satisfactory, owing to the probable existence of several other uncontrolled variations. If the temperature cannot be kept under control, it is fair to assume that other factors, known or unknown, also cannot be controlled, and variations in these factors will tend to mask the effect of temperature and may be sufficient to mask it altogether. If the temperature varies as a result of variation in some other factor, misleading results as to the effect of temperature would be obtained.

Whenever possible the relationship between variables should be determined from controlled experiments. Examination of relationships between variables on the basis of process records should usually be considered as a preliminary to controlled experiments.

Parallel line assays

7·7   Regression equations are frequently used for assay purposes when comparing some property of a sample against a standard curve for that property. One example of such an assay in biological work has already been described § 7·54]. Similar examples arise when assessing the amount of a given dye stuff present in a sample by means of colorimetric and spectrophotometric methods; such methods are useful for estimating the strength of dyestuffs when there is no simple specific chemical test for this purpose.

We shall illustrate the method by considering a numerical example. The strength of a sample of a dyestuff is generally expressed in terms of that of a standard. Table 7·3 gives the logarithms of the optical densities of varying concentrations of solutions of a sample and of a standard. The problem is to determine the strength of the sample in terms of that of standard. In these circumstances a series of dilutions of both sample and standard should be carried out in the same experiment because, as shown below, the results on the series of dilutions of the sample can be used to obtain an improved estimate of the standard curve. It is not always necessary to take a series of dilutions of the sample to compare with the standard—an estimate can be obtained from one dilution only, but a series of dilutions gives a higher degree of accuracy which may be required in particular circumstances. "Standard curves" are standard only for the conditions appertaining at the time and may vary slightly from time to time.

Figure 7·6 shows the graphs of the logarithms of the optical densities plotted against the logarithms of the concentrations. The relation between these transformed variables was expected to be linear, but it will be apparent

Table 7·3
LOG OPTICAL DENSITIES

Relative Concentrations	log (10 × Concentration)	Standard	Sample
0·80	0·903	0·521	0·519
0·90	0·954	0·579	0·570
1·00	1·000	0·626	0·622
1·10	1·041	0·672	0·666

N

from what follows that there is an additional reason for choosing a logarithmic scale for the concentrations.

Whatever transformation of the optical density is used, a horizontal line drawn through any point on the vertical axis will cut the lines for standard and sample respectively at points corresponding to values x_1 and x_2 of the concentration. Since x_1 and x_2 give the same response, the concentration of pure dyestuff present in each should be the same. The ratio x_1/x_2 then measures the strength of the sample in terms of standard. If the only difference between the sample and the standard material is the amount of diluent present, then the ratio x_1/x_2 will be the same for all values of the optical density. On the logarithmic scale for the concentration, $\log x_1 - \log x_2$ will be constant, and this means that the horizontal distance between the curve for the standard and the curve for the sample will be the same for all values of the optical density, irrespective of the scale in which the latter is expressed. The logarithmic scale is thus the natural one to use for the concentration.

The best transformation to use for the optical density is the one which gives the simplest relationship—linear if possible—between optical density and log (concentration), and in addition makes the variance of the response the same at every point of the range considered. When such a transformation does not exist the method of fitting becomes more complicated, and reference should be made to Finney [7·3].

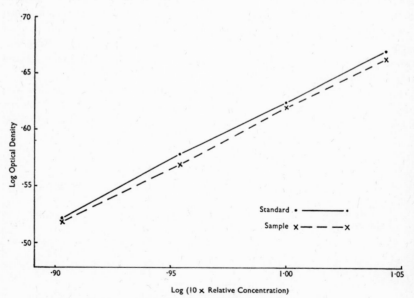

Fig. 7·6. Optical density and concentration of dyestuff

For most applications in the industrial field the ranges of the variables can be so chosen that the above conditions—linearity and equality of variances—are approximately satisfied.

Transformations commonly used for the response are the logarithm, square root, reciprocal, and sometimes $\log (y + a)$, $\sqrt{(y + a)}$, or $1/(y + a)$, where y is the observed response and a a constant to be determined from the data.

The concentration can be set up without appreciable error and can be assumed exact. The regression of log (optical density) on log (concentration) is then an estimate of the functional relationship between these two variables, and is the relationship to use for the purpose of estimating concentration from a measure of the optical density.

In the experiment represented by the data of Table 7·3 and graphed in Figure 7·6 the range of optical density is small and the variance of log (optical density) can be assumed to be constant.

The stages in the estimation of the strength of the sample in terms of the standard are:

(i) Fit separate straight lines to the results for the sample and for the standard.

(ii) Compare the regression coefficients and combine them if they do not differ appreciably, to obtain the slope of the best fitting parallel lines to represent the two sets of results.

(iii) Estimate the horizontal distance between the parallel lines. This gives the logarithm of the ratio of the strength of the sample to that of the standard.

(iv) Calculate the confidence limits for the ratio.

These steps will now be applied to the data of Table 7·3, where we take $x = \log (10 \times \text{relative concentration})$ and $y = \log (\text{optical density})$.

Fitting parallel lines to the data of Table 7·3

7·71 The calculations are given in Table 7·4.

Standard error of the difference between the two regression coefficients $= 0·018\sqrt{2} = 0·025$. Actual difference $= 0·016$.

The regression coefficients for the sample and standard clearly do not differ appreciably, and we can proceed to derive the best-fitting pair of parallel lines. If the regression coefficients differed appreciably it would not be possible to give a unique value for the strength of the sample. This could happen if the active ingredients of the two samples were not chemically identical.

Table 7·4

CALCULATION INVOLVED IN THE ANALYSIS OF THE DATA
OF TABLE 7·3

	x	y	
		Standard	Sample
N	4	4	4
Sum	3·898	2·398	2·377
Mean	0·9745	0·5995	0·5943
Crude sum of squares..	3·809206	1·450142	1·424701
Correction = (sum)²/N	3·798601	1·437601	1·412532
Corrected sum of squares	0·010605	0·012541	0·012169
Crude sum of products of x and y ..	—	2·348381	2·327743
Correction	—	2·336851	2·316387
Corrected sum of products	—	0·011530	0·011356
Regression coefficient	—	1·0872	1·0708
Sum of squares due to regression ..	—	0·012536	0·012160
Sum of squares about regression ..	—	0·000005	0·000009
Combined variance = 0·000014/4 = 0·0000035. d.f. = 4			
Standard error of each regression coefficient	$\sqrt{(0·0000035/0·010605)} = \sqrt{0·000330}$ = 0·018		

The regression coefficient b for the pair of parallel lines, obtained by combining b_1 and b_2, is given by

$$b = \frac{\Sigma_1(x - \bar{x})(y - \bar{y}) + \Sigma_2(x - \bar{x})(y - \bar{y})}{\Sigma_1(x - \bar{x})^2 + \Sigma_2(x - \bar{x})^2}$$

where Σ_1 denotes summation over the observations for the standard and Σ_2 denotes summation over the observations for the sample.

$$\therefore b = \frac{0·011530 + 0·011356}{0·010605 + 0·010605} = \frac{0·022886}{0·021210} = 1·0790 \quad \ldots \ldots (7·7)$$

In this case, since the same values of the concentration were used for both sample and standard, b is simply the average of b_1 and b_2.

The pair of parallel lines are then

Standard: $Y = 0·5995 + 1·0790(x - 0·9745)$

Sample: $Y = 0·5943 + 1·0790(x - 0·9745)$

Estimation of the ratio of the strengths and the confidence limits of the ratio

7·72 The horizontal distance between the two parallel lines:

$$Y = \bar{y}_1 + b(x - \bar{x}_1), \text{ i.e. } x = \frac{Y - \bar{y}_1}{b} + \bar{x}_1$$

and

$$Y = \bar{y}_2 + b(x - \bar{x}_2), \text{ i.e. } x = \frac{Y - \bar{y}_2}{b} + \bar{x}_2$$

is

$$\frac{\bar{y}_2 - \bar{y}_1}{b} - (\bar{x}_2 - \bar{x}_1) \quad \dots\dots\dots\dots\dots\dots(7{\cdot}71)$$

For the present example $\bar{x}_1$ is equal to $\bar{x}_2$ and the horizontal distance is simply $(\bar{y}_2 - \bar{y}_1)/b$, which has the value $- 0{\cdot}00482$.

This is the logarithm of the ratio of the strength of sample to standard, and its antilogarithm then gives the actual ratio. The antilogarithm is $0{\cdot}9890$. In other words, the strength of the sample is found to be $98{\cdot}9\%$ of that of the standard.

The next step is to find the confidence limits for this result. The confidence limits for a ratio of two parameters have been derived by Fieller, and details will be found in Appendix 7D. For this type of problem, however, the following method gives a sufficiently accurate approximation. We have first to estimate the variance about the regression. The sum of squares of the observations accounted for by the pair of parallel lines is given by

$$\frac{[\Sigma_1(x - \bar{x})(y - \bar{y}) + \Sigma_2(x - \bar{x})(y - \bar{y})]^2}{\Sigma_1(x - \bar{x})^2 + \Sigma_2(x - \bar{x})^2} = \frac{(0{\cdot}022886)^2}{0{\cdot}021210} = 0{\cdot}024694$$

The total corrected sum of squares is $0{\cdot}012541 + 0{\cdot}012169 = 0{\cdot}024710$. The sum of squares about the parallel regressions is therefore $0{\cdot}000016$.

Since we have fitted three constants—two means and one regression coefficient—the degrees of freedom are $8 - 3 = 5$. The variance about the regression is therefore $0{\cdot}0000032$.

Using the method of § 3·72, the variance of Expression (7·71) is approximately

$$\frac{V(\bar{y}_2 - \bar{y}_1)}{b^2} + \frac{(\bar{y}_2 - \bar{y}_1)^2}{b^2} \frac{V(b)}{b^2} + V(\bar{x}_2 - \bar{x}_1)$$

which reduces to

$$\frac{V(\bar{y}_2 - \bar{y}_1)}{b^2} + \left[\frac{(\bar{y}_2 - \bar{y}_1)}{b}\right]^2 \frac{V(b)}{b^2} \quad \dots\dots\dots\dots(7{\cdot}72)$$

since the error variance of the x observations is zero.

$\bar{y}_1$ and $\bar{y}_2$ are each means of four observations, and therefore $V(\bar{y}_2 - \bar{y}_1) = \frac{1}{2}\sigma^2$, where σ^2 is the variance about the regression. Also $V(b) = \sigma^2/0{\cdot}021210$.

By substituting these values in Expression (7·72) we have:

Variance of log ratio of strengths $= (\sigma^2/b^2)[\frac{1}{2} + (0{\cdot}00482)^2/0{\cdot}02121]$

The second expression inside the brackets is clearly small compared with $\frac{1}{2}$ and can be neglected. We then obtain

$$\text{Variance of log ratio} = \tfrac{1}{2} \times 0 \cdot 0000032/(1 \cdot 079)^2 = 0 \cdot 00000137$$

$$\text{Standard error of log ratio} = 0 \cdot 00117$$

To find the 95% confidence limits we note that the appropriate value of t for 5 degrees of freedom is 2·57, and the confidence limits are $- 0 \cdot 00482 \pm 0 \cdot 00301 = - 0 \cdot 00783$ and $- 0 \cdot 00181$, the antilogs of which are 0·982 and 0·996.

The relative strength of the sample is then 98·9% with 95% confidence limits of 98·2% to 99·6%.

The narrowness of the confidence limits indicates that this method of estimating the concentration is fairly accurate.

ALLOWANCE FOR CONCOMITANT VARIATION

7·8 Suppose we require to compare the quality of a chemical product made on the plant by two processes, A and B. The usual method is to make a number of batches by each of A and B, measure the quality of each batch, calculate the means of the two groups, the difference between the two means, and the confidence limits for the difference [§ **4·231**].

When variations are known to exist between lots of raw materials used in the manufacture of the chemical, it is usual to make a batch of A and a batch of B from each lot [§ **4·25**]; but there are situations where each lot of raw material is insufficient to make both a batch of A and a batch of B, and blending of lots may not be practicable or economical. The quality of the raw material may be well defined, for example by its purity, its crystallising point, or the percentage of a given impurity, and these may be related to the quality of the final product. In these circumstances one batch is made from each lot of raw material and the purity or other relevant property of each lot is also determined.

7·81 Data obtained from an experiment of this kind are given in Table 7·5. The finished product is a dyestuff, and one quality of interest is its tinctorial strength, which is determined by comparing the samples of dyestuff with a standard material by spectrophotometric means; the figures quoted are percentage differences from the standard. This tinctorial strength is affected by an impurity in the raw material. This impurity, an unwanted isomer which is difficult to remove, is present in amounts that vary from about 3% to about 10%. There is a lower limit to the impurity, and the standard deviation is large compared with the mean; in such circumstances the distribution is almost certainly skew, and a transformation is desirable. In this case the logarithmic transformation is satisfactory, and therefore the figures quoted in Table 7·5 for the quality of the raw material are the logarithms of the percentage of the impurity.

Table 7·5

QUALITY OF DYESTUFF: COMPARISON OF TWO PROCESSES

	Process A		Process B	
	Tinctorial strength of dyestuff	Log (% impurity) in raw material	Tinctorial strength of dyestuff	Log (% impurity) in raw material
	3	0·84	1	0·73
	− 2	0·89	8	0·46
	8	0·58	− 3	0·82
	4	0·60	5	0·54
	1	0·95	− 3	0·77
	1	0·73	− 2	0·84
	8	0·65	0	0·59
	− 2	1·00	− 6	1·01
	5	0·73	3	0·58
	4	0·68	0	0·70
Means	3·0	0·77	0·3	0·70

The quality of the raw material varies from lot to lot, and an inspection suffices to show that the tinctorial strength of the dyestuff is related to the quality of the raw material. This relationship can be seen more clearly in Figure 7·7, where these two properties are plotted, the two processes A and B being shown separately.

The mean value of log (% impurity) in the raw materials used for A differs a little from that in the materials used for B, and this alone would be expected to give rise to a difference in the mean tinctorial strengths of the products made from them. The effect of the process used on the tinctorial strength of the product is thus confused to a certain extent with that of differences in the quality of the material used. It is desirable to separate these two effects, and this is one of the purposes of the method of analysis developed in this section. Another important purpose of the analysis is to allow for the variation between the lots of raw material used in each group and thereby improve the sensitivity of the comparison between the processes.

7·82 The lots of raw material used for processes A and B were selected at random, and if no information were available on the quality of the raw

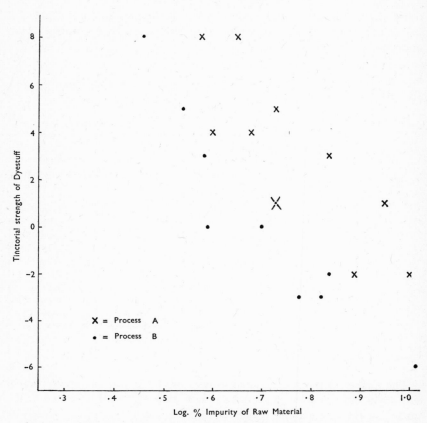

Fig. 7·7. Tinctorial strength of dyestuff and impurity of raw material

material the data would have to be analysed using the usual method for the
comparison of the means of two groups as follows:

Mean A $= 3·0$ Mean B $= 0·3$ Difference $= 2·7$

Sum of squares within groups $= 270·1$

Variance within groups $= 270·1/18 = 15·01$

Variance of the difference between the two means $= 3·00$

Standard error of the difference between the two means $= 1·73$

95% confidence limits $= 2·70 \pm 3·63 = -0·93$ to $6·33$

The confidence limits include the value zero, therefore we cannot conclude
with this degree of confidence that there is a real difference between the
tinctorial strengths of materials produced by the two processes.

A substantial proportion of the variation in tinctorial strength of the
dyestuff from batch to batch is caused by the variation in the raw material,

and this contributes to the uncertainty in the estimate of the difference between the two processes. It will be shown in the next section that the variation in the purity of the raw materials can be allowed for, and the result of this is to improve the precision of the experiment to that (or almost that) which would be obtained if the raw material had been kept constant for the whole experiment.

Method of analysis

7·83   The method of analysis resembles very closely the method discussed in § **7·71** for the comparison of two regression lines. To make the explanations clearer we plot in Figure 7·8 an exaggerated situation in which the points by the two systems are separated.

Assume that the relationship between the tinctorial strength of dyestuff and the logarithm of the percent impurity in the raw material is linear and that the regression lines for the two processes A and B are parallel. This

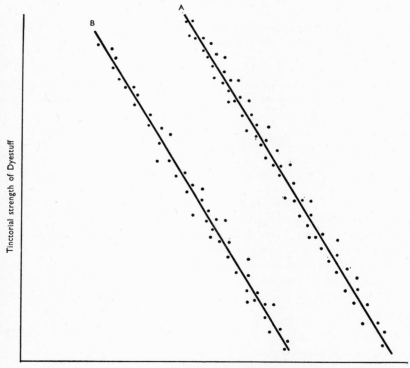

Fig. 7·8. Separate regressions (exaggerated)

means that the relationship is the same for the two processes; this is usually a safe assumption to make.

The distributions of the qualities of the raw materials depicted in Figure 7·8 are different for A and B. If the two regression lines coincide or do not differ appreciably, then we could say that the apparent difference in mean tinctorial strength by the two processes is due to the variation in the raw materials. If the two lines are differently placed and the difference is appreciable, then an appreciable difference exists in the tinctorial strength of dyestuff produced by the two processes irrespective of whether or not there are differences in the quality of raw materials used for each.

It is clear that the difference between the two processes, allowing for the effect of the differences in the distribution of impurities of raw materials, is given by the *vertical* distance between the two regression lines.

The regression lines, assumed to have the same slope, are:

$$Y_A = \bar{y}_A + b(x - \bar{x}_A)$$
$$Y_B = \bar{y}_B + b(x - \bar{x}_B)$$

where the independent variable x is the logarithm of the percent impurity in the raw material. The vertical displacement is:

$$Y_A - Y_B = (\bar{y}_A - \bar{y}_B) - b(\bar{x}_A - \bar{x}_B)\ldots\ldots\ldots(7\cdot8)$$

The assumption is usually made that the errors in the x-variable are not appreciable, which assumption is reasonable in this case. The variance of $(Y_A - Y_B)$ is therefore

$$V(\bar{y}_A - \bar{y}_B) + (\bar{x}_A - \bar{x}_B)^2\, V(b)$$

$$= \sigma^2\left[\left(\frac{1}{n} + \frac{1}{m}\right) + (\bar{x}_A - \bar{x}_B)^2/\{\Sigma_A(x - \bar{x})^2 + \Sigma_B(x - \bar{x})^2\}\right]..(7\cdot81)$$

where n and m are the numbers of samples tested by A and B respectively.

We now require to estimate σ^2. This is the variance about the regression lines and is calculated in the same way as in § 7·72. It is the variance of the tinctorial strength from batch to batch *after allowing for the variations in the percentage of impurity in the raw materials*, and is the same variance that would be obtained had it been possible to use one homogeneous lot of raw material for all 20 batches of product. Following the details given in § 7·72, σ^2 is estimated by

$$s^2 = \frac{\Sigma_A(y - \bar{y})^2 + \Sigma_B(y - \bar{y})^2 - \dfrac{[\Sigma_A(x - \bar{x})(y - \bar{y}) + \Sigma_B(x - \bar{x})(y - \bar{y})]^2}{\Sigma_A(x - \bar{x})^2 + \Sigma_B(x - \bar{x})^2}}{m + n - 3}$$

We have now to consider the situation in which the two regression lines are not parallel. Under these circumstances the effect of changing the process is not unique and will depend on the percent impurity in the raw materials. The two lines are:

$$Y_A = \bar{y}_A + b_A(x - \bar{x}_A)$$
$$Y_B = \bar{y}_B + b_B(x - \bar{x}_B)$$
$$\therefore \ Y_A - Y_B = (\bar{y}_A - \bar{y}_B) + b_A(x - \bar{x}_A) - b_B(x - \bar{x}_B)$$
$$\text{and} \quad V(Y_A - Y_B) = V(\bar{y}_A - \bar{y}_B) + (x - \bar{x}_A)^2 V(b_A) + (x - \bar{x}_B)^2 V(b_B)$$

Both the estimate of the difference in tinctorial strength of dyestuff by the two processes and the variance of the difference depend on the value of x considered.

When the slopes are different, the relation between tinctorial strength of dyestuff and percent impurity of raw material differs for the two production processes A and B. Although difficulties of interpretation may arise, this difference in itself shows that the two processes give different results in certain circumstances.

Application to the data of Table 7·5

7·84 It is convenient to summarise the calculations in the form of the following table.

Table 7·51

CALCULATION INVOLVED IN ANALYSIS OF
DATA OF TABLE 7·5

	Process A		Process B	
	Tinctorial strength (y)	Log % impurity (x)	Tinctorial strength (y)	Log % impurity (x)
Number of batches ..	10		10	
Mean	3·0	0·765	0·3	0·704
Sum of squares about mean	114·0	0·1950	156·1	0·2454
Degrees of freedom ..	9		9	
Sum of products of x and y about means	− 3·920		− 5·772	
Slope	− 20·1		− 23·5	
Sum of squares about regressions	35·20		20·34	

Combining the sums of squares about the two separate regressions gives a variance of 3·471 based on 16 degrees of freedom. The standard errors of the slopes are therefore 4·2 and 3·8 respectively, from which it is clear that the two slopes do not differ appreciably and can be assumed to be equal.

The combined slope is then $- 9·692/0·4404 = - 22·0$

Sum of squares due to the pair of parallel regressions
$$= (9·692)^2/0·4404 = 213·3$$

Sum of squares about the pair of parallel regressions
$$= 270·1 - 213·3 = 56·8$$

This is based on $20 - 3 = 17$ degrees of freedom; therefore,

Variance about regressions $= 56·8/17 = 3·341$

The two regression lines are
$$Y = 3·0 - 22·0(x - 0·765) = 19·83 - 22·0x$$
$$Y = 0·3 - 22·0(x - 0·704) = 15·79 - 22·0x$$

The vertical distance between the regressions $= 4·04$. This is the estimate of the difference in tinctorial strengths produced by the two processes, A being superior to B. The variance of this estimate using Formula (7·81) is
$$3·341[1/5 + (0·061)^2/0·4404] = 0·696$$
$$\text{Standard error} = 0·834$$

For 17 degrees of freedom the value of t for $P = 0·025$ is 2·11, and therefore the 95% confidence limits for the estimate of the difference in tinctorial strength of dyestuff produced by the two processes, allowing for the variation in percent impurities, are 2·28 to 5·80. There is thus an appreciable difference between the two processes which was not revealed by the analysis ignoring the information on the variation in the raw materials. The error variance of the corrected tinctorial strength per batch is reduced from 15·01 to 3·34, which represents a considerable improvement.

Reference to Equation (7·8) shows that the estimated difference in tinctorial strengths produced by the two processes, 4·04, is composed of two parts. One is the difference in mean observed tinctorial strengths amounting to 2·70, and the other part a correction for the difference in mean percent impurity in the raw materials. This difference is $0·765 - 0·704 = 0·061$, which when multiplied by the slope of the regression lines results in the correction of 1·34.

Alternative methods of analysis

7·85   There are other methods of analysing data of the type given in Table 7·5. All are equivalent, but the method given in the previous section shows most clearly the various stages involved and the assumptions which may have to be made. Some of these assumptions are disguised in the more formal method called the "Analysis of Covariance." This method, which is the one usually given in textbooks, can be more readily generalised for more complicated situations.

When more than one "nuisance" factor is operating, then the analysis is carried out by the method of multiple regression, which is considered in the next chapter.

CORRELATION

7·9   There is a class of problems in descriptive statistics involving two or more related variables where the main interest is not in estimating one variable from another, but in the distribution of the variables and in the association between them. This is the class of problem in which correlation methods are most useful. The following provides an illustration.

A hat manufacturer would be interested in the distribution of the head measurements of a population, because this must have a bearing on the number of hats of any given shape and size he is likely to sell. Suppose he takes a random sample of individuals in his potential market and measures the head length and breadth of each individual. This supplies him with a mass of data which will imply very little unless it is presented in a condensed form in order to bring out the essential features. As shown in Chapter 2, any one measurement, e.g. the length, can be completely described by means of a distribution, e.g. a histogram, and if this is of the Normal form, two statistics

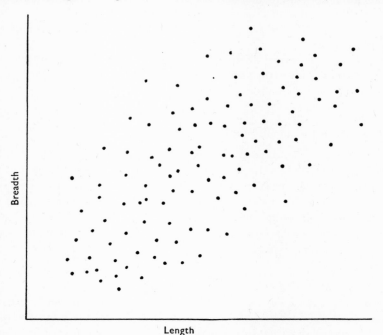

Fig. 7·9. Distribution of head measurements

—the mean and standard deviation—give a complete description. If we take length and breadth and make the assumption that both measurements are Normally distributed—for biometric data this will usually be true—then each can be represented by its mean and standard deviation. These four figures, although adequate to describe each property separately, do not give a complete description of the whole data, because no information is supplied on the relationship between the two measurements. As shown previously, a convenient method of exhibiting the relationship is to plot the two measurements, one against the other, for all the individuals in the form of a scatter diagram, as in Fig. 7·9.

An association or a correlation between the two measurements is indicated by the diagonal tendency. Long heads tend to be associated with wide heads and vice versa, but for any given value of each measurement there is a considerable spread in the other.

The Normal surface

7·91 As an alternative to the scatter diagram, the distribution can be represented by a solid histogram formed by first of all dividing the area into rectangles, and then erecting on each one a block whose volume is proportional to the number of observations covered by the rectangle. In the limit for an indefinitely large sample and indefinitely small areas we arrive at a smooth surface.

There exists a Normal distribution for two variables, just as for one; it is referred to as the Bivariate Normal Distribution. It can be represented by the expression

$$\frac{1}{2\pi\sigma_x\sigma_y\sqrt{(1-\rho^2)}} \exp\left[-\frac{1}{2(1-\rho^2)} \times \left\{\frac{(x-\mu)^2}{\sigma_x{}^2} - 2\rho\frac{(x-\mu)(y-\eta)}{\sigma_x\sigma_y} + \frac{(y-\eta)^2}{\sigma_y{}^2}\right\}\right]$$

where $\sigma_x{}^2$ and $\sigma_y{}^2$ are respectively the variances of the two variables x and y, μ and η their means, and ρ is the additional coefficient which measures the association between the two variables. These five coefficients give a complete description of the Normal bivariate distribution; the means and variances are estimated from the sample in the usual way (Chapter 3); ρ is the Correlation Coefficient and is also estimated from the sample. To determine this value we need to calculate another statistic called the Covariance, which has the expression

$$\text{cov }(xy) = \Sigma(x - \bar{x})(y - \bar{y})/(n - 1)$$

In words, this is the sum of the products of the deviation of each x from the mean $\bar{x}$ and the deviation of the corresponding y from the mean $\bar{y}$ divided by the number of degrees of freedom $(n - 1)$. The covariance has thus a similar form to the variance except that product terms are involved. This similarity is brought out more clearly by displaying all these expressions as follows:

$$s_x{}^2 = \Sigma(x - \bar{x})(x - \bar{x})/(n - 1)$$
$$\text{cov } (xy) = \Sigma(x - \bar{x})(y - \bar{y})/(n - 1)$$
$$s_y{}^2 = \Sigma(y - \bar{y})(y - \bar{y})/(n - 1)$$

The correlation coefficient is a derived statistic given by $\text{cov } (xy)/s_x s_y$, and is denoted by the letter r. Since the divisors $(n - 1)$ cancel, an alternative expression for r is $\Sigma(x - \bar{x})(y - \bar{y})/\sqrt{\{\Sigma(x - \bar{x})^2 \Sigma(y - \bar{y})^2\}}$. All the quantities used in calculating the correlation coefficient have already been encountered in calculating a regression coefficient and its confidence limits.

Properties of the correlation coefficient
7·92   The correlation can be negative or positive. When it is positive, one variable tends to increase as the other increases; when it is negative, one variable tends to decrease as the other increases. It can be readily shown that the correlation coefficient cannot take values outside the limits $- 1$ and $+ 1$. A high absolute value of r indicates a close relationship and a small value, a less definite relationship. When the absolute value of r is unity, the variables fall on a straight diagonal line and the relationship is perfect. When $r = 0$ the points scatter in all directions, and the variables are independent. Typical scatter diagrams for a low and a high correlation are shown in the following figure (Fig. 7·91).

It must be remembered that the correlation coefficient is an estimate (calculated from the sample) of the association between two variables, and this estimate is only valid when the sample is randomly drawn from the Universe.

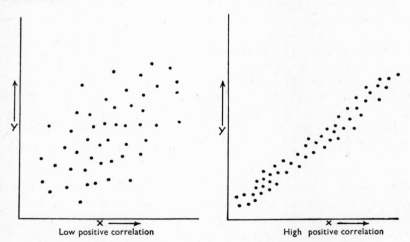

Low positive correlation   High positive correlation

Fig. 7·91. Scatter diagrams for low and high correlations

The correlation coefficient is of less value when the bivariate distribution is not Normal, but it can still be of use as an overall measure of *linear* association between the variables.

Examples of calculation of the correlation coefficient

7·93   Using the data of Table 7·1 and letting x be hardness and y be abrasion loss, the following quantities required for the calculation of r are derived in Appendix 7A:

$$n = 30 \qquad \Sigma y = 5{,}263 \qquad \Sigma xy = 346{,}867$$
$$\Sigma x = 2{,}108 \qquad \Sigma y^2 = 1{,}148{,}317 \qquad (\Sigma x)(\Sigma y)/n = 369{,}813$$
$$\Sigma x^2 = 152{,}422 \qquad (\Sigma y)^2/n = 923{,}306$$
$$(\Sigma x)^2/n = 148{,}122$$

Whence
$$\Sigma(x - \bar{x})^2 = 152{,}422 \quad - 148{,}122 = 4{,}300$$
$$\Sigma(y - \bar{y})^2 = 1{,}148{,}317 - 923{,}306 = 225{,}011$$
$$\Sigma(x - \bar{x})(y - \bar{y}) = 346{,}867 \quad - 369{,}813 = - 22{,}946$$

$$r = - 22{,}946/\sqrt{(4{,}300 \times 225{,}011)} = - 0{\cdot}738$$

Significance of the correlation coefficient

7·94   One question usually of interest is whether the value of the correlation coefficient found for a sample could have arisen with a given probability from a Normal Universe with $\rho = 0$, i.e. with x and y uncorrelated. A table exists for this purpose (Table E at the end of this volume), which gives the 0·10 0·05, 0·02 and 0·01 significance points for various numbers of degrees of freedom. In assessing the significance of the correlation coefficient the table is entered with $(n - 2)$ for the degrees of freedom. For the correlation of hardness and abrasion loss $(n - 2) = 28$ and the 5% and 1% points obtained by interpolation are $\pm 0{\cdot}36$ and $\pm 0{\cdot}46$ respectively. The actual value of $- 0{\cdot}738$ for the correlation coefficient is therefore highly significant, and we conclude that the sample of observations was drawn from a Universe in which a negative correlation existed.

This assessment of the significance of the correlation coefficient gives precisely the same result as that of comparing the regression coefficient with its standard error, using the t-table [§ **7·24**]. In order to determine the confidence limits for a correlation coefficient we make use of a transformation which we consider below in § **7·96**.

Grouped data

7·95   The above method for the calculation of the correlation coefficient is applicable in all cases, but as in the calculation of the variance, considerable simplification is possible for large samples (say > 60 observations) by the process of grouping. The details of the method together with an example are given in Appendix 7C.

Comparison of correlation coefficients and confidence limits

7·96   In order to compare correlation coefficients a useful transformation due to R. A. Fisher may be used. This is

$$z = \tfrac{1}{2}\{\log_e (1 + r) - \log_e (1 - r)\}$$

which is very nearly Normally distributed with standard deviation $1/\sqrt{(n - 3)}$. This transformation enables us to calculate approximate confidence limits for a correlation coefficient and for a difference between two correlation coefficients, and also to combine correlation coefficients from two or more samples and calculate the confidence limits. The factors used to calculate the confidence limits are obtained from the table of Normal deviates (Table A) and not from the t-table.

The correlation coefficients to be compared or combined are first transformed to their z values, using the above expression; these z values, considered as though each were the mean of $(n - 3)$ observations of unit standard deviation, may then be used in the calculation of confidence limits or in any of the tests appropriate for comparisons or combinations of such means.

7·97   Difficulties may arise in the interpretation of a correlation coefficient when the observations are taken over a period of time. Consider, for example, the correlation of quality of a product with quality of raw materials taken at intervals over a period of manufacture, say one year. During this period let us assume that there has been a gradual tightening up on supervision, which would of itself result in improved yield. Assume also that during the same period a certain small impurity that does not affect the yield has also shown a gradual increase. If the yield is plotted against this impurity a high correlation may result, but it does not follow that the yield increase is due to increase in the impurity. Therefore a significant correlation does not necessarily indicate a causal relationship between the two variables, since this correlation may be due to a common factor, particularly if a time or space factor is involved. This type of correlation is commonly referred to as Spurious Correlation. In certain circumstances the effect of time can be removed by the use of multiple regression methods, which are considered in the next chapter.

Relation between the coefficients of correlation and regression

7·98   The sample estimates of the correlation coefficient and the regression coefficients are:

$$r = \frac{\Sigma(x - \bar{x})(y - \bar{y})}{\sqrt{\{\Sigma(x - \bar{x})^2 \Sigma(y - \bar{y})^2\}}} = \frac{\text{cov}(xy)}{s_x s_y}$$

and

$$b = \frac{\Sigma(x - \bar{x})(y - \bar{y})}{\Sigma(x - \bar{x})^2} = \frac{\text{cov}(xy)}{s_x^2} = r\frac{s_y}{s_x}$$

O

The regression equation of y upon x can be written as

$$\frac{Y - \bar{y}}{s_y} = r\frac{x - \bar{x}}{s_x}$$

In other words, the correlation coefficient is numerically the same as the regression coefficient when the variates are expressed in standard measure [§ **2·43**].

The regression equation of x upon y is similarly

$$\frac{X - \bar{x}}{s_x} = r\frac{y - \bar{y}}{s_y}$$

The sum of squares due to the regression of y upon x is

$$b^2\Sigma(x - \bar{x})^2 = [\Sigma(x - \bar{x})(y - \bar{y})]^2/\Sigma(x - \bar{x})^2 = r^2\Sigma(y - \bar{y})^2$$

In words, r^2 represents the proportion of the total sum of squares in one variable accounted for by the other. The sum of squares about the regression is $(1 - r^2)\Sigma(y - \bar{y})^2$, and therefore the ratio of the mean square due to regression to the mean square about the regression is $(n - 2)r^2/(1 - r^2)$.

These relationships show that "correlation" and "regression" are mathematically equivalent; but on the practical side they represent different types of problems, and it is best to keep them separate. In industrial work the problems classed under regression are by far the more important ones, and for this reason they have received prominence in this chapter.

REFERENCES

[7·1] LINDLEY, D. V. "Regression Lines and Linear Functional Relationship," *Royal Stat. Soc., Series B*, Vol. 9, pp. 218–44 (1947).

[7·2] BARTLETT, M. S. "Fitting a Straight Line when Both Variables are subject to Error," *Biometrics*, Sept. 1949, Vol. 5, No. 3, pp. 207–12.

[7·3] FINNEY, D. J. *Statistical Method in Biological Assay.* Charles Griffin & Co. Ltd. (London, 1952).

APPENDIX 7A

TO FIT A STRAIGHT LINE TO DATA
BY THE METHOD OF LEAST SQUARES

Let y be the dependent variable and x be the independent variable and let (x_1, y_1), (x_2, y_2), (x_3, y_3), . . . represent the observations. Suppose the scatter diagram to be that represented by Figure 7A.

A straight line is represented mathematically by an equation of the first degree, i.e.

$$Y = a + bx\dots\dots\dots\dots\dots\dots\dots(7A\cdot1)$$

where a and b are constants.

Let AB on the figure be any such line, and let (x_1, y_1) be any given observation. If we were to use this line to predict the value of y_1 from x_1 we should get the point P (Fig. 7A), which is given by substituting x_1 in Equation (7A·1), i.e.

$$\text{Predicted value of } y_1 = Y_1 = a + bx_1$$

The difference between the predicted value and the actual value (dotted line on the figure) is therefore

$$y_1 - (a + bx_1)$$

We wish to choose the line which on an average will give the best prediction for all the points. This is done by choosing the line for which the sum of squares of the deviations from it measured in a vertical direction is a minimum. This is the Method of Least Squares.

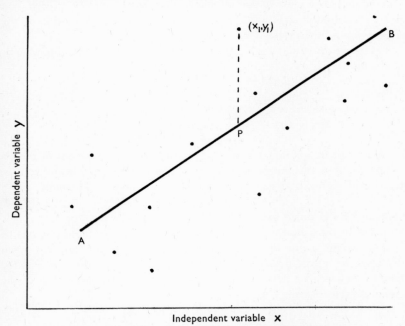

Fig. 7A. Diagram illustrating method of least squares

The square of the deviation (x_1, y_1) from the line is $\{y_1 - (a + bx_1)\}^2$, and the sum of squares of these for all the points is

$$Q = \{y_1 - (a + bx_1)\}^2 + \{y_2 - (a + bx_2)\}^2 + \cdots$$
$$= \Sigma\{y - (a + bx)\}^2 \quad \ldots\ldots\ldots\ldots\ldots\ldots\ldots\ldots(7A\cdot11)$$

a and b are then chosen to make Q a minimum. This can be done by the differential calculus in the usual way, by differentiating Q partially with respect to a and b separately, equating each derivative to zero, and solving the resulting equations for a and b. Thus:

$$\partial Q/\partial a = -2\Sigma\{y-(a+bx)\} = 0$$
$$\partial Q/\partial b = -2\Sigma x\{y-(a+bx)\} = 0$$

Rearranging, we get

$$\Sigma y = na + b\Sigma x \quad \dots\dots\dots\dots\dots\dots(7A\cdot2)$$
$$\Sigma xy = a\Sigma x + b\Sigma x^2 \quad \dots\dots\dots\dots\dots(7A\cdot3)$$

where n is the number of observations.

From Equation (7A·2) we get

$$a = \Sigma y/n - b\Sigma x/n$$
$$= \bar{y} - b\bar{x} \quad \dots\dots\dots\dots\dots\dots(7A\cdot31)$$

where $\bar{y}$ = mean of y's and $\bar{x}$ = mean of x's.

This result is the same as that obtained by substituting $(\bar{x}, \bar{y})$ in Equation (7A·1). The best line of fit, therefore, passes through the mean of the scattered points of the figure.

Substituting the value of $a = \bar{y} - b\bar{x}$ in Equation (7A·3), we obtain, after rearranging:

$$b = (\Sigma xy - n\bar{x}\bar{y})/(\Sigma x^2 - n\bar{x}^2)$$

Note that

$$\Sigma(x-\bar{x})(y-\bar{y}) = \Sigma(x-\bar{x})y - \Sigma(x-\bar{x})\bar{y}$$

Now, $\bar{y}$ is a constant and $\Sigma(x-\bar{x}) = 0$. Therefore

$$\Sigma(x-\bar{x})(y-\bar{y}) = \Sigma(x-\bar{x})y = \Sigma xy - \bar{x}\Sigma y$$
$$= \Sigma xy - n\bar{x}\bar{y}$$

The numerator of b is thus the sum of products of the deviations of the x's and the y's from their respective means. The denominator is the sum of squares of the x's about their mean (see § **3·34**, footnote). Therefore

$$b = \Sigma(x-\bar{x})(y-\bar{y})/\Sigma(x-\bar{x})^2 \dots\dots\dots\dots(7A\cdot4)$$

The quantity b is called the Regression Coefficient of y upon x.

In order to calculate the value of the sum of squares of the deviations of the observations about the best-fitting line, we note that for any given observation (x, y) the deviation of y from the line can be expressed as the difference between its deviation from the mean $\bar{y}$ and the deviation of the regression value Y from $\bar{y}$, i.e.:

$$y - Y = (y - \bar{y}) - (Y - \bar{y})$$

This is seen to be an identity.

The sum of squares of the deviations of the observed values of y from the line is

$$Q = \Sigma(y-Y)^2 = \Sigma[(y-\bar{y})-(Y-\bar{y})]^2$$

Expanding, we get

$$Q = \Sigma(y-\bar{y})^2 - 2\Sigma(y-\bar{y})(Y-\bar{y}) + \Sigma(Y-\bar{y})^2$$

Using $Y - \bar{y} = b(x-\bar{x})$, where $b = \Sigma(x-\bar{x})(y-\bar{y})/\Sigma(x-\bar{x})^2$, this can be reduced to

$$Q = \Sigma(y-\bar{y})^2 - \Sigma(Y-\bar{y})^2$$

The first part of the expression for Q is the sum of squares of the y observations about their mean, and the second part is the sum of squares of the predicted values about the mean. The latter expression is termed the sum of squares due to the regression. An alternative expression useful for numerical calculation is $b^2 \Sigma(x - \bar{x})^2$.

These sums of squares, together with degrees of freedom and variances, may be conveniently presented in the form of an Analysis of Variance table* giving an analysis of the total variation into that due to regression and that about the regression. Thus:

Table 7A·1

ANALYSIS OF VARIANCE OF REGRESSION

Source of Variation	Sum of Squares	Degrees of Freedom	Mean Squares
(1) Due to regression ..	$b^2 \Sigma(x - \bar{x})^2$	1	
(2) About regression ..	$\Sigma(y - \bar{y})^2$ $- b^2 \Sigma(x - \bar{x})^2$	$n - 2$	
Total	$\Sigma(y - \bar{y})^2$	$n - 1$	

It can be shown that for random samples from a Universe in which the observations of y are independent and Normally distributed, the sums of squares (1) and (2) divided by their appropriate degrees of freedom give two independent and unbiased estimates of the variance of the y's of the Universe. It follows that if the estimate of the variance from (1) is significantly greater (by the F-test, § 4·8) than the estimate from (2), then the regression is significant.

Example with step-by-step calculations

In the data of Table 7·1 let y = abrasion loss and x = hardness.

(i) *Calculate Sum of Squares of Hardness about Mean.*

Number of observations $= 30$
Sum x $= 2,108$
∴ $\bar{x}$ $= 70·27$
Crude sum of squares $= 152,422$
Correction for the mean $= (2,108)^2/30 = 148,122$
∴ Sum of squares about mean $= \Sigma(x - \bar{x})^2$
$= 152,422 - 148,122 = 4,300$

---

* This Analysis of Variance, although customarily carried out, is not necessary for the application of regression and for this reason has not been dealt with in the text.

(ii) *Calculate Sum of Squares of Abrasion Loss about Mean.*

Sum y	$= 5{,}263$
$\therefore \bar{y}$	$= 175 \cdot 4$
Crude sum of squares	$= 1{,}148{,}317$
Correction for the mean	$= (5{,}263)^2/30 = 923{,}306$
$\therefore$ Sum of squares about mean	$= \Sigma(y - \bar{y})^2$
	$= 1{,}148{,}317 - 923{,}306 = 225{,}011$

(iii) *Calculate Sum of Products of Abrasion Loss and Hardness about their respective Means.*

For this we use the formula:

$$\Sigma(x - \bar{x})(y - \bar{y}) = \Sigma xy - n\bar{x}\bar{y} = \Sigma xy - \Sigma x \Sigma y/n$$

Σxy is called the Crude Sum of Products, and $\Sigma x \Sigma y/n$ is called the Correction For the Means.

Crude Sum of Products of abrasion loss and hardness	
$= x_1 y_1 + x_2 y_2 + \ldots + x_n y_n$	$= 346{,}867$
Correction for the means	$= (2{,}108 \times 5{,}263)/30$
	$= 369{,}813$
Sum of Products about means	$= \Sigma(x - \bar{x})(y - \bar{y})$
	$= 346{,}867 - 369{,}813 = -22{,}946$

(iv) *Calculate Regression Coefficient of y upon x.*

Regression coefficient	$= \Sigma(x - \bar{x})(y - \bar{y})/\Sigma(x - \bar{x})^2$
	$= -22{,}946/4{,}300 = -5 \cdot 336$

(v) *Calculate Regression Equation of y upon x.*

This is
$$y = \bar{y} + b(x - \bar{x}),$$
i.e.
$$y = 175 \cdot 4 - 5 \cdot 336(x - 70 \cdot 27)$$
$$= 550 \cdot 4 - 5 \cdot 336x$$

(vi) *Calculate Sum of Squares due to Regression.*

This is
$$b^2 \Sigma(x - \bar{x})^2 = \{\Sigma(x - \bar{x})(y - \bar{y})\}^2/\Sigma(x - \bar{x})^2$$
$$= 122{,}446$$

The Analysis of Variance table may be constructed as Table 7A·11.

To assess the significance of the regression we calculate the ratio of the variances due to and about the regression. This gives $122{,}446/3{,}663 = 33 \cdot 4$. For 1 and 28 degrees of freedom the 5% and 1% values of F are $4 \cdot 20$ and $7 \cdot 64$ respectively. The regression is thus highly significant.

The regression coefficient of hardness on abrasion loss (x upon y) is

$$\Sigma(x - \bar{x})(y - \bar{y})/\Sigma(y - \bar{y})^2 = -22{,}946/225{,}011 = -0 \cdot 1020$$

The corresponding regression equation is
$$X = 70 \cdot 27 - 0 \cdot 1020(y - 175 \cdot 4)$$
$$= 88 \cdot 16 - 0 \cdot 1020y$$

Table 7A·11

ANALYSIS OF VARIANCE OF REGRESSION OF ABRASION LOSS
ON HARDNESS
(Based on Table 7·1)

	Source of Variation	Sum of Squares	Degrees of Freedom	Mean Square
(1)	Due to regression ..	122,446	1	122,446
(2)	About regression ..	102,565	28	3,663
(3)	Total	225,011	29	—

Item (2) is obtained by subtracting (1) from (3).

The Analysis of Variance for the regression of hardness on abrasion loss is shown in Table 7A·12.

Table 7A·12

ANALYSIS OF VARIANCE—HARDNESS ON ABRASION LOSS
(Based on Table 7·1)

	Source of Variation	Sum of Squares	Degrees of Freedom	Mean Square
(1)	Due to regression ..	2,340	1	2,340
(2)	About regression ..	1,960	28	70
	Total	4,300	29	—

Note that the ratio of the mean squares is 33·4, which is identical with that for Table 7A·11. From the standpoint of statistical significance both regressions are equivalent.

It is generally more informative to calculate the standard error of the regression coefficient (see Appendix 7B) and derive the confidence limits, $b \pm t_a S.E.(b)$. If required the significance of b can be assessed from the ratio $b/S.E.(b)$, which is distributed as t with $(n - 2)$ degrees of freedom. This gives precisely the same probability levels as those given by Tables 7A·11 and 7A·12.

Appendix 7B

STANDARD ERROR OF REGRESSION COEFFICIENT

The regression coefficient of y upon x is given by

$$b = \frac{\Sigma(x - \bar{x})(y - \bar{y})}{\Sigma(x - \bar{x})^2} = \frac{\Sigma(x - \bar{x})y}{\Sigma(x - \bar{x})^2}$$

Expanding, we obtain

$$b = \frac{1}{\Sigma(x - \bar{x})^2}\{(x_1 - \bar{x})y_1 + (x_2 - \bar{x})y_2 + \ldots + (x_n - \bar{x})y_n\} \quad \ldots (7B\cdot1)$$

The quantities $y_1, y_2, \ldots, y_n$ are the observed values of y for given values of x, which is our independent variable. The expression b is then of the form

$$a_1 y_1 + a_2 y_2 + \ldots + a_n y_n \quad \ldots \ldots \ldots \ldots (7B\cdot2)$$

where y_1 to y_n are independent observations and the a's are constants.

The variance of b is therefore [§ 3·71]

$$V(b) = \Sigma a_i^2 V(y_i) = s^2 \Sigma a_i^2 = s^2 \frac{\Sigma(x - \bar{x})^2}{\{\Sigma(x - \bar{x})^2\}^2} \quad \ldots \ldots (7B\cdot3)$$

$$\therefore \ S.E.(b) = s/\sqrt{\{\Sigma(x - \bar{x})^2\}}$$

In deriving this expression for the standard error of the regression coefficient we have assumed that the coefficients of the y's in Expression $(7B\cdot1)$ are free from error. This would certainly be true if the x-variable could be measured without error. The expression, however, is not restricted to such cases, because we can consider all those random samples of n observations (from the Universe) for which we have the same set of observed values of x, that is, $x_1, x_2, \ldots, x_n$. This is perfectly legitimate, because the regression of y upon x is the locus of mean values of observed y for *given observed* values of x.

The $100(1 - 2a)\%$ confidence limits for the regression coefficient are

$$b \pm t_a s/\sqrt{\{\Sigma(x - \bar{x})^2\}}$$

where t_a has the same number of degrees of freedom as s.

The significance of b may be assessed from

$$t = b\sqrt{\{\Sigma(x - \bar{x})^2\}}/s$$

which is also based on $(n - 2)$ degrees of freedom.

Appendix 7C

CALCULATION OF CORRELATION COEFFICIENT AND REGRESSION EQUATION FROM GROUPED DATA

The method is best described by illustrating it on a particular example. The example selected refers to the correlation between the breaking loads and the extensibilities at break of lengths of yarn taken from a hank which had been subjected to a rotproof treatment. To determine the correlation, 134 individual lengths (25 cm. each) were tested separately on a Goodbrand Single Thread Tester. The load (in grammes) and the extension of the yarn at break (measured as a percentage of original length) were recorded and the results grouped in the form of the two-way table shown in Table 7C·1.

Table 7C·1*

CORRELATION OF LOAD AND EXTENSIBILITY AT BREAK OF TREATED COTTON YARN

Breaking Load $= x$

		1	2	3	4	5	6	7	8	9	10	11	Total No.
		1180 to 1220	1220 to 1260	1260 to 1300	1300 to 1340	1340 to 1380	1380 to 1420	1420 to 1460	1460 to 1500	1500 to 1540	1540 to 1580	1580 to 1620	
13	8·2–8·6								1	2		1	4
12	7·8–8·2						1	1	2	2	1	3	10
11	7·4–7·8				1		2	2	3	6	8	1	23
10	7·0–7·4						3	3	1	5	1		13
9	6·6–7·0					1	2	4	6	3	1	1	18
8	6·2–6·6				1		2	8	2	1			14
7	5·8–6·2				1	1	1	5	2	1	1		12
6	5·4–5·8				1	1	3	1	1				7
5	5·0–5·4			2	1	1	2	2					8
4	4·6–5·0			1		3							4
3	4·2–4·6	1	2	2		2							7
2	3·8–4·2	1	3	2	3								9
1	3·4–3·8	2	1	2									5
	Total No.	4	6	9	8	9	16	26	18	20	12	6	134

Extensibility $= y$

* All results which fell exactly on the dividing lines between two groups were placed in the higher group (App. 2B).

The figure in each cell represents the number of yarns with results indicated by the marginal figures, e.g. there are 8 yarns having a breaking load of between 1,420 g. and 1,460 g. and an extensibility between 6·2% and 6·6%.

The grouping units are 40 g. for breaking load and 0·4% for extensibility. The column totals and row totals are given in the margins. These represent respectively the distributions of the breaking load and extensibility. The whole table is, in effect, the distribution with respect to both variables simultaneously.

As in the calculation of the variances for grouped data (App. 3C), the grouping units may be given an arbitrary value of unity. This simplifies the calculation. We may also take any point as origin. The mid-point of almost any group will be convenient. In this example we shall take the mid-point of the lowest group for both variables to be 1. The mid-points of the other groups will then have the values 2, 3, 4, . . . , as shown in the margins of Table 7C·1. A simple inspection suffices to show that the regression may be assumed to be linear, and therefore the correlation coefficient will be an adequate measure of the association between the two variables.

Three quantities are required for the calculation of the correlation coefficient:

    (i) The sum of squares of breaking load about the mean,
    (ii) The sum of squares of extensibility about the mean,
    (iii) The sum of products of extensibility and breaking load about their means.

These are calculated as follows:

    (i) *Sum of Squares of Breaking Load about the Mean.*

Denote this variable by x.

The frequency distribution of x is given by the column totals, and from inspection of Table 7C·1 this is seen to be:

Table 7C·2

FREQUENCY DISTRIBUTION OF x

Mid-point of group = x	1	2	3	4	5	6	7	8	9	10	11	Total
Frequency = f	4	6	9	8	9	16	26	18	20	12	6	134

The method of calculating the sum of squares about the mean has already been given in Appendix 3C. We have:

$$\Sigma x \qquad\qquad = 4 \times 1 + 6 \times 2 + \ldots + 6 \times 11 = 908$$

Crude sum of squares $\quad = 4 \times 1^2 + 6 \times 2^2 + \ldots + 6 \times 11^2 = 7{,}010$

Correction for the mean $\quad = 908^2/134 = 6{,}153$

$\therefore$ Sum of squares about

$$\text{mean} \qquad = \Sigma(x - \bar{x})^2 = 7{,}010 - 6{,}153 = 857$$

Variance of x $\qquad\qquad = 857/133 = 6\cdot44$

(ii) *Sum of Squares of Extensibility about Mean.*

Denote this variable by y.

The frequency distribution of y as seen from the row totals of Table 7C·1 is:

Table 7C·3

FREQUENCY DISTRIBUTION OF y

Mid-point of group = y	1	2	3	4	5	6	7	8	9	10	11	12	13	Total
Frequency = f	5	9	7	4	8	7	12	14	18	13	23	10	4	134

$$\Sigma y = 5 \times 1 + 9 \times 2 + \ldots + 4 \times 13 = 1{,}055$$

Crude sum of squares $= 5 \times 1^2 + 9 \times 2^2 + \ldots + 4 \times 13^2 = 9{,}761$

∴ Sum of squares about

mean $= \Sigma(y - \bar{y})^2 = 9{,}761 - 8{,}306 = 1{,}455$

(iii) *Sum of Products of Extensibility and Breaking Load about Means.*

In order to calculate this quantity we make use of the formula:

$$\Sigma(x - \bar{x})(y - \bar{y}) = \Sigma xy - (\Sigma x)(\Sigma y)/n$$

The first term on the right-hand side is the crude sum of products, and the second term is the correction for the means. The first step is to evaluate the crude sum of products. Let the value of x for the rth column be r, and the value of y for the sth row be s. The value of xy for each observation in this particular cell is therefore rs. If there are f observations in this cell, their contribution to the crude sum of products of the observations is frs. Calculating this for each cell in the rth column and adding, we obtained $r\Sigma fs$, which is simply "r times the sum of extensibilities for all the observations of the rth column." We use this to calculate the crude sum of products by summing over all columns. The details are:

Determine the sum of the y's for all observations in each column separately. Referring to Table 7C·1, we have:

Column 1 ($x = 1$); $\Sigma y = 2 \times 1 + 1 \times 2 + 1 \times 3 = 7$
Column 2 ($x = 2$); $\Sigma y = 1 \times 1 + 3 \times 2 + 2 \times 3 = 13$

.   .

.   .

Column 6 ($x = 6$); $\Sigma y = 2 \times 5 + 3 \times 6 + 1 \times 7 + 2 \times 8 + 2 \times 9$
$+ 3 \times 10 + 2 \times 11 + 1 \times 12$

$= 133$

etc.

These results are recorded in Table 7C·4 (second row). Multiply each column sum by the corresponding value of x, and add. This is given in row 3 of Table 7C·4, and the total is the crude sum of products.

Table 7C·4

x			1	2	3	4	5	6	7	8	9	10	11	Total
Σy			7	13	26	43	45	133	215	170	208	126	69	1055
$x\Sigma y$			7	26	78	172	225	798	1505	1360	1872	1260	759	8062

$\therefore$ Crude sum of products $= 8,062$

Correction for the means $= \Sigma x \Sigma y/n$

$\qquad = 908 \times 1,055/134 = 7,149$

$\therefore$ Sum of products of deviations
of x and y from means $= 8,062 - 7,149 = 913$

Covariance of x and y $= 913/133 = 6\cdot86$

The correlation coefficient is given by

$$r = \frac{\Sigma(x - \bar{x})(y - \bar{y})}{\sqrt{\{\Sigma(x - \bar{x})^2 \Sigma(y - \bar{y})^2\}}} = \frac{913}{\sqrt{(857 \times 1,455)}}$$

$$= 0\cdot818$$

The regression coefficient of extensibility on breaking load is

$$913/857 = 1\cdot065$$

Sum of squares about the regression

$$= \Sigma(y - \bar{y})^2 - [\Sigma(x - \bar{x})(y - \bar{y})]^2/\Sigma(x - \bar{x})^2$$
$$= 1,455 - 972\cdot7 = 482\cdot3$$

Variance about the regression

$$= 482\cdot3/132 = 3\cdot654$$

Standard error about the regression

$$= 1\cdot912$$

Standard error of regression coefficient

$$= 1\cdot912/\sqrt{857} = 0\cdot065$$

95% confidence limits for the regression coefficient

$$= 1\cdot065 \pm 0\cdot129$$
$$= 0\cdot936 \text{ to } 1\cdot194$$

APPENDIX 7D
FIELLER'S THEOREM

Confidence limits are sometimes required for the ratio of two estimated parameters, e.g. the ratio of two means, the ratio of two regression coefficients, or the ratio of two potencies such as that used in § 7·7.

Let a, b be unbiased estimates of two parameters, and assume that a and b are Normally distributed. We require to determine the confidence limits for the true value of the ratio a/b.

Put $a/b = \rho$, and form the expression $x = a - \rho b$. This is a linear function of Normally distributed variables, and x is therefore itself Normally distributed with variance $V = V(a) - 2\rho \operatorname{cov}(ab) + \rho^2 V(b)$. The expected value of x is zero, so that $x/\sqrt{V}$ is distributed as t, i.e. $(a - \rho b)^2/V$ is distributed as t^2. The confidence limits for ρ are therefore given by the values which satisfy the equation

$$(a - \rho b)^2/V = t^2$$

using the appropriate value of t. This is a quadratic in ρ, and the confidence limits of ρ are:

$$\frac{\dfrac{a}{b} - \dfrac{t^2 \operatorname{cov}(ab)}{b^2} \pm \dfrac{t}{b} \sqrt{\left\{ V(a) - \dfrac{2a}{b} \operatorname{cov}(ab) + \dfrac{a^2}{b^2} V(b) - \dfrac{t^2 V(b)}{b^2} \left(V(a) - \dfrac{[\operatorname{cov} ab]^2}{V(b)} \right) \right\}}}{1 - \dfrac{t^2 V(b)}{b^2}}$$

The approximate formula, derived in a different manner and used in § 7·72, is

$$\frac{a}{b} \pm \frac{t}{b} \sqrt{\left\{ V(a) + \frac{a^2}{b^2} V(b) \right\}}$$

In this situation a and b are independent, so that $\operatorname{cov}(ab) = 0$. Making this substitution in Fieller's formula and comparing with the approximate formula, we see that in the latter the assumption has been made that $V(b)/b^2$ is small compared with unity. This is generally the case in a well-designed experiment.

APPENDIX 7E

FITTING A LINEAR FUNCTIONAL RELATION WHEN BOTH VARIABLES ARE SUBJECT TO ERROR

The procedure for fitting a straight line when the error variances of both x and y are unknown has been outlined in § 7·62. Suppose we wish to fit the line

$$Y = a + bX \dots\dots\dots\dots\dots\dots(7E\cdot1)$$

to a set of n pairs of observations (x, y). Two relations are required in order to determine the values of a and b. One is readily obtained from the result, derived by the method of least squares, that the line passes through the mean $(\bar{x}, \bar{y})$ of the observations. The second relation is an estimate of the slope of the line; plot the n observations and divide them into three non-overlapping groups [§ 7·62], the two end groups having equal numbers, p, of observations, where p is chosen as near $n/3$ as possible. Denote the means of these groups by $(\bar{x}_1, \bar{y}_1)$, $(\bar{x}_2, \bar{y}_2)$ and $(\bar{x}_3, \bar{y}_3)$ respectively; the slope b is then estimated by the ratio $(\bar{y}_3 - \bar{y}_1)/(\bar{x}_3 - \bar{x}_1)$. The confidence limits for this estimate are provided by the solutions β_1, β_2 of the quadratic equation:

$$\tfrac{1}{2}p(\bar{x}_3 - \bar{x}_1)^2(b - \beta)^2 = t^2(C_{yy} - 2\beta C_{xy} + \beta^2 C_{xx})/(n-3) \quad ..(7E\cdot2)$$

where C_{yy}, C_{xy}, and C_{xx} are the sums of the sums of squares and products within the three groups, and t is the value of t for the chosen confidence limits corresponding to $(n - 3)$ degrees of freedom.

We shall illustrate the method by applying it to the following data:

$x =$	2	5	6	7	11	13	16	17	19	20	21	23	24
$y =$	11	10	13	16	20	18	25	22	26	30	32	30	32

Here $n = 13$ and the nearest value to $n/3$ is $p = 4$. Plotting the points, we find that there is no overlapping of the groups considered in either the x direction or the y direction, so that there is no ambiguity and the above method applies. From the first 4 pairs of observations:

$$\bar{x}_1 = 20/4 = 5, \; \bar{y}_1 = 50/4 = 12\cdot5$$

and from the last 4 pairs of observations:

$$\bar{x}_3 = 88/4 = 22, \; \bar{y}_3 = 124/4 = 31\cdot0$$

Therefore $b \to (31\cdot0 - 12\cdot5)/(22 - 5) = 1\cdot088$

The overall means are $\bar{x} = 184/13 = 14\cdot154$, $\bar{y} = 285/13 = 21\cdot923$.

The estimated equation of the line is therefore

$$Y = 21\cdot923 + 1\cdot088(X - 14\cdot154)$$

or
$$Y = 6\cdot523 + 1\cdot088X$$

To derive 95% confidence limits for the estimate of the slope we require the following quantities:

$$\begin{aligned}
C_{yy} &= [11^2 + 10^2 + 13^2 + 16^2 - (11 + 10 + 13 + 16)^2/4] \\
&\quad + [20^2 + \ldots + 26^2 - (20 + \ldots + 26)^2/5] \\
&\quad + [30^2 + \ldots + 32^2 - (30 + \ldots + 32)^2/4] = 7{,}003 - 6{,}933\cdot2 \\
&= 69\cdot8
\end{aligned}$$

$$\begin{aligned}
C_{xy} &= [2 \times 11 + \ldots + 7 \times 16 - 20 \times 50/4] \\
&\quad + [11 \times 20 + \ldots + 19 \times 26 - 76 \times 111/5] \\
&\quad + [20 \times 30 + \ldots + 24 \times 32 - 88 \times 124/4] = 4{,}714 - 4{,}665\cdot2 \\
&= 48\cdot8
\end{aligned}$$

$$\begin{aligned}
C_{xx} &= [2^2 + \ldots + 7^2 - (2 + \ldots + 7)^2/4] \\
&\quad + [11^2 + \ldots + 19^2 - (11 + \ldots + 19)^2/5] \\
&\quad + [20^2 + \ldots + 24^2 - (20 + \ldots + 26)^2/4] = 3{,}256 - 3{,}191\cdot2 \\
&= 64\cdot8
\end{aligned}$$

The value of t in Table C for $\alpha = 0\cdot025$, $\phi = n - 3 = 10$ is $2\cdot23$.

Substituting in $(7E\cdot2)$, the 95% confidence limits for the slope are the solutions of the equation

$$2 \times 10 \times 17^2(1\cdot088 - \beta)^2 = 2\cdot23^2(69\cdot8 - 2\beta \times 48\cdot8 + 64\cdot8\beta^2)$$

or
$$5{,}458\beta^2 - 2 \times 6{,}046\beta + 6{,}495 = 0$$

i.e.
$$\beta = 1\cdot108 \pm 0\cdot193$$

The 95% confidence limits for the slope are therefore (0·915, 1·301), the estimated value being 1·088.

The variance estimate used above, namely $(C_{yy} - 2\beta C_{xy} + \beta^2 C_{xx})/(n-3)$ is based on $(n-3)$ degrees of freedom, since three degrees of freedom have been used in the estimation of the group means. Only two of these degrees of freedom are really necessary for the above method, one for estimating the overall mean and the other for the difference between the mean of the two end groups; the third degree of freedom is available for a comparison of the mean of the second group with the combined mean of the first and third groups (i.e. for curvature). When n is small it is advisable to use this degree of freedom to obtain a better estimate of the variance based on one additional degree of freedom. The variance estimate is then given by

$$\frac{C_{yy} - 2\beta C_{xy} + \beta^2 C_{xx} + \{(\bar{y}_1 + \bar{y}_3 - 2\bar{y}_2) - \beta(\bar{x}_1 + \bar{x}_3 - 2\bar{x}_2)\}^2 \left\{\frac{2}{p} + \frac{4}{n-2p}\right\}^{-1}}{n-2}$$

$$\ldots\ldots(7E\cdot3)$$

the additional quantity in the numerator being the contribution to the sum of squares due to curvature. The quadratic equation for the confidence limits of the slope is similar to Equation ($7E\cdot2$) except that the coefficient of t^2 on the right-hand side is replaced by Formula ($7E\cdot3$) and t will be the value of t corresponding to $(n-2)$ degrees of freedom.

CHAPTER 8

MULTIPLE AND CURVILINEAR
REGRESSION

FREQUENTLY a quantity of interest such as the yield of a product
will be dependent on the levels of not one but a number of
variables. The situation is often complicated by the fact that these
variables are themselves related. This chapter shows how such
multiple relationships can be elucidated and how some common
pitfalls may be avoided. In the later part of the chapter the theory
is applied to the case in which two quantities are related not by a
straight line but by a curve.

Introduction

8·1 In the previous chapter a relationship was obtained [§ **7·27**] between the
abrasion loss and hardness of rubber samples of the form:

Abrasion loss (g./h.p.-hour) = 550·4 — 5·336 hardness (degrees Shore)

$$\text{i.e.} \quad y = a + bx_1$$

The value of this equation is that it shows how measurement of a property
which can be fairly readily and rapidly determined—in this instance hardness
—may be used as an indication of a more important but less readily determined property such as abrasion loss. It is, however, by no means an exact
relationship; the residual scatter of points about the line defined by the
relationship still has standard deviation 60·5 g./h.p.-hour compared with a
standard deviation of 88·1 g./h.p.-hour for the overall variation of all abrasion
loss results. Thus it is unlikely that in practice a knowledge of hardness
alone would be a sufficient guide to abrasion loss. It is possible, however, that
other information on a sample in addition to a knowledge of hardness might
enable us to predict abrasion loss more precisely while still avoiding the
elaborate testing called for by a direct determination. We might, in fact,
attempt to relate abrasion loss to more than one other property of a sample
and fit a Multiple Regression Equation showing its dependence on each of the
several factors considered rather than the simple regression on hardness alone.
Techniques are available for the fitting of such equations analogous to those
already described for the fitting of simple regressions, and these are discussed
in the present chapter. The same techniques may be applied to the fitting
of curvilinear (polynomial) relationships, since successive powers of a single
independent variable are formally equivalent to additional independent
variables. Thus, a section of the chapter [§ **8·3**] is devoted to the fitting of

curvilinear regressions.* Measures of precision and tests of significance for multiple and curvilinear regression are also described, and the use of regression equations for purposes of prediction is discussed.

MULTIPLE REGRESSION EQUATIONS

8·2   In the example already considered, a further property of a sample of rubber which might reasonably be expected to be related to abrasion loss is its tensile strength.   Results for tensile strength are shown alongside those for hardness and abrasion loss in Table 8·1, and Figure 8·1 is a scatter diagram of abrasion loss versus tensile strength.

The diagram shows few signs of any association between abrasion loss and tensile strength, and it does not seem, at first sight, that the additional

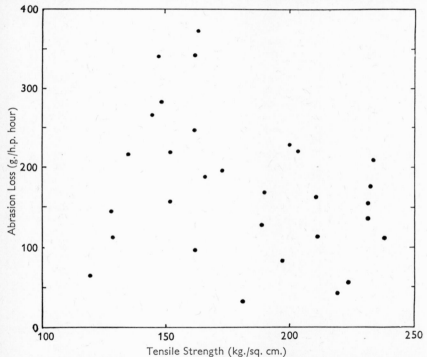

Fig. 8·1. Scatter diagram. Abrasion loss v. tensile strength for rubber samples

* While the fitting of curvilinear regressions is most conveniently and informatively treated as a special case of multiple regression, certain difficulties which arise in the interpretation of multiple dependence are absent when a dependence on one variable only is considered. The reader interested only in the fitting of curvilinear regressions on a single variable may therefore omit the more difficult material of §§ **8·261, 8·262, 8·263, 8·272, 8·273 and 8·274.**

P

Table 8·1

PHYSICAL PROPERTIES OF RUBBER SAMPLES

Sample No.	Abrasion Loss (g./h.p.-hour) (y)	Hardness (degrees Shore) (x_1)	Tensile Strength (kg./sq. cm.) (x_2)
1	372	45	162
2	206	55	233
3	175	61	232
4	154	66	231
5	136	71	231
6	112	71	237
7	55	81	224
8	45	86	219
9	221	53	203
10	166	60	189
11	164	64	210
12	113	68	210
13	82	79	196
14	32	81	180
15	228	56	200
16	196	68	173
17	128	75	188
18	97	83	161
19	64	88	119
20	249	59	161
21	219	71	151
22	186	80	165
23	155	82	151
24	114	89	128
25	341	51	161
26	340	59	146
27	283	65	148
28	267	74	144
29	215	81	134
30	148	86	127

information will be of much value for purposes of prediction. Figure 8·1 does not, however, tell the whole story. If we are to use tensile strength to assist in the prediction of abrasion loss, we must relate the observed variations in tensile strength to the as yet unexplained variations in abrasion loss, i.e. to the variations of abrasion loss *about the regression of abrasion loss on hardness*, rather than to the overall variation. If we do this, then we should also eliminate any variations in tensile strength which can be associated with variations in hardness, since, in removing from the abrasion loss the cal- culated effect of hardness, we will remove simultaneously any effect of the associated variations in tensile strength. Thus we must look for a relationship between the residual variations in abrasion loss after allowing for hardness, and the residual variations in tensile strength, again after allowing for any effects of hardness. The scatter diagram of these residual variations is shown as Figure 8·2.

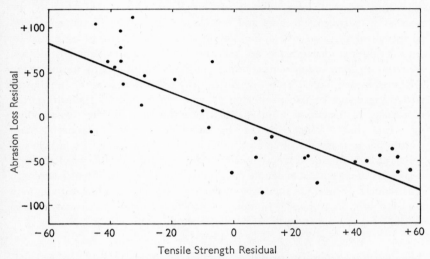

Fig. 8·2. Scatter diagram. Residual variations in abrasion loss and tensile strength after allowing for hardness

There is now a clear indication of a relationship. It follows that a know- ledge of tensile strength as well as hardness *will* permit more precise prediction of abrasion loss than a knowledge of hardness alone; the residual scatter will be reduced from that about the regression on hardness only (the overall scatter in Figure 8·2) to that about the relationship which may be fitted to the values in Figure 8·2. The slope of the latter is calculated as $-1·374$, i.e. unit increases in tensile strength are associated with decreases of $1·374$ g./h.p.-hour in abrasion loss, and the residual scatter is found to have standard deviation 36·5 g./h.p.-hour. The details of the calculations are given later.

Separation of effects

8·21 By eliminating the effects of hardness (x_1) we have effectively studied variations in abrasion loss (y) and tensile strength (x_2) at constant hardness.

Because it applies to variations at constant hardness, the relationship revealed by Figure 8·2 will be a true measure of the effect of tensile strength on abrasion loss when both hardness and tensile strength are considered. Conversely, however, the relationship between abrasion loss (y) and hardness (x_1) derived earlier will not be applicable when both hardness (x_1) and tensile strength (x_2) are used for prediction, since it does not relate to variations in abrasion loss and hardness at *constant tensile strength*. The Total Regression Coefficient then found will differ from the Partial Regression Coefficient now applicable, because the former describes the effects both of variations in hardness, and of any associated variations in tensile strength. The difference will be greater or smaller depending on the extent of the association between hardness and tensile strength. The partial regression coefficient of abrasion loss on hardness (i.e. of y on x_1) may be estimated by considering the dependence on hardness of the *adjusted* abrasion losses, adjusting to some convenient common tensile strength (x_2) by means of the relationship just found. In other words, if we use b to denote the (unknown) partial regression coefficient of y on x_1, and c to denote the (known) partial regression coefficient of y on x_2, then b is the slope of the regression of $(y - cx_2)$ on x_1. While this may be found directly, it is practically more convenient to make use of an algebraic identity which will give b in terms of values already found. Let b_0 denote the *total* regression coefficient of abrasion loss on hardness and let m denote the slope of the regression of tensile strength on hardness. Since c is the slope of the regression of residual variations in abrasion loss on residual variations in tensile strength, the equation fitted to allow for the dependence on tensile strength (x_2) is:

$$\{(y - \bar{y}) - b_0(x_1 - \bar{x}_1)\} = c\{(x_2 - \bar{x}_2) - m(x_1 - \bar{x}_1)\}$$

The deviations from this regression are inexplicable in terms of either hardness or tensile strength, so that the equation in fact represents the multiple regression of y on x_1 and x_2. Rearrangement gives:

$$(y - \bar{y}) = (b_0 - mc)(x_1 - \bar{x}_1) + c(x_2 - \bar{x}_2),$$

while further rearrangement gives:

$$\{(y - \bar{y}) - c(x_2 - \bar{x}_2)\} = (b_0 - mc)(x_1 - \bar{x}_1)$$

which is the equation representing the regression of $(y - cx_2)$ (the adjusted abrasion loss) on x_1 (hardness). This last step is not necessary to prove the desired result

$$b = b_0 - mc \quad \dots\dots\dots\dots\dots\dots\dots\dots(8\cdot1)$$

which is clear from the previous equation, but it helps to show the identity of the algebraic with the direct approach.

The value obtained for b is $- 6\cdot571$, so that the partial effect of hardness is greater than the total effect found earlier. The explanation lies in the negative correlation which exists between hardness and tensile strength; hard samples tend to have a low tensile strength, so that the effect of hardness is partially offset by the contrary effect of associated variations in tensile strength.

Since the mean abrasion loss (175·4) corresponds to mean hardness (70·27) and also to mean tensile strength (180·5), we may express the estimated dependence of abrasion loss (y) on hardness (x_1) and tensile strength (x_2) by the multiple regression equation

$$(y - 175·4) = -6·571(x_1 - 70·27) - 1·374(x_2 - 180·5) \quad ..(8·2)$$

i.e. Abrasion loss $= 885·2 - 6·571$ hardness $- 1·374$ tensile strength $..(8·21)$

Total and partial regression coefficients

8·22   The distinction between total and partial regression coefficients is an important one, and one which should never be overlooked. It is sometimes the practice, when a dependence on more than one factor is suspected, to plot the values of the "dependent" variable against the corresponding values of each of the "independent" variables in turn, and to assume that a dependence exists wherever this seems indicated by such a plot. This, however, may be completely misleading; the relationships shown by such two-dimensional plots are all total regressions, and these may depend much more on the arrangement of the observations with respect to the independent variables than on any real effects of the factors concerned. To illustrate the distinction

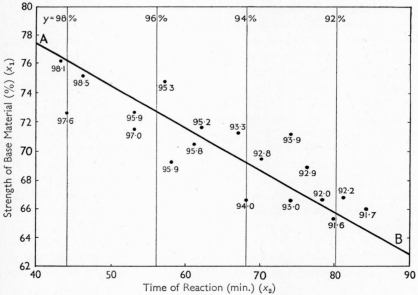

Fig. 8·3.   Manufacture of an organic chemical. Plot of results, showing estimated contours of constant product purity

it is convenient to make use of a more extreme example than that discussed above on the physical properties of rubber samples. Figure 8·3 is a (schematic) plot of results obtained in the manufacture of an organic chemical. The ordinate (x_1) is the "strength" of the base material, i.e. the proportion of the active ingredient, and the abscissa (x_2) is the time required for completion of the reaction. Each point plotted represents a single batch. The dependent variable y was the purity of the final product; this was related to strength of base material and time of reaction by means of a multiple regression equation, and it was found that, in fact, purity depended only on time of reaction—the longer the time of reaction, the lower the purity. Thus contours of constant purity (lines joining all points for which a given purity would be predicted from the regression equation) are the vertical lines shown in the figure. Such a contour diagram is often a useful practical representation of a multiple regression equation with two independent variables.

The effect which must be assigned to either factor when both are considered—i.e. the partial regression coefficient—is the rate of change of y with the factor when the other is held constant. It is thus the rate at which contours are crossed by a point travelling parallel to the appropriate co-ordinate axis. Figure 8·3 shows that, while purity is related to time of reaction (x_2), it is not related to strength of base material (x_1), since no contours are ever crossed in the x_1 direction. The observations available are not, however, spread parallel to either axis; they show a general diagonal tendency, lower strengths being associated with longer reaction times. Thus, in the results available, movement in the x_1 direction takes place, on the average, along the line AB—the regression of x_2 on x_1. This line does cross the "purity" contours, at a rate determined by the slope of the regression of x_2 on x_1. If we ignore or lose sight of the fact that, *in the results available*, movement in the x_1 direction is only obtained at the cost of movement in the x_2 direction, we will then conclude that purity of product is affected by strength of base material. Such a conclusion had in fact been drawn, before the multiple regression analysis showed it to be fallacious, from a plot [Figure 8·4] of purity of product against strength of base material; the apparent plausibility of the result—decreasing purity associated with decreasing strength of base material—served to distract attention from the important connection between strength of base material and reaction time. The rate of change of y with x_1 as we move along the line AB is the total regression coefficient for y on x_1, and in this instance it gives a completely false impression of the role of x_1 (strength of base material), since the apparent dependence of y on x_1 which it shows results solely from the correlation between x_1 and x_2, i.e. from the arrangement of the observations with respect to x_1 and x_2. If, by accident or design, this arrangement had been different, a different total regression coefficient would necessarily have been obtained. The partial regression coefficients would not, however, have been affected, except by inevitable sampling fluctuations; they do not, as the representation shows, depend on the arrangement of the observations.

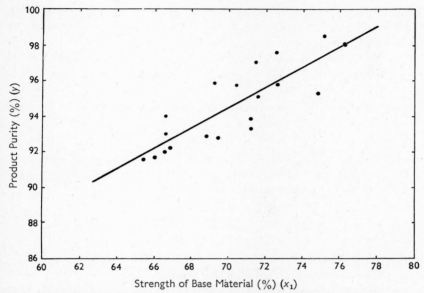

Fig. 8·4. Manufacture of an organic chemical. Apparent dependence of product purity on strength of base material

It will be observed that, in the present instance, the total regression coefficient for the regression of y (purity) on x_2 (time of reaction) is the same as the corresponding partial regression coefficient, and is unaffected by the arrangement of the observations. The reason for this is that there is no real dependence of y on x_1 (strength of base material). Usually, however, the contours will be inclined, and both partial regression coefficients will exist. The general effect of correlation between the independent variables is then to throw part of the real effect of x_1 into the apparent effect of x_2, and part of the real effect of x_2 into the apparent effect of x_1, so that both total regression coefficients are affected.

Generalisation of the method of least squares
8·23 The discussion above [§§ **8·2**, **8·21**] shows how, in principle, a multiple regression equation may be fitted, but the method used is not a particularly practical one—especially when more than two "independent" variables must be considered. It will be remembered, however, that the separate regressions

are fitted by the Method of Least Squares [§ **7·22**], in which the sums of squares of deviations from the relationship are minimised. This same method may be applied directly to the fitting of multiple regression equations, and short-circuits the repeated fitting and adjustment carried out above. For a dependence of one variable on two other variables, where the relationship to be fitted is of the form $y = a + bx_1 + cx_2$, the Least Squares equations for a, b and c are:

$$\left.\begin{aligned}
b\Sigma(x_1 - \bar{x}_1)^2 + c\Sigma(x_1 - \bar{x}_1)(x_2 - \bar{x}_2) &= \Sigma(x_1 - \bar{x}_1)(y - \bar{y}) \\
b\Sigma(x_1 - \bar{x}_1)(x_2 - \bar{x}_2) + c\Sigma(x_2 - \bar{x}_2)^2 &= \Sigma(x_2 - \bar{x}_2)(y - \bar{y}) \\
a &= \bar{y} - b\bar{x}_1 - c\bar{x}_2
\end{aligned}\right\} \quad ..(8\cdot3)$$

We may also write the first two equations more concisely as

$$\left.\begin{aligned}
bC_{11} + cC_{12} &= C_{y1} \\
bC_{12} + cC_{22} &= C_{y2}
\end{aligned}\right\} \dots\dots\dots\dots\dots(8\cdot31)$$

where C_{11} denotes $\Sigma(x_1 - \bar{x}_1)^2$, C_{12} denotes $\Sigma(x_1 - \bar{x}_1)(x_2 - \bar{x}_2)$, and so on.

For the regression of abrasion loss (y) on hardness (x_1) and tensile strength (x_2) discussed above, the equations are:

$$\left.\begin{aligned}
4{,}300b - 3{,}862c &= -22{,}946 \\
-3{,}862b + 38{,}733c &= -27{,}857
\end{aligned}\right\} \dots\dots\dots\dots(8\cdot311)$$

These may readily be solved to give

$$b = -6\cdot571 \qquad c = -1\cdot374$$

so that the solution is identical with that quoted earlier.

For the more general problem, in which the dependence of a variable y on a number of other variables $x_1, \dots, x_p$ is to be estimated, the relationship may be written as

$$y = b_0 + b_1x_1 + b_2x_2 + \dots + b_px_p$$

and the Least Squares equations are:

$$\left.\begin{aligned}
b_1C_{11} + b_2C_{12} + \dots + b_pC_{1p} &= C_{y1} \\
b_1C_{12} + b_2C_{22} + \dots + b_pC_{2p} &= C_{y2} \\
\vdots \qquad \vdots \qquad\qquad \vdots \qquad\; \vdots \qquad& \\
b_1C_{1p} + b_2C_{2p} + \dots + b_pC_{pp} &= C_{yp} \\
b_0 = \bar{y} - b_1\bar{x}_1 - b_2\bar{x}_2 - \dots - b_p\bar{x}_p&
\end{aligned}\right\} \dots\dots\dots(8\cdot32)$$

In the notation used above, C_{11} denotes $\Sigma(x_1 - \bar{x}_1)^2$, C_{12} denotes $\Sigma(x_1 - \bar{x}_1)(x_2 - \bar{x}_2)$, etc. The derivation of these equations is given in Appendix 8A.

The number of equations is equal to the number of constants to be estimated, i.e. ($p + 1$), and the coefficients (apart from those in the equation of means defining b_0) form a symmetrical pattern, with sums of squares along the principal (N.W.–S.E.) diagonal, and sums of products elsewhere. This symmetry is helpful in setting out the equations in practice.

Solution of the equations

8·24 When there are only two independent variables, the solutions can be written out at once; we have

$$b_1 C_{11} + b_2 C_{12} = C_{y1}$$
$$b_1 C_{12} + b_2 C_{22} = C_{y2}$$

and hence, by appropriate cross-multiplication and subtraction,

$$b_1(C_{11}C_{22} - C_{12}{}^2) = C_{22}C_{y1} - C_{12}C_{y2}$$
$$b_2(C_{11}C_{22} - C_{12}{}^2) = C_{11}C_{y2} - C_{12}C_{y1}$$

i.e.
$$\left. \begin{aligned} b_1 &= (C_{22}C_{y1} - C_{12}C_{y2})/(C_{11}C_{22} - C_{12}{}^2) \\ b_2 &= (C_{11}C_{y2} - C_{12}C_{y1})/(C_{11}C_{22} - C_{12}{}^2) \end{aligned} \right\} \quad \dots\dots\dots(8\cdot33)$$

Generally speaking, however, some systematic method of solution, with appropriate arithmetical checks, is required.

Several methods are available, of which the simplest and most readily comprehensible is the schoolroom method of systematic elimination of unknowns. A more rapid method is that outlined in Appendix 8B; the advantages of this method become progressively greater as the number of independent variables increases. An alternative method which is particularly useful when many independent variables have to be tested for significance and, if significant, included in the representation, is given in [8·1].

Solution to give standard errors

8·241 One form of solution of the equations of considerable practical importance is obtained by solving, not the original set of p equations, but the p sets of p equations obtained by successively substituting on the right of the original equations the sets of values $(1, 0, 0, \ldots, 0)$, $(0, 1, 0, \ldots, 0)$, $(0, 0, 1, \ldots, 0)$, $\ldots$, $(0, 0, 0, \ldots, 1)$. The importance arises from the fact that this form of solution gives as a by-product the standard errors of the regression coefficients. It does not, in practice, greatly increase the amount of calculation required, whatever the method of solution used, since many of the steps depend only on the coefficients on the left of the equations, and others are simplified by the large numbers of zeroes introduced.

With, for example, three independent variables, the Least Squares equations are

$$b_1 C_{11} + b_2 C_{12} + b_3 C_{13} = C_{y1}$$
$$b_1 C_{12} + b_2 C_{22} + b_3 C_{23} = C_{y2}$$
$$b_1 C_{13} + b_2 C_{23} + b_3 C_{33} = C_{y3}$$

We replace these by the three sets of equations

$$pC_{11} + qC_{12} + rC_{13} = 1, \quad 0, \quad 0$$
$$pC_{12} + qC_{22} + rC_{23} = 0, \quad 1, \quad 0$$
$$pC_{13} + qC_{23} + rC_{33} = 0, \quad 0, \quad 1$$

each set corresponding to a particular column of figures on the right. Let the solutions to the first set (right-hand sides 1, 0, 0 respectively) be

$$p_1 = C^{11}$$
$$q_1 = C^{21}$$
$$r_1 = C^{31}$$

Let those to the second set be similarly

$$p_2 = C^{12}$$
$$q_2 = C^{22}$$
$$r_2 = C^{32}$$

and those to the third set be

$$p_3 = C^{13}$$
$$q_3 = C^{23}$$
$$r_3 = C^{33}$$

We may write the three sets of solutions as the array of numbers

$$C^{11} \quad C^{12} \quad C^{13}$$
$$C^{21} \quad C^{22} \quad C^{23}$$
$$C^{31} \quad C^{32} \quad C^{33}$$

each set of solutions forming one column of the array.

Readers familiar with matrix algebra will recognise this array as the inverse of the matrix of sums of squares and products formed by the coefficients on the left-hand sides of the original equations. Subscripts are used to indicate the coefficients C_{ij} of the original matrix and superscripts to indicate the corresponding elements C^{ij} of the inverse matrix. The symmetry of the pattern of coefficients in the equations leads to a corresponding symmetry in the inverse matrix, so that $C^{12} = C^{21}$, $C^{13} = C^{31}$ and $C^{23} = C^{32}$. This property may be used as a check on the correctness of the solutions, as an indication of the accuracy attained, or as a means of avoiding part of the calculation which would otherwise be necessary. In work with a desk calculating machine of limited capacity, using straightforward elimination of unknowns, the second alternative is perhaps the most useful. Using the inverse matrix, the solutions to the original equations are given by

$$\left. \begin{array}{l} b_1 = C^{11}C_{y1} + C^{12}C_{y2} + C^{13}C_{y3} \\ b_2 = C^{21}C_{y1} + C^{22}C_{y2} + C^{23}C_{y3} \\ b_3 = C^{31}C_{y1} + C^{32}C_{y2} + C^{33}C_{y3} \end{array} \right\} \quad \ldots \ldots \ldots \ldots \ldots (8\cdot34)$$

Thus, b_1 is obtained by summing the products of successive terms in the first row of the inverse matrix with the corresponding quantities on the right-hand sides of the original equations, b_2 by using similarly the second row of the matrix, and b_3 by using the third row. Since in practice the matrix is symmetric, we may equally well use the columns.

The standard errors of the estimated regression coefficients are also obtained from the inverse matrix. If σ^2 is the experimental error variance of the observed y-values, then the standard errors of the estimates of b_1, b_2, b_3 are given by

$$\left.\begin{aligned} S.E.(b_1) &= \sigma\sqrt{C^{11}} \\ S.E.(b_2) &= \sigma\sqrt{C^{22}} \\ S.E.(b_3) &= \sigma\sqrt{C^{33}} \end{aligned}\right\} \dots\dots\dots\dots\dots(8·35)$$

i.e. by σ times the square root of the appropriate diagonal term. The non-diagonal terms give the covariances of the estimates. Thus

$$\left.\begin{aligned} \text{cov } (b_1b_2) &= \sigma^2 C^{12} \,(= \sigma^2 C^{21}) \\ \text{cov } (b_1b_3) &= \sigma^2 C^{13} \,(= \sigma^2 C^{31}), \text{ etc.} \end{aligned}\right\} \dots\dots\dots\dots(8·36)$$

Usually, of course, σ^2 will not be known in advance. If, however, the regression equation is correctly formulated (i.e. if all relevant factors have been included), then σ^2 may be estimated from the residual variation of the observed y-values about the values predicted from the fitted relationship. Denoting the estimate of σ^2 by s^2, then the estimated standard error of b_1 is $s\sqrt{C^{11}}$, and so on. Estimation of σ^2 and of the standard errors and covariances of regression coefficients is discussed in § **8·26** below.

The standard errors give a measure of the uncertainties attaching to the separate estimates, while the covariances show how chance errors in the estimation of any one coefficient will affect the estimates of the other coefficients. Both standard errors and covariances are required in assessing the accuracy of prediction using the regression equation.

Orthogonality

8·242   Of the coefficients in the least squares equations, the sums of squares are essentially positive and, in practice, different from zero; for if a sum of squares, say C_{11}, were equal to zero, this would imply that all observed values of x_1 were the same, and hence that C_{12}, C_{13}, ..., C_{1p} were also zero. Thus all coefficients of b_1 in the least squares equations would be zero and b_1 would be completely indeterminate; whatever value were assigned to it, the equations would still be satisfied. The indeterminacy accords with the common-sense view that, if x_1 does not vary in the set of observations, no information can be obtained from these observations about the effects of variations in x_1.

The vanishing of a sum of products does not, however, impose any such drastic limitations on the observed values, and the presence of the zero somewhat simplifies the arithmetic in the solution of the equations. The special case when all products vanish is of particular interest. The least squares equations reduce to

$$b_r C_{rr} = C_{yr} \,(r = 1, \dots, p) \dots\dots\dots\dots(8·37)$$

and each b_r is obtained directly from the appropriate equation. The solution, it will be noted, is the same as that for the total regression coefficient;

it does not matter whether we consider the variables separately or together. The reason for this is that the vanishing of the sums of products means that the observed values of any independent variable are completely uncorrelated with those of any other, and hence that changes in any one of them are not associated, overall, with changes in any of the others. Each total regression coefficient thus reflects only the effect of the variable concerned.

A further simplification arises in the expressions for the variances and covariances of the estimates; the variances reduce to

$$V(b_r) = \sigma^2/C_{rr} \qquad \dots\dots\dots\dots\dots\dots\dots(8.38)$$

while all covariances are zero. The mutual independence of the estimates implies that each may be tested separately for significance [§§ 8·26, 8·27], while the effect of adding or suppressing a term in the regression equation may be ascertained at once.

The vanishing of a sum of products defines what is known as the "orthogonality" of the two sets of values. Such orthogonality may arise by chance, but this is rather unlikely. When, however, the values of the independent variables may be assigned at will, as in a planned investigation rather than an examination of accumulated data, orthogonality may be deliberately imposed, and will lead to considerable saving of effort in the analysis of the results, as well as to some gain in the precision of estimation. The principle underlies the whole development of the statistical design of experiments, and is most clearly in evidence in the balanced factorial designs discussed in, for example, Chapters 7 and 8 of "Design and Analysis." A more general discussion of methods of attaining orthogonality is given in [8·2], where it is shown how orthogonal designs for any number of factors and tests may be derived.

It should be noted that the vanishing of the product terms need not in any sense imply a functional independence of the variables considered; this will be evident when we come to consider curvilinear relationships [§ 8·3, and particularly § 8·34]. The mutual independence of the so-called "independent" variables is in fact of little theoretical consequence, and the term is used only for convenience in description.

Example 8·1: Flow of sulphate of ammonia

8·25 It is important that sulphate of ammonia should flow freely when being packed, in order that automatic sack filling and weighing machines should be able to function correctly. Occasionally, however, the crystals stick, and cause difficulties in the packing sheds. The sticking is caused in part by dampness, but may depend also on crystal shape or size. The adsorption of moisture by the material may also be affected by traces of impurity present in the product. To investigate causes of sticking, a test was devised, corresponding approximately to packing conditions, in which a quantity of

Table 8·2

RATES OF FLOW AND OTHER DATA ON SAMPLES OF SULPHATE OF AMMONIA

Sample Number	Flow Rate (g./sec.) (y)	Initial Moisture Content (in units of 0·01%) (x_1)	Length/ Breadth Ratio for Crystals (x_2)	Percent Impurity (in units of 0·01%) (x_3)
1	5·00	21	2·4	0
2	4·81	20	2·4	0
3	4·46	16	2·4	0
4	4·81	18	2·5	0
5	4·46	16	3·2	0
6	3·85	18	3·1	1
7	3·21	12	3·2	1
8	3·25	12	2·7	0
9	4·55	13	2·7	0
10	4·85	13	2·7	0
11	4·00	17	2·7	0
12	3·62	24	2·8	0
13	5·15	11	2·5	0
14	3·76	10	2·6	0
15	4·90	17	2·0	0
16	4·13	14	2·0	0
17	5·10	14	2·0	1
18	5·05	14	1·9	0
19	4·27	20	2·1	2
20	4·90	12	1·9	1
21	4·55	11	2·0	2
22	5·32	10	2·0	7
23	4·39	10	2·0	2
24	4·85	16	2·0	2
25	4·59	17	2·2	3
26	5·00	17	2·4	4
27	3·82	17	2·4	0
28	3·68	15	2·4	2
29	5·15	17	2·2	3
30	2·94	21	2·2	4
31	3·18	23	2·2	10
32	2·28	22	2·0	7
33	5·00	21	1·9	4

Table 8·2 (*continued*)

Sample Number	Flow Rate (g./sec.) (y)	Initial Moisture Content (in units of 0·01%) (x_1)	Length/ Breadth Ratio for Crystals (x_2)	Percent Impurity (in units of 0·01%) (x_3)
34	2·43	24	2·1	8
35	0	37	2·3	14
36	4·10	21	2·4	2
37	3·70	28	2·4	5
38	3·36	29	2·4	7
39	3·79	23	3·6	7
40	3·40	32	3·3	8
41	1·51	26	3·5	4
42	0	28	3·5	12
43	1·72	21	3·0	3
44	2·33	22	3·0	6
45	2·38	34	3·0	8
46	3·68	29	3·5	5
47	4·20	17	3·5	3
48	5·00	11	3·2	2

sulphate was allowed to flow through a small funnel, and its rate of flow determined. Rates of flow and other data on the samples examined are given in Table 8·2.

From these figures we obtain:

$$\bar{y} = 3·843 \qquad \bar{x}_1 = 18·98 \qquad \bar{x}_2 = 2·550 \qquad \bar{x}_3 = 3·125$$
$$C_{yy} = 74·15 \qquad C_{11} = 2{,}052·98 \qquad C_{22} = 12·46 \qquad C_{33} = 577·25$$
$$C_{12} = 49·15 \qquad C_{13} = 782·12 \qquad C_{23} = 13·50$$
$$C_{y1} = -257·59 \qquad C_{y2} = -11·720 \qquad C_{y3} = -141·37$$

The least squares equations are thus:

$$2{,}052·98b_1 + 49·15b_2 + 782·12b_3 = -257·59$$
$$49·15b_1 + 12·46b_2 + 13·50b_3 = -11·72$$
$$782·12b_1 + 13·50b_2 + 577·25b_3 = -141·37$$

and the solutions are:

$$b_1 = -0·04882$$
$$b_2 = -0·56877$$
$$b_3 = -0·16545$$

Hence the estimated dependence of flow rate (y) on percent moisture (x_1), crystal length/breadth ratio (x_2) and percent impurity (x_3) is:
$$(y - 3·843) = - 0·04882(x_1 - 18·98) - 0·56877(x_2 - 2·550)$$
$$- 0·16545(x_3 - 3·125)$$
i.e. $$y = 6·737 - 0·0488x_1 - 0·5688x_2 - 0·1655x_3$$

The inverse matrix is obtained by solution of the three sets of equations:
$$2,052·98b_1 + 49·15b_2 + 782·12b_3 = 1, \quad 0, \quad 0$$
$$49·15b_1 + 12·46b_2 + 13·50b_3 = 0, \quad 1, \quad 0$$
$$782·12b_1 + 13·50b_2 + 577·25b_3 = 0, \quad 0, \quad 1$$

It is thus:
$$10^{-3} \times \begin{bmatrix} 1·0931 & - 2·7775 & - 1·4160 \\ - 2·7775 & 89·4009 & 1·6725 \\ - 1·4160 & 1·6725 & 3·6119 \end{bmatrix}$$

where the multiplication by 10^{-3} is understood to apply to each term of the matrix separately.

We thus have, as before:
$$b_1 = 10^{-3}[- (1·0931 \times 257·59) + (2·7775 \times 11·72) + (1·4160 \times 141·37)]$$
$$= - 0·0488$$
$$b_2 = 10^{-3}[(2·7775 \times 257·59) - (89·4009 \times 11·72) - (1·6725 \times 141·37)]$$
$$= - 0·5688$$
$$b_3 = 10^{-3}[(1·4160 \times 257·59) - (1·6725 \times 11·72) - (3·6119 \times 141·37)]$$
$$= - 0·1655$$

Standard errors and confidence limits: Prediction using the regression equation

8·26 For one independent variable the sum of squares due to regression is given by $b\Sigma(x - \bar{x})(y - \bar{y})$, i.e. by bC_{xy} in the notation used above. For more than one independent variable the sum of squares due to regression is given similarly by
$$b_1C_{y1} + b_2C_{y2} + \ldots + b_pC_{yp} \quad \ldots\ldots\ldots\ldots\ldots(8·4)$$
It represents p degrees of freedom; the residual sum of squares
$$C_{yy} - b_1C_{y1} - b_2C_{y2} - \ldots - b_pC_{yp}\ldots\ldots\ldots\ldots(8·41)$$
thus gives an estimate of residual variance based on $n - p - 1$ degrees of freedom, where n denotes the number of sets of observations used in deriving the regression equation, since in all $p + 1$ parameters have been estimated. It should be noted, however, that the residual variance will only estimate the true "error" mean square if the regression equation is correctly formulated. If significant variables have been omitted, or if the true relationship is non-linear, the estimate will be biased [8·3].

The estimate of the residual variance is
$$s^2 = \frac{1}{n - p - 1}(C_{yy} - b_1C_{y1} - \ldots - b_pC_{yp})\ldots\ldots\ldots(8·411)$$

As mentioned earlier, the standard errors of the estimated regression coefficients are obtained by way of the inverse matrix. Thus

$$S.E.(b_1) = s\sqrt{C^{11}}$$
$$S.E.(b_2) = s\sqrt{C^{22}}$$
$$S.E.(b_3) = s\sqrt{C^{33}}$$

etc.

The non-diagonal terms of the inverse matrix give, similarly, the covariances of the estimates. We have

$$\text{cov}\,(b_1 b_2) = s^2 C^{12} = s^2 C^{21}$$

and similar expressions for the other covariances. The covariances of the estimates indicate the extent to which chance errors in the estimate of any one coefficient will affect the estimates of other coefficients; they reflect any correlations between observed values of the independent variables.

Limits within which the true regression coefficients $\beta_1, \ldots, \beta_p$ probably ie, i.e. the confidence limits, are calculated from the standard errors by means of the appropriate t-multipliers (Table C). Thus the $(1 - 2a)$ confidence limits for β_1 are

$$b_1 \pm t_a s\sqrt{C^{11}} \dots\dots\dots\dots\dots\dots\dots(8\cdot42)$$

where t has the same number of degrees of freedom $(n - p - 1)$ as the estimate of s^2. The precision with which β_1 is estimated depends on the magnitude of s^2, i.e. on the residual scatter about the regression, on the number of observations available (which determines the appropriate t-multiplier) and also on the inverse matrix term C^{11}. This last depends on the spread of the observed x_1-values, and also on the extent to which the variations in x_1 are correlated with variations in the other "independent" variables. The greater the spread, and the less the correlation, the smaller will be the value of C^{11}. Its reciprocal, $1/C^{11}$, is in fact the residual sum of squares of the x_1-values about a regression of x_1 on the other independent variables $x_2, \ldots, x_p$, and this is used to derive the standard error of b_1 in the same way as the overall sum of squares of the x-values was used to derive the standard error of a regression coefficient b for a simple regression on one variable [§ 7·24]. Reference to Figure 8·2 and the accompanying discussion illustrates the point.

The significance of b_1 is measured by its ratio to its standard error, i.e. by

$$t = b_1/s\sqrt{C^{11}} \dots\dots\dots\dots\dots\dots\dots(8\cdot43)$$

The degrees of freedom for t are, as for t_a, $n - p - 1$.

For the example discussed in § 8·25, the sum of squares due to regression is
$$0\cdot0488 \times 257\cdot59) + (0\cdot5688 \times 11\cdot72) + (0\cdot1655 \times 141\cdot37) = 42\cdot63$$
The residual sum of squares is thus

$$74\cdot15 - 42\cdot63 = 31\cdot52$$

and corresponds to $(48 - 3 - 1) = 44$ degrees of freedom. The estimated residual variance is thus

$$s^2 = \frac{1}{44}(31\cdot52) = 0\cdot7164$$

giving

$$s = 0\cdot8464$$

Hence

$$S.E.(b_1) = 0\cdot8464\sqrt{(1\cdot0931 \times 10^{-3})} = 0\cdot0280$$
$$S.E.(b_2) = 0\cdot8464\sqrt{(89\cdot4009 \times 10^{-3})} = 0\cdot2531$$
$$S.E.(b_3) = 0\cdot8464\sqrt{(3\cdot6119 \times 10^{-3})} = 0\cdot0509$$

95% confidence limits for the true regression coefficients are:

For β_1: $- 0\cdot0488 \pm 0\cdot0564$, i.e. $- 0\cdot1052, + 0\cdot0076$
β_2: $- 0\cdot5688 \pm 0\cdot5100$, i.e. $- 1\cdot0788, - 0\cdot0588$
β_3: $- 0\cdot1655 \pm 0\cdot1026$, i.e. $- 0\cdot2681, - 0\cdot0629$

while the calculated t-values for testing the significance of the b's are $- 1\cdot74$, $- 2\cdot25$ and $- 3\cdot25$ respectively. We see from the confidence limits that none of the coefficients is very precisely determined, and that the estimate of β_1 is so imprecise that it is not unlikely that the true value is zero. The t-value for b_1 fails, similarly, to reach the $0\cdot05$ significance level.

Confidence regions for simultaneous estimates

8·261   The standard errors of the regression coefficients, and the confidence limits calculated therefrom, measure the overall uncertainty of each estimated regression coefficient taken separately. The uncertainty as to the true value of (say) β_1 springs in part, however, from uncertainty about the true values of β_2 and β_3; the estimate b_1 of β_1 is obtained after making allowance for the *apparent* effects of the other two factors. Any errors of estimation in b_2 and b_3 will cause related errors in b_1, so that the separate estimates will be correlated one with another. In the example just discussed, the covariance of b_1, b_3 is given by s^2C^{13}, i.e. by $s^2(- 1\cdot4160 \times 10^{-3})$. The correlation coefficient measuring the correlation between b_1 and b_3 is thus

$$r = C^{13}/\sqrt{C^{11}C^{33}}$$
$$= - 1\cdot4160/\sqrt{(1\cdot0931 \times 3\cdot6119)}$$
$$= - 0\cdot71$$

This correlation coefficient is associated with $(48 - 4) = 44$ degrees of freedom and is highly significant.

The negative correlation between b_1 and b_3 implies that errors of estimation which cause the estimate b_1 to be high will tend also to cause the estimate b_3 to be low, and conversely. The correlation is not perfect, so that there will not be perfect association between estimates of β_1 and the corresponding estimates of β_3. It is high enough, however, for the scatter in the values of

Q

b_1 associated with any particular value of b_3 to be appreciably less than the overall scatter of possible values of b_1. Thus confidence limits for β_1 at any specified value of b_3 will be narrower than those for b_3 unspecified. Because of the association, also, the positions of the limits will change as the value of b_3 is changed. In general, therefore, we should not consider b_1 without also considering b_3.

It may be shown that, if the true values of the regression coefficients are β_1, β_3, then

$$\frac{C^{33}(b_1 - \beta_1)^2 - 2C^{13}(b_1 - \beta_1)(b_3 - \beta_3) + C^{11}(b_3 - \beta_3)^2}{2s^2[C^{11}C^{33} - (C^{13})^2]} \quad ..(8·44)$$

is distributed as an F-ratio with 2 and (in this instance) 44 degrees of freedom. The last figure is of course the number of degrees of freedom on which the estimate of s^2 is based. A $(1 - a)$ confidence region for the simultaneous uncertainty of β_1 and β_3 is obtained by setting the ratio above equal to the value of F, with the appropriate degrees of freedom, exceeded with probability a. With $a = 0·05$, and degrees of freedom as stated, this value is $3·21$. Thus, the boundary of the region is given by

$$C^{33}(b_1 - \beta_1)^2 - 2C^{13}(b_1 - \beta_1)(b_3 - \beta_3) + C^{11}(b_3 - \beta_3)^2$$
$$= 6·42s^2[C^{11}C^{33} - (C^{13})^2]$$

or, substituting numerical values:

$$3·61(\beta_1 - b_1)^2 + 2·83(\beta_1 - b_1)(\beta_3 - b_3) + 1·09(\beta_3 - b_3)^2$$
$$= 0·8936 \times 10^{-2}......(8·441)$$

The equation defines an ellipse, with axes inclined, centred on the point (b_1, b_3). It is shown in Figure 8·5 below. The region bounded by the ellipse is one which may be expected, with 95% confidence, to include the point representing the two true regression coefficients (β_1, β_3). Also shown in the figure is a rectangle bounded by lines parallel to the axes. These lines indicate the separate $(1 - \frac{1}{2}a)$ confidence intervals for β_1, β_3 taken separately; the confidence coefficient is taken as $(1 - \frac{1}{2}a)$, since the chance that both β_1 and β_3 are contained by the relevant limits is $(1 - \frac{1}{2}a)^2 \simeq (1 - a)$. The rectangle is an alternative 95% confidence region for the pair of values, but the area contained is greater than that bounded by the ellipse, a result which may be shown to be generally true. We obtain the smallest possible confidence region, for a given confidence coefficient, when we plot the ellipse defined as above. It may be noted that the confidence coefficient applies to the joint statement that both β_1 and β_3 are represented by some point in the region. The statement is thus equivalent to two separate statements with confidence approximately equal to $(1 - \frac{1}{2}a)$ concerning β_1 and β_3 separately, for if we make n statements with confidence $(1 - \Delta)$, the chance that all n will be simultaneously correct is only $(1 - \Delta)^n \simeq 1 - n\Delta$ for Δ small. This last is a point all too frequently overlooked in practice.

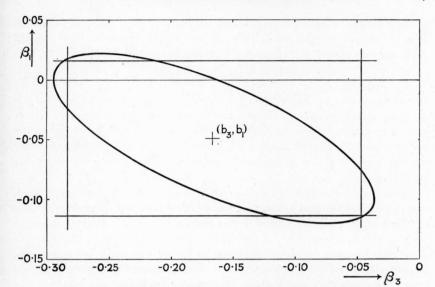

Fig. 8·5. Confidence regions for simultaneous estimation
of two regression coefficients

Omission of a variable

8·262   The covariance $s^2 C^{13}$ of the estimates b_1 and b_3 implies, as we have seen, that in repeated sampling particular values of b_3 tend to be associated with particular values of b_1, and vice versa. It implies that there is a regression of b_3 on b_1, or of b_1 on b_3. The slope of the regression of b_3 on b_1 is given in the usual way by (Covariance)/(Variance), i.e. by C^{13}/C^{11}. Thus unit change in b_1 is accompanied on average by a change of C^{13}/C^{11} in b_3. If we omit the independent variable x_1 from the regression equation, we are in effect "adjusting" the value of b_1 to zero. To allow for this adjustment we must also adjust b_3 by an amount $- b_1 C^{13}/C^{11}$.

Thus the value of b_3 corresponding to $b_1 = 0$ is

$$b_3' = b_3 - b_1 C^{13}/C^{11} \quad \dots \dots \dots \dots \dots \dots (8 \cdot 45)$$

This is the regression coefficient describing the estimated dependence of y on x_3 when x_1 is not included in the regression equation, and the equation shows how regression coefficients must be adjusted to allow for the omission of a variable. The variance of b_3 at a given value of b_1 is the variance about the regression of b_3 on b_1, i.e.

$$s^2 C^{33}(1 - r^2) = s^2 [C^{33} - (C^{13})^2/C^{11}] \quad \dots \dots \dots \dots (8 \cdot 46)$$

This shows that the inverse matrix element C^{33} should be modified to

$$(C^{33})' = C^{33} - (C^{13})^2/C^{11} \quad \dots \dots \dots \dots \dots (8 \cdot 461)$$

to allow for the dropping of x_1 from the regression equation. Other diagonal elements are similarly adjusted, while the form of adjustment for non-diagonal terms may be shown to be (taking C^{23} as an example)

$$(C^{23})' = C^{23} - C^{12}C^{13}/C^{11} \dots\dots\dots\dots(8·462)$$

It is thus possible to derive the whole of the new inverse matrix without the necessity of recalculation from the least squares equations. Of more immediate importance, however, is the fact that the equation $(8·461)$ gives the variance of the adjusted regression coefficient b_3' in terms of s^2 and hence may be used to derive confidence limits about this figure or to test it for significance.

When observed values of two independent variables are highly correlated, it may well happen that neither regression coefficient, tested against its own standard error, is significantly different from zero, but that the regression on both variables accounts for a significant part of the total variation of the dependent variable. This is equivalent to saying that the appropriate confidence ellipse for joint estimation of both coefficients cuts both axes, but does not include the point $(0, 0)$, so that we may not reasonably conclude that both true regression coefficients are simultaneously zero. We may reach the same conclusion by omitting one of the variables and then examining the significance of the *adjusted* coefficient for the regression on the other variable. We would not, however, be justified in omitting both variables on the basis of their unadjusted regression coefficients and standard errors. The point is discussed in more detail later in the chapter [§ **8·27**].

Regression on many variables

8·263 The concept of simultaneous confidence regions may clearly be extended to the simultaneous estimation of several regression coefficients. Unfortunately, however, the bounding surfaces, which are ellipsoids or hyperellipsoids in a space of many dimensions, cannot conveniently be represented diagrammatically, nor can the equations of the surfaces be compactly represented in terms of the elements of the inverse matrix and the estimates of the coefficients without using matrix notation. Detailed discussion is therefore outside the scope of the present chapter. It will be noted, however, that the concept is principally of value when the estimated regression coefficients are highly correlated; when the correlation is fairly small, say less than 0·5, the limits for one coefficient are very little affected by the value taken for another. Thus, even when many regression coefficients are estimated simultaneously, it will usually be sufficient to measure the precision of most of them by their standard errors or conventional confidence limits, and to consider confidence regions only for such occasional pairs of coefficients as are closely correlated with one another.

Prediction using the regression equation

8·264   The regression equation is of the form
$$y = b_0 + b_1 x_1 + \ldots + b_p x_p$$
$$\text{where } b_0 = \bar{y} - b_1 \bar{x}_1 - \ldots - b_p \bar{x}_p$$
We may therefore write the equation as
$$y = \bar{y} + b_1(x_1 - \bar{x}_1) + \ldots + b_p(x_p - \bar{x}_p) \quad \ldots\ldots\ldots (8\cdot5)$$
Corresponding to any set of assigned values $(X_1, \ldots, X_p)$ of the "independent" variables $x_1, \ldots, x_p$, there is a predicted value Y of y which may be calculated from the equation. This value is subject to uncertainty, since it is derived by using coefficients which are themselves subject to uncertainty. It may be shown that the estimate $\bar{y}$ is independent of the estimates $b_1, \ldots, b_p$, but the estimates $b_1, \ldots, b_p$ are not, as we have seen, independent of one another. Hence
$$V(Y) = V(\bar{y}) + (X_1 - \bar{x}_1)^2 V(b_1) + \ldots + (X_p - \bar{x}_p)^2 V(b_p)$$
$$+ 2(X_1 - \bar{x}_1)(X_2 - \bar{x}_2) \operatorname{cov}(b_1 b_2) + \ldots \quad \ldots\ldots (8\cdot51)$$
We may write this as
$$V(Y) = s^2 \left[\frac{1}{n} + C^{11}(X_1 - \bar{x}_1)^2 + \ldots + C^{pp}(X_p - \bar{x}_p)^2 \right.$$
$$\left. + 2C^{12}(X_1 - \bar{x}_1)(X_2 - \bar{x}_2) + \ldots \right] \ldots\ldots (8\cdot511)$$
where s^2 is the residual variance about the regression. Since the estimates $b_1, \ldots, b_p$ are not, in general, independent of one another, we must allow for their $\frac{1}{2}p(p-1)$ covariances, as well as their p variances, in arriving at the variance of the regression estimate. We see here another advantage of orthogonality.

For Example 8·1, where there are three independent variables, we have that
$$y = 6\cdot737 - 0\cdot0488x_1 - 0\cdot5688x_2 - 0\cdot1655x_3$$
Thus the rate of flow estimated for an initial moisture content of $0\cdot18\%$ ($x_1 = 18$), length/breadth ratio (x_2) of $2\cdot7$ and an impurity of $0\cdot03\%$ ($x_3 = 3$) is
$$6\cdot737 - (0\cdot0488 \times 18) - (0\cdot5688 \times 2\cdot7) - (0\cdot1655 \times 3) = 3\cdot83 \text{ g./sec.}$$
For the calculation of the variance of this regression estimate we have
$$n = 48$$
$$s^2 = \quad 0\cdot7164$$
$$X_1 - \bar{x}_1 = -0\cdot98$$
$$X_2 - \bar{x}_2 = \quad 0\cdot15$$
$$X_3 - \bar{x}_3 = -0\cdot125$$
The inverse matrix elements are as given earlier. Hence
$$V(Y) = 0\cdot7164 \left[\tfrac{1}{48} + 10^{-3} \{ 1\cdot09(0\cdot98)^2 + 89\cdot40(0\cdot15)^2 + 3\cdot61(0\cdot125)^2 \right.$$
$$+ 5\cdot55(0\cdot98)(0\cdot15) - 2\cdot83(0\cdot98)(0\cdot125) - 3\cdot34(0\cdot15)(0\cdot125) \}]$$
$$= 0\cdot7164 \times 0\cdot0244$$
$$= 0\cdot0175$$

The standard error of Y is thus $0{\cdot}132$, and 95% confidence limits are found by using the appropriate value of t for 44 degrees of freedom, since the estimate s^2 is based on this number of degrees of freedom. They are thus

$$3{\cdot}83 \pm (2{\cdot}015 \times 0{\cdot}132)$$
$$\text{i.e.}\quad 3{\cdot}56 \text{ and } 4{\cdot}10$$

These limits refer to the errors of the regression estimate only; the result of an individual test will be subject also to the residual variance of $0{\cdot}7164$ (see § 7·26).

Variance of the constant term

8·265　The constant term b_0 in the regression equation, when this is written in the form

$$y = b_0 + b_1 x_1 + \ldots + b_p x_p$$

is simply the estimate of y for $X_1 = X_2 = \ldots = X_p = 0$. In some problems this constant term may be expected to be zero. It may be tested for significance against its standard error, which may also be used to derive appropriate confidence limits. The standard error is given by

$$\sqrt{[V(\bar{y}) + \bar{x}_1^2\, V(b_1) + \ldots + \bar{x}_p^2\, V(b_p)}$$
$$+ 2\bar{x}_1\bar{x}_2 \text{ cov } (b_1 b_2) + \ldots] \ldots \ldots (8{\cdot}52)$$

or

$$s\sqrt{\left[\frac{1}{n} + C^{11}\bar{x}_1^2 + \ldots + C^{pp}\bar{x}_p^2 + 2C^{12}\bar{x}_1\bar{x}_2 + \ldots\right]} \ldots (8{\cdot}521)$$

Analysis of Variance for multiple regressions

8·27　The sum of squares due to regression is given by

$$b_1 C_{y1} + b_2 C_{y2} + \ldots + b_p C_{yp}$$

and is associated with p degrees of freedom. The residual sum of squares is

$$C_{yy} - b_1 C_{y1} - b_2 C_{y2} - \ldots - b_p C_{yp}$$

and is associated with $n - p - 1$ degrees of freedom. We may thus draw up an Analysis of Variance table as follows:

Table 8·3

ANALYSIS OF VARIANCE FOR MULTIPLE REGRESSION

Source	Sum of Squares	Degrees of Freedom	Mean Square
Due to regression	$b_1 C_{y1} + b_2 C_{y2} + \ldots + b_p C_{yp}$	p	
About regression	$C_{yy} - b_1 C_{y1} - \ldots - b_p C_{yp}$	$n - p - 1$	
Total ..	C_{yy}	$n - 1$	

The F-ratio calculated from this table may be used to test for the significance of the apparent dependence, but such a test of the combined dependence on all independent variables is not usually sufficient, since it tells us nothing about the significance of particular terms in the regression equation. To test whether the introduction of a particular term (say that involving x_p) had led to any significant improvement in the fit of the representation, we could test b_p against its estimated standard error, using the t-test described in § **8·26** above. An alternative procedure, which is instructive because it shows more clearly what is being done in such a test, is as follows:

Using only $x_1, \ldots, x_{p-1}$ to predict y, we obtain by the Method of Least Squares or by means of the adjustment described in § **8·262** estimates $b_1', \ldots, b_{p-1}'$ of the coefficients in the regression equation. The sum of squares attributable to this regression is

$$b_1'C_{y1} + b_2'C_{y2} + \ldots + b_{p-1}'C_{y,p-1}$$

and this represents $p - 1$ degrees of freedom. The residual sum of squares represents, in consequence, $n - p$ degrees of freedom. Using $x_1, \ldots, x_p$ to predict y, we have estimates $b_1, \ldots, b_p$ of the regression coefficients, and the sum of squares due to regression is given by

$$b_1C_{y1} + b_2C_{y2} + \ldots + b_pC_{yp}$$

In general, the coefficients will be different from those for the regression on $p - 1$ independent variables. The full "regression" sum of squares represents p degrees of freedom and the corresponding residual sum of squares represents $n - p - 1$ degrees of freedom. The effect of the introduction of x_p is thus measured by the variance associated with the extra degree of freedom

Table 8·4

TESTING FOR SIGNIFICANCE OF AN
ADDITIONAL INDEPENDENT VARIABLE:

ANALYSIS OF VARIANCE TABLE

Source	Sum of Squares	Degrees of Freedom	Mean Square
Regression on pth variable	$b_1C_{y1} + b_2C_{y2} + \ldots + b_pC_{yp}$ $- b_1'C_{y1} - \ldots - b_{p-1}'C_{y,p-1}$	1	
Regression on first $(p - 1)$ variables	$b_1'C_{y1} + b_2'C_{y2} + \ldots$ $+ b_{p-1}'C_{y,p-1}$	$p - 1$	
Residual	$C_{yy} - b_1C_{y1} - \ldots - b_pC_{yp}$	$n - p - 1$	
Total ..	C_{yy}	$n - 1$	

which is abstracted from the residual. This variance may be found by difference, and is tested for significance against the new "residual" mean square in the usual way. If it is not significant, we conclude that the introduction of x_p into the representation does not significantly improve the fit; the extra variation explained is not significantly greater than could reasonably be expected to be associated, purely by chance, with the variations in x_p, if x_p in fact bore no relationship to y. The Analysis of Variance table corresponding to the test is shown in Table 8·4.

The test is equivalent to the t-test of b_p against its standard error; the F-ratio with 1 and $n - p - 1$ degrees of freedom is the square of the corresponding value of t.

Examples

8·271 For the first of the examples discussed above (regression of abrasion loss on hardness and tensile strength, § **8·2**), the sum of squares due to the multiple regression on two variables is

$$(6·571 \times 22,946) + (1·374 \times 27,857) = 189,054$$

The sum of squares due to regression on hardness alone [§ **7·271**] is 122,446. There are thirty sets of results. Thus the Analysis of Variance is:

Table 8·41

TESTING FOR SIGNIFICANCE OF EFFECT OF
TENSILE STRENGTH

Source	Sum of Squares	Degrees of Freedom	Mean Square
Regression on tensile strength after allowing for hardness	66,608	1	66,608
Regression on hardness ..	122,446	1	122,446
Residual	35,957	27	1,332
Total ..	225,011	29	—

The F-ratio for the additional effect of tensile strength is $66,608/1,332 = 50·0$, with degrees of freedom 1 and 27. For these degrees of freedom the 0·01 probability level is only 7·68, so that there is no doubt of the significance of the effect. In fact, the introduction of tensile strength reduces the residual variance from 3,663 to 1,332, i.e. by about 60%.

For the second example considered (flow of sulphate of ammonia, § **8·25**), the sum of squares attributable to the regression on three variables is [§ **8·26**]

42·63. If, however, we fit a regression on x_2 (length/breadth ratio) and x_3 (percent impurity) only, the least squares equations are:

$$12\cdot46b_2 + 13\cdot50b_3 = -11\cdot72$$
$$13\cdot50b_2 + 577\cdot25b_3 = -141\cdot37$$

which give $b_2 = -0\cdot6928$, $b_3 = -0\cdot2287$, and a sum of squares due to regression of

$$(0\cdot6928 \times 11\cdot72) + (0\cdot2287 \times 141\cdot37) = 40\cdot45$$

Thus the Analysis of Variance for the significance of the additional effect of initial moisture content is as given in Table 8·42.

Table 8·42

TESTING FOR SIGNIFICANCE OF EFFECT OF
INITIAL MOISTURE CONTENT

Source	Sum of Squares	Degrees of Freedom	Mean Square
Additional effect of initial moisture content	2·18	1	2·18
Regression on L/B ratio and percent impurity	40·45	2	20·23
Residual	31·52	44	0·72
Total ..	74·15	47	—

The F-ratio for the additional effect of initial moisture content is 3·03, with degrees of freedom 1 and 44. Since the 0·05 probability level for these degrees of freedom is 4·06, the additional effect cannot be adjudged significant. The conclusion is the same as that of § **8·26** above, the F-ratio of 3·03 being the square of the t-value of $-1\cdot74$ then calculated. There is in fact a high correlation between initial moisture content and percent impurity ($r = 0\cdot72$), and it is clear that, in practice, both the initial moisture content and the rate of flow reflect a hygroscopicity engendered by the traces of impurity. So far as the regression relationship is concerned, a knowledge of initial moisture content, in addition to length/breadth ratio and percent impurity, does not appreciably improve prediction of flow rates. So far as plant operation is concerned, it is more important to limit the traces of impurity than to attempt a closer control of the drying of the salt if sticking is to be avoided.

Alternative analyses: Regression on many variables

8·272 The analyses of variance described above are by no means the only analyses that may be applied. For example, in considering the dependence of abrasion loss on hardness and tensile strength we might have first fitted a regression on tensile strength and then tested for the significance of the additional effect of hardness, while in the example on flow of sulphate of ammonia the additional effect of any of the three variables after allowing for a regression on the other two might have been tested. There are thus two possible Analyses of Variance like that of Table 8·41, and three like that of Table 8·42. Each analysis is equivalent to the *t*-test of a regression coefficient against its standard error. It is instructive to construct the Analysis of Variance (corresponding to that of Table 8·41) to test for the significance of the effect of hardness on abrasion loss. The sum of squares attributable to a regression on tensile strength alone is

$$(27,857)^2/38,733 = 20,035$$

The residual sum of squares and the sum of squares due to regression on both variables remain as before. Thus the Analysis of Variance is as follows:

Table 8·43

TESTING FOR SIGNIFICANCE OF EFFECT OF HARDNESS

Source	Sum of Squares	Degrees of Freedom	Mean Square
Regression on hardness after allowing for tensile strength	169,019	1	169,019
Regression on tensile strength	20,035	1	20,035
Residual	35,957	27	1,332
Total ..	225,011	29	—

The improvement consequent on the introduction of hardness after tensile strength is even more significant than the improvement consequent on the introduction of tensile strength after hardness; clearly, neither variable by itself is as satisfactory for prediction of abrasion loss as the two taken together. It is noteworthy, however, that before any allowance is made for hardness the apparent residual variance is

$$204,976/28 = 7,321$$

Thus the *F*-ratio for the effect of tensile strength, had this been taken alone, would have been only $20,035/7,321 = 2·74$, which does not reach even the

0·10 probability level. Had tensile strength and not hardness been considered first, it might well have been concluded that it bore no relation to abrasion loss, and the effect of tensile strength might not have been found.

The example serves to illustrate a difficulty in testing for significance which becomes progressively more marked as the number of independent variables is increased—that of the order in which the variables should be considered. Ideally, all possible orders and combinations of the independent variables should be examined, since otherwise there is always the possibility that a significant contribution may be overlooked, but this rapidly becomes impracticable. For example, with six possible independent variables, $2^6 - 1 = 63$ separate regressions would have to be fitted, and solution would be required of (among others) one set of six equations, six sets of five equations and fifteen sets of four equations.

Few general rules can be given for the handling of problems involving many variables, and a good deal of reliance must usually be placed on informed opinion of the relative importance of the variables concerned. If, however, a regression is fitted using all independent variables, the standard errors of the coefficients will give some guidance as to which may without loss be omitted, though this approach must be used with some care; as shown above, the standard errors may be markedly altered—particularly when there are high correlations between the independent variables—by the omission of a variable. Where the number of independent variables is so large (as may be the case in some exploratory investigations) that it is preferable to avoid, if possible, the fitting of a regression on all variables simultaneously, it is common practice to begin by fitting a regression on that single variable which is most closely correlated with, or is thought most likely to be related to, the dependent variable, and then to introduce other variables in turn (e.g. by the method given in [8·1]), retaining those which significantly increase the regression sum of squares. The advantages of orthogonality are clear against this background, since all coefficients can be calculated and tested separately, and are unaffected by the omission or inclusion of other variables. It should, however, be added that, in practice, the difficulties inherent in multiple regression analysis with many independent variables can usually be resolved by the exercise of good sense and an appreciation of the technical background of the problem. In connection with the inversion of large matrices, the potentialities of large-scale electronic computers and the commercial services based on such machines must nowadays also be borne in mind.

Use of significance tests

8·273 It must be appreciated that the non-significance of a particular regression coefficient does not in any way imply that the independent variable concerned does not affect, or is not related to, the dependent variable. It implies merely that, at the level of significance adopted, the confidence limits for the estimated effect, or slope, include zero as a possible value. Where, additionally, the confidence limits are so narrow that any true effect which may exist is small and of little importance over the range for which the relationship is required, we may be justified in ignoring the term. In other cases, however, we may only be justified in concluding that further work is required to define the relationship more precisely.

There are two classes of problems to which regression analysis may be applied; in one, as in the example above on abrasion loss of rubber samples, a regression equation is required only for purposes of prediction, and there is no assumption of an underlying functional relationship. In such problems, provided that the data on which the regression equation is based correspond to a random sample of individuals from the population for which prediction is required, we may usually ignore non-significant terms, which do not add significantly to the precision of prediction and may even lessen it. The other class of problems, however, is that which makes use of regression analysis to derive, from experiment, exact or approximate functional relationships. In such problems we cannot generally ignore non-significant terms; it would be, for example, absurd to conclude from the non-significance of a regression coefficient that pressure did not affect the rate of a chemical reaction if kinetic theory could be used to show that it must. The important feature is not the significance of the effect, but how precisely the effect is determined. If the confidence limits are wide (whether or not they include zero), then further work is almost certainly necessary—possibly over a wider range of conditions —to estimate the effect more closely. The uncritical use of tests of significance, without thought to the implications of the corresponding Null Hypothesis, should be scrupulously avoided. The Analysis of Variance, which often leads to such uncritical use of significance tests, should not be applied indiscriminately.

Regression analysis of plant records
8·274   Problems of the second class mentioned above often arise in the study of established processes; data accumulated in normal running, possibly over a period of years, are subjected to regression analysis in order to ascertain the effects of operating conditions on, for example, yield or conversion. There is no harm in such a study, and in many cases it represents a useful first step towards a better understanding of the process on a plant scale rather than on a laboratory scale. It should never, however, be considered as more than a first step. The natural variations which occur with time will seldom, if ever, satisfactorily replace a planned experiment—if only because the usual aim in plant operation is to maintain conditions as steady as possible, and in particular to keep efficiency high. Changes in operating conditions are likely

to be small, and will be determined more by the ease with which the factors concerned can be controlled than by their importance; in addition, they will usually show high intercorrelations and time trends. Estimated regression coefficients may thus be subject to considerable uncertainty, and fundamentally important factors may not show significant effects. In these circumstances it is better to quote all regression coefficients with their appropriate confidence limits—or confidence regions for the most highly correlated pairs of effects—than to carry out any tests of significance. The confidence limits will not only indicate which effects are in fact significant, but will, at the same time, set some limits to the likely magnitudes of suspected effects, and thus indicate where further work would be advantageous. It may well be found that a comparatively small but properly designed experiment will then give more information than all the available process records.

Even greater dangers than the apparent non-significance of real effects may sometimes arise in the analysis of plant records; in some circumstances the plant may be run in such a way as to introduce a completely spurious apparent dependence. An example is given by a study of conversion efficiency for a particular exothermic reaction. Since the reaction was exothermic and the converters were uncooled, the conversion was very closely proportional to the temperature rise through the converter. The aim in plant operation had usually been to keep the exit temperature steady, since at unduly high temperatures undesirable side reactions occurred: regulation was effected by varying the temperature of the inlet gas. A study of accumulated data was proposed, to ascertain the effects on the conversion efficiency of, for example, the composition of the inlet gas. One of the factors put forward for study was temperature; since the temperature varied through the converter, the most representative figure appeared to be the average temperature, which was considered to be, nearly enough, the average of inlet and exit temperatures. What was not immediately obvious, but soon became so, was that the use of this average temperature as an independent variable in the regression analysis would lead to completely nonsensical conclusions, such as, for example, that the conversion showed no dependence on the composition of the inlet gas. The reason lies in the mode of operation of the converter. Because exit temperatures are held steady, the average temperature is almost perfectly correlated with temperature rise, which in turn closely reflects conversion. Thus a regression of conversion efficiency on average temperature is effectively a regression of conversion on itself; all the variation except that attributable to errors of measurement is explained by the regression, and there is no chance of any other effects being found. The slope of the regression of conversion efficiency on average temperature does not, moreover, give the real effect of temperature; it is merely, at second or third remove, a statement that $x = x$. Such pitfalls are not uncommon, and are an added reason why regression analysis of process records should be undertaken with some caution and the fullest attention given to all details of plant running.

Applicability of the method

8·28 There is one major assumption implicit in the above treatment of multiple regression which should be noted. This is the assumption that all the residual variation is, or may be considered to be, attributable to the dependent variable. The implications of this assumption were dealt with— for regression on a single variable—in § **7·3**; they may be summarised as follows. Where the residual variation represents inherent variability of the individuals tested (as is largely true in the example discussed above on the testing of rubber samples) and there is only a statistical relationship between the values of "dependent" and "independent" variables, the regression equation is a convenient and legitimate representation of this. Where a relationship is required for the prediction of "observed" values from ob-served values and the data fitted are a random sample of possible sets of observations, the regression equation is again applicable. Where, however, there is an underlying functional relationship which is obscured only by errors of measurement, the regression equation only estimates this without bias if the errors are all in the values of the dependent variable. The problem of the estimation of a functional relationship when there are errors in the independent as well as in the dependent variables is by no means fully solved, and a general discussion is outside the scope of the present handbook; a brief survey is, however, attempted in § **8·5** below.

CURVILINEAR REGRESSION

8·3 Where a linear representation of the relationship between observed values of two variables appears inadequate, an equation of higher order may be sought to improve the fit. This will be of the general form

$$y = b_0 + b_1 x + b_2 x^2 + \ldots + b_p x^p$$

A similar generalisation of the multiple regression equation, involving powers and products of the several independent variables, is also possible; it arises, for example, in the representation of response surfaces in the neighbourhood of a maximum or minimum [8·3 and *Design and Analysis*]. This problem does not, however, raise any new point of principle, so that the discussion which follows is, for clarity, confined to the case of dependence between two variables.

Fitting of curvilinear relationships

8·31 The fitting of a curvilinear relationship is exactly the same as the fitting of a multiple regression, with the powers $x^1, \ldots, x^p$ of the observed values of the independent variable x replacing the observed values of the independent variables $x_1, \ldots, x_p$. This is shown in Appendix 8 A. Thus, a parabolic regression of y on x would be fitted precisely as if it were a multiple regression on two distinct independent variables x and x^2. That the two variables are in no sense independent of one another is of no consequence in the setting up of the equations. The only point requiring special mention is that, in practice, it is usual to round the powers of the x-values to the same number of significant figures as the x-values themselves. The figures sacrificed by the rounding are meaningless, and the coefficients in the least squares equations are kept to a common order of magnitude, which makes for ease in the solution of the equations.

Multiple curvilinear regressions

8·311   Multiple curvilinear regressions are fitted in a precisely similar manner; each power or product entering into the regression equation is treated as a separate independent variable in setting up the least squares equations for the regression coefficients. The only difficulties which arise spring from the numbers of equations which may have to be solved; even for as few as three independent variables the fitting of a general quadratic relationship may require the estimation of nine regression coefficients and hence the solution of a set of nine simultaneous equations, while for four independent variables the number of possible coefficients rises to fourteen, and for five independent variables to twenty. There is an equally rapid increase in the number of possible coefficients as the order of the regression equation is increased.

Tests of significance and measures of precision for curvilinear regressions

8·32   Standard errors and confidence limits are calculated, and tests of significance carried out, exactly as if a multiple linear regression were being fitted. There are, however, certain differences in interpretation and presentation which arise from the fact that the effects estimated are not the effects of separate factors, but are each part of the overall effect of a single factor.

Tests of significance

8·321   The order of the equation required will not, in most cases, be known or predictable in advance. It is usual, therefore, to introduce successive powers of x seriatim into the representation and to test for the significance of the additional effect of each. The fitted equation is taken to that order beyond which the addition of extra terms produces no significant reduction in the residual variance. It is common, particularly when using orthogonal polynomials [§ 8·34], to check that neither the next higher odd power of x nor the next higher even power adds significantly to the regression sum of squares.

Such tests of significance, to determine the order of the equation necessary for adequate representation of the data, are quite legitimate. When, however, the order of the equation has been established, it is not in general either legitimate or necessary to test the significance of lower-order terms, and all terms up to the highest order required should be included in the representation. If we suppress a lower-order term we are imposing on the relationship a constraint which we have no reason to suppose corresponds with reality. If, for example, we suppress a non-significant linear term in a parabolic regression, we imply that the minimum or maximum of the parabola occurs precisely at the origin—possibly only a working origin—that we have chosen for our x-values. Thus tests of significance of particular terms, once the order of the equation has been established, should be avoided.

Measures of precision

8·322   The regression coefficients attaching to the separate powers of x will generally be highly correlated with one another. Thus the standard errors of the coefficients are, in themselves, of little value as measures of the precision with which the overall effect of x has been estimated. The calculation of confidence regions for sets of coefficients is also somewhat unsatisfactory: it is difficult, for example, to assess mentally the practical effect of a decrease in the coefficient of x accompanied by an increase in the coefficient of x^2. The most convenient representation of the precision with which the effect of x has been determined is thus a plot of the fitted relationship together with confidence limits for the predicted values of y. These are calculated in the same way as for a multiple regression, except of course that specification of a value of x specifies also the associated values of x^2, x^3, etc. Such a plot is shown below (Figure 8·7) in connection with the example which follows.

Extrapolation

8·323   There is one point which applies to all use of fitted regression equations for prediction, but particularly to curvilinear regressions, and that is, that prediction outside the range covered by the data should be made only with considerable reserve. The only exception is when it is known that the fitted relationship is of the correct functional form, which is seldom the case when a curvilinear regression is fitted.

Example 8·2: Efficiency of a water-gas plant

8·33   The data given in Table 8·5 are monthly "efficiencies" for a water-gas plant, expressed in working units. Air and steam are blown alternately through a bed of hot coke to produce a mixture of gases of which the principal components are nitrogen, hydrogen and carbon monoxide. The measure of efficiency is coke used per 1,000 m.³ of ($H_2 + CO$) produced; since the nitrogen collected is already present in the air used, and is collected incidentally, it does not enter into the calculated efficiencies. Also given are the corresponding air/steam ratios (1,000 m.³ air/tonne steam). The data are plotted in Figure 8·6.

Table 8·5

MONTHLY COKE USAGE AND AIR/STEAM RATIOS FOR A WATER-GAS PLANT

Month	Coke Usage (working units)	Air/Steam Ratio	Month	Coke Usage (working units)	Air/Steam Ratio
1	120	2·11	15	51	1·76
2	122	2·29	16	53	1·33
3	128	2·32	17	50	1·23
4	124	2·31	18	34	1·40
5	118	2·25	19	68	1·38
6	114	2·22	20	70	1·96
7	119	2·20	21	49	1·47
8	149	2·41	22	50	1·42
9	141	2·19	23	66	1·33
10	86	2·06	24	46	1·65
11	78	1·99	25	40	1·26
12	31	1·62	26	51	1·61
13	51	1·59	27	51	1·74
14	72	1·70			

While there is considerable scatter, which is attributable to errors of sampling and analysis of coke and gas as well as to any real variations in efficiency, the plot shows clearly that coke usage is related to air/steam ratio. It also suggests that the relationship is not linear, but tends to level out at the lower air/steam ratios used. A parabolic regression was therefore fitted. If we denote coke efficiency by y, air/steam ratio by x, and (air/steam ratio)² for convenience by z, then

$$\bar{y} = 78·96 \qquad \bar{x} = 1·807 \qquad \bar{z} = 3·409$$
$$C_{yy} = 34,849·0 \qquad C_{xx} = 3·8559 \qquad C_{zz} = 51·2192$$
$$C_{xy} = 325·29 \qquad C_{yz} = 1,215·99 \qquad C_{xz} = 14·0118$$

and the fitted regression is

$$y = 280·9 - 323·54x + 112·25z$$

i.e.
$$y = 280·9 - 323·54x + 112·25x^2$$

The calculations for this example are given in Appendix 8C.

The equation represents a parabola having a minimum at $x = 1·44$.

The sum of squares attributable to the parabolic regression is

$$(- 323·54 \times 325·29) + (112·25 \times 1,215·99) = 31,250·6$$

R

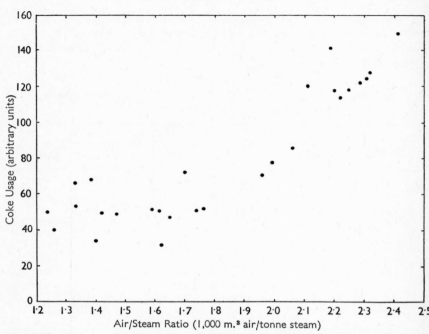

Fig. 8·6. Scatter diagram. Coke usage v. air/steam ratio for a water-gas plant

Thus the residual sum of squares, corresponding to 24 degrees of freedom, is 3,598·4.

If a linear regression only were fitted, the sum of squares attributable to the regression would be

$$(325·29)^2/3·8559 = 27,442·0$$

Thus the Analysis of Variance for the significance of the parabolic term is as given in Table 8·6.

The F-ratio for the additional effect of the parabolic term is $3,808·6/149·9 = 25·4$, which is significant at the 0·001 probability level. Thus the fit of the representation is improved by the inclusion of the term in x^2.

The fitted relationship is plotted in Figure 8·7. This figure also shows the 95% confidence limits for the predicted values of y; these are calculated in the usual way, using the variances and covariances of the estimated regression coefficients (see Appendix 8C).

Orthogonal polynomials

8·34 The advantages of orthogonality in the fitting of multiple regressions were discussed in § 8·242, and it is natural to seek for a similar means simplifying the fitting of curvilinear regressions. It is not possible, in general,

Table 8·6

ANALYSIS OF VARIANCE FOR SIGNIFICANCE OF PARABOLIC
TERM IN REGRESSION OF COKE USAGE ON AIR/STEAM RATIO

Source	Sum of Squares	Degrees of Freedom	Mean Square
Additional due to x^2 term ..	3,808·6	1	3,808·6
Due to linear regression only..	27,442·0	1	27,442·0
Total due to parabolic regression	31,250·6	2	—
Residual	3,598·4	24	149·9
Total ..	34,849·0	26	—

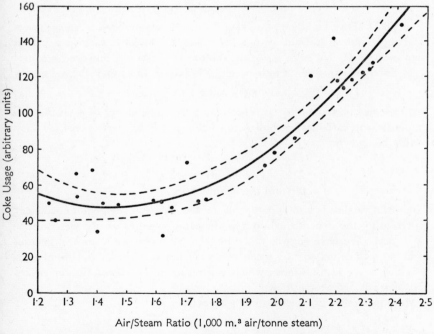

Fig. 8·7. Parabolic regression of coke usage on air/steam ratio, with 95%
confidence limits for predicted values

to arrange for the orthogonality of successive powers of a series of x-values; thus, for example, if the straight line fitted by least squares to a set of data is written

$$(y - \bar{y}) = b_1(x - \bar{x})$$

and the parabola fitted by least squares is written

$$(y - \bar{y}) = b_2(x - \bar{x}) + c_2(x^2 - \overline{x^2})$$

b_2 will not usually equal b_1, and the estimate b_2 of the coefficient of x in the parabolic regression will not be independent of the estimate c_2 of the coefficient of x^2. In fitting the regression, however, x^2 is treated exactly as if it were a second independent variable in a multiple regression; hence, c_2 is the slope of the regression of residual deviations in y, after allowing for a linear regression on x, on the residual deviations in x^2, again after allowing for a linear regression on x. Let m, where

$$m = \frac{\Sigma(x - \bar{x})(x^2 - \overline{x^2})}{\Sigma(x - \bar{x})^2}$$

denote the slope of the *linear* regression of x^2 on x. Then the estimated dependence of y on x^2 is shown by the equation

$$\{(y - \bar{y}) - b_1(x - \bar{x})\} = c_2\{(x^2 - \overline{x^2}) - m(x - \bar{x})\} \quad \ldots \ldots (8 \cdot 6)$$

In § 8·21 above an equation of this form was manipulated to show how a total regression coefficient such as b_1 could be adjusted to give a partial regression coefficient such as b_2. In the present instance, however, a somewhat different approach is more useful. Equation $(8 \cdot 6)$ may be written as

$$(y - \bar{y}) = b_1(x - \bar{x}) + c_2\{(x^2 - \overline{x^2}) - m(x - \bar{x})\} \quad \ldots \ldots (8 \cdot 61)$$

and this may be thought of as representing the dependence of y on the two "independent variables" x and $(x^2 - mx)$. These are orthogonal, as may readily be shown:

$$\Sigma(x - \bar{x})\{(x^2 - \overline{x^2}) - m(x - \bar{x})\}$$
$$= \Sigma(x - \bar{x})(x^2 - \overline{x^2}) - m\Sigma(x - \bar{x})^2$$
$$= 0 \text{ (from the definition of } m)$$

The orthogonality is also apparent in the fact that the regression coefficient representing the dependence on x is the same whether or not we consider $(x^2 - mx)$. We have shown, therefore, that although we cannot in general make x^2 orthogonal to x, we can construct a second-order polynomial, in which x^2 is the leading term, which will represent any second-order effects and which is orthogonal to x.

More generally, if we wish to fit a regression

$$y = a_0 + a_1 x + a_2 x^2 + \ldots$$

we may represent this as

$$y = b_0 + b_1 \xi_1 + b_2 \xi_2 + \ldots$$

where the functions ξ_1, ξ_2, etc., are polynomials of the first, second, etc., order in x, which are chosen to be all mutually orthogonal. To any value of x, say x_i, will correspond appropriate values $(\xi_1)_i$, $(\xi_2)_i$, ... of the ξ-functions, and the orthogonality implies that, for the summation over the n observed x-values:

$$\sum_{i=1}^{n}(\xi_j)_i(\xi_k)_i = 0$$

for all j and k which are not equal. The coefficients in the regression equation, when this is written in terms of the ξ-functions, are thus given (because of the orthogonality) simply by (*cf.* § 8·242)

$$b_k = \sum_{i=1}^{n} y_i(\xi_k)_i \bigg/ \sum_{i=1}^{n} (\xi_k)_i^2 \quad \dots\dots\dots\dots(8\cdot62)$$

and their standard errors are estimated by

$$S.E.(b_k) = s \bigg/ \sqrt{\left\{\sum_{i=1}^{n}(\xi_k)_i^2\right\}} \quad \dots\dots\dots\dots(8\cdot63)$$

Provided we have the values of the ξ-functions, successive terms may be added to the regression equation without difficulty, and their significance tested at once; because of the orthogonality, the coefficients and the contributions to the regression sum of squares are unaltered by the addition or deletion of other terms.

Use of orthogonal polynomials

8·341 The second-order polynomial ξ_2 is, as we have seen, the residual deviation of x^2 from a *linear* regression of x^2 on x. More generally, ξ_k is the deviation of x^k from a multiple *linear* regression of x^k on all powers of x up to x^{k-1}. Thus, while the use of orthogonal functions is theoretically possible for any set of x-values, the construction and use of them is, in the majority of cases, as tedious a task as the fitting of the usual regression equation, and there is little to recommend them except when several responses (e.g. yield, purity) must be related to the same independent variable. There is, however, one very important class of problems in which the use of orthogonal functions so simplifies the fitting of non-linear relationships that it is worth while in planned experimental work to go to some trouble to realise the necessary conditions. The requirement is simply that the x-values shall be equally spaced over the whole range covered. For this case appropriate ξ-functions and the corresponding sums of squares are extensively tabulated and do not require calculation except for extreme instances beyond the range of the tables. Even then, the forms of the functions are such that they may readily be calculated. For values of x spaced at unit interval the functions are given by

$$\left.\begin{aligned}
\xi_1 &= x - \bar{x} \\
\xi_2 &= (x - \bar{x})^2 - (n^2 - 1)/12 \\
\xi_3 &= (x - \bar{x})^3 - \frac{(3n^2 - 7)}{20}(x - \bar{x}) \\
\xi_4 &= (x - \bar{x})^4 - \frac{(3n^2 - 13)}{14}(x - \bar{x})^2 + \frac{3(n^2 - 9)(n^2 - 1)}{560}
\end{aligned}\right\} \quad ..(8·64)$$

etc.

where n is the number of observations.

For details of the method of construction, and for tables giving ξ_1 to ξ_5 for $n = 3(1)75$, see [8·4]. The tabular entries are not generally the values of the ξ-functions themselves but convenient multiples or submultiples of these. The purposes of the multiplication are twofold—to ensure that the tabular values are all integral, and also to ensure that they are as small as possible, i.e. that any common factors are removed. For example, ξ_3 for $n = 5$ is given by

$$\xi_3 = (x - \bar{x})^3 - \tfrac{17}{5}(x - \bar{x})$$

The successive values of $(x - \bar{x})$ are $- 2, - 1, 0, 1, 2$, so that successive values of ξ_3 are $- 6/5, + 12/5, 0, - 12/5, + 6/5$. To make these integral we must first multiply by 5; having done this we may take out a common factor of 6, leaving us with the successive values $- 1, + 2, 0, - 2, + 1$. These are tabulated as ξ_3', where in this instance

$$\xi_3' = \tfrac{5}{6}\xi_3$$

More generally, $\xi_k' = \lambda\xi_k$. The tables give the values of ξ_k' and of $\Sigma(\xi_k')^2$, and also show the corresponding value of λ. Since multiplication of successive values of a ξ-function by a constant does not affect the conditions of orthogonality $\Sigma\xi_j\xi_k = 0$, the ξ'-functions are also orthogonal polynomial functions of x, and may equally well (in fact more conveniently, since the numbers involved are smaller) be used to fit curvilinear regressions. As before, the coefficients in the regression equation are given by

$$b_k = \sum_{i=1}^{n} y_i(\xi_k')_i \bigg/ \sum_{i=1}^{n} (\xi_k')_i^2$$

and their standard errors by

$$S.E.(b_k) = s \bigg/ \sqrt{\left\{\sum_{i=1}^{n} (\xi_k')_i^2\right\}}$$

Thus, to calculate the regression coefficient attaching to any polynomial ξ_k' we simply accumulate the products $y\xi_k'$, reading the ξ_k' direct from the tables, and divide the sum $\sum_{i=1}^{n} y_i(\xi_k')_i$ by the corresponding tabulated value of $\sum\limits_{i=1}^{n}(\xi_k{}')^2$. The contribution to the regression sum of squares of the $\xi_k{}'$ term is

$$\left\{\sum_{i=1}^{n}y_i(\xi_k{}')_i\right\}^2 \bigg/ \left\{\sum_{i=1}^{n}(\xi_k{}')_i^2\right\}$$

and this is also readily evaluated.

8·342 The tables of ξ'-functions and the method of construction apply only for values of x spaced at unit intervals; where the intervals are equal, but not of unit width, unit spacing may always be arranged by appropriate scaling. x-values which are equally spaced on a logarithmic scale, i.e. in geometrical progression on a linear scale, may be dealt with by using $\log x$ rather than x as the independent variable, and similar simple transformations may be used whenever appropriate [§ **7·7**].

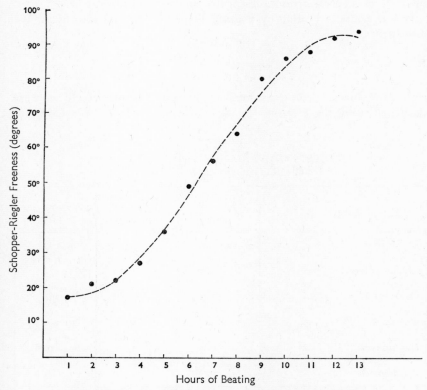

Fig. 8·8. Schopper-Riegler freeness test of paper pulp during beating

Example 8·3. Schopper-Riegler freeness test of paper pulp samples

8·35   The data given in Table 8·7 are for the Schopper-Riegler freeness tests on paper pulp samples taken at hourly intervals during beating.

Table 8·7

TESTS ON PAPER PULP SAMPLES

Hours of beating ..	1	2	3	4	5	6	7	8	9	10	11	12	13
Schopper-Riegler ..	17	21	22	27	36	49	56	64	80	86	88	92	94

These results are plotted in Figure 8·8. It is clear from this that at least a cubic curve is necessary to represent the points satisfactorily.

Denote hours of beating by x and Schopper-Riegler freeness by y. We then have:

$$\bar{x} = 7$$
$$\bar{y} = 56\cdot3$$
$$\Sigma(y - \bar{y})^2 = 10,494\cdot8$$

y gives the constant b_0 in the regression equation. The other coefficients are calculated using the ξ'-values for $n = 13$ given in [8·4]. We have, for

Table 8·8

ANALYSIS OF VARIANCE FOR REGRESSION,
USING ORTHOGONAL POLYNOMIALS

Source	Sum of Squares	Degrees of Freedom	Mean Square
Linear term	10,177·6	1	10,177·6
Quadratic term..	2·7	1	2·7
Cubic term	264·5	1	264·5
Quartic term	0·1	1	0·1
Quintic term	10·6	1	10·6
Residual	39·3	7	5·6
Total ..	10,494·8	12	—

example, $\Sigma y \xi_1' = 17 \times (-6) + 21 \times (-5) + \ldots + 94 \times (+6) = 1{,}361$, and, from the tables, $\Sigma(\xi_1')^2 = 182$, so that $b_1 = 1{,}361/182 = 7 \cdot 478$. Similar calculations give:

$$\Sigma y \xi_2' = -73 \quad \Sigma(\xi_2')^2 = 2{,}002 \quad \text{i.e. } b_2 = -0 \cdot 0365$$
$$\Sigma y \xi_3' = -389 \quad \Sigma(\xi_3')^2 = 572 \quad \text{i.e. } b_3 = -0 \cdot 6801$$
$$\Sigma y \xi_4' = 81 \quad \Sigma(\xi_4')^2 = 68{,}068 \quad \text{i.e. } b_4 = 0 \cdot 0012$$
$$\Sigma y \xi_5' = 256 \quad \Sigma(\xi_5')^2 = 6{,}188 \quad \text{i.e. } b_5 = 0 \cdot 0414$$

The contributions to the regression sum of squares for individual terms are given by $b \Sigma y \xi'$ or by $(\Sigma y \xi')^2 / \Sigma \xi'^2$. We thus derive the Analysis of Variance shown in Table 8·8.

The quartic and quintic terms are not significant, so that a cubic provides a satisfactory fit. The fitted relationship is

$$y = 56 \cdot 3 + 7 \cdot 478 \xi_1' - 0 \cdot 0365 \xi_2' - 0 \cdot 6801 \xi_3'$$

where the ξ''s are the functions tabulated in [8·4] and not necessarily the ξ's defined in Equation (8·64) above. From the table it is found that the λ's for ξ_1' and ξ_2' are unity, but that for ξ_3' is 1/6. Thus, on substitution, the fitted equation becomes

$$y = 56 \cdot 8 + 10 \cdot 31(x - 7) - 0 \cdot 0365(x - 7)^2 - 0 \cdot 1133(x - 7)^3$$

For estimating standard errors or confidence limits for predicted values, however, it is more convenient to deal with the equation in terms of the ξ''s.

Applicability of the methods

8·36 It is noted, as in § **8·28**, that the assumption throughout the above treatment of curvilinear regression is that the residual variation is, or may be considered to be, entirely attributable to the dependent variable. Difficulties arise in the estimation of non-linear functional relationships when observed values of both variables are affected by errors of measurement. These are discussed briefly in § **8·5** below.

ALLOWANCE FOR CONCOMITANT VARIATION (ANALYSIS OF COVARIANCE)

8·4 In the previous chapter [§ **7·8**] the problem was discussed of comparing the tinctorial strengths of batches of a dyestuff made by two processes, A and B, when unavoidable batch-to-batch variations arose because of variations in the purity of the raw material. It was shown that comparison between the two groups of results was made appreciably more precise if the effects of varying purity were eliminated, using a combined "within groups" regression of tinctorial strength on purity as an estimate of the rate of change of tinctorial strength with purity.

A similar allowance for concomitant variation may be made when the comparison between groups is affected by more than one "nuisance factor"; the methods are a direct extension of those given in the previous chapter, and the only new feature is the additional complexity of the calculations introduced by the necessity of fitting multiple regressions. Since the necessity for such an analysis seldom arises in industrial applications of statistics only a brief account of the general procedure is given below.

Allowance for concomitant variation

8·41 Let the variable which is of interest be denoted by y, and let there be two "nuisance factors" denoted by variables x_1 and x_2. Let the two groups of results to be compared be denoted by suffixes A and B, and let there be n_A results in the first group and n_B results in the second group. We may use the notation $(C_{11})_A$, etc., to denote the corrected sums of squares and products within groups. Then the average "within groups" regression slopes are given by

$$\left. \begin{array}{l} b_1[(C_{11})_A + (C_{11})_B] + b_2[(C_{12})_A + (C_{12})_B] = [(C_{y1})_A + (C_{y1})_B] \\ b_1[(C_{12})_A + (C_{12})_B] + b_2[(C_{22})_A + (C_{22})_B] = [(C_{y2})_A + (C_{y2})_B] \end{array} \right\} \quad \dots (8 \cdot 7)$$

The equations are the usual least squares equations $(8 \cdot 31)$, but the coefficients are the combined "within groups" sums of squares and products.

The sum of squares within groups attributable to the average "within groups" regression is given (*cf.* Expression $(8 \cdot 4)$) by

$$b_1[(C_{y1})_A + (C_{y1})_B] + b_2[(C_{y2})_A + (C_{y2})_B] \quad \dots (8 \cdot 71)$$

and represents two degrees of freedom. The residual sum of squares within groups (of the deviations about the average regression) thus represents $(n_A - 1) + (n_B - 1) - 2 = n_A + n_B - 4$ degrees of freedom, and the residual variance is given by

$$s^2 = \frac{1}{(n_A + n_B - 4)}[\{(C_{yy})_A + (C_{yy})_B\}$$
$$- b_1\{(C_{y1})_A + (C_{y1})_B\} - b_2\{(C_{y2})_A + (C_{y2})_B\}] \dots (8 \cdot 72)$$

The adjusted difference in means is

$$d = (\bar{y}_A - \bar{y}_B) - b_1[(\bar{x}_1)_A - (\bar{x}_1)_B] - b_2[(\bar{x}_2)_A - (\bar{x}_2)_B] \dots (8 \cdot 73)$$

and its estimated variance is

$$V(d) = s^2\left[\frac{1}{n_A} + \frac{1}{n_B}\right] + [(\bar{x}_1)_A - (\bar{x}_1)_B]^2 V(b_1) + [(\bar{x}_2)_A - (\bar{x}_2)_B]^2 V(b_2)$$
$$+ 2[(\bar{x}_1)_A - (\bar{x}_1)_B][(\bar{x}_2)_A - (\bar{x}_2)_B] \text{ cov } (b_1 b_2) \dots (8 \cdot 74)$$

the variances $V(b_1)$, $V(b_2)$ and the covariance cov $(b_1 b_2)$ being estimated in the usual way [§ 8·26].

Confidence limits for the adjusted difference in means may be set, or tests of significance made, using the appropriate values of t with $n_A + n_B - 4$ degrees of freedom.

8·411 Where, more generally, there are k "nuisance factors" to be considered, the procedure is the same except that, of course, there are k least squares equations to be solved and k adjustments to be made to the difference in means, while the residual variance is based on $n_A + n_B - k - 2$ degrees of freedom.

8·412 In the more formal "Analysis of Covariance," to which reference is made in § 7·85, the significance of the adjusted difference in means is assessed by an F-test in an Analysis of Variance table, the value of F found being the square of the t-value obtained by comparing d with its standard error as indicated above. When more than two groups must be compared simultaneously and an overall significance test is required, this necessarily takes the form of an F-test, and the more formal method is more convenient. For details of this method the reader is referred to [8·5].

Comparison of regressions "within groups"

8·42 In allowing for concomitant variation by means of an average "within groups" regression we make the tacit assumption that the true regression slopes are the same in each of the groups compared. This assumption may itself be tested. For purposes of exemplification we consider once more the case of two "nuisance factors." The regression slopes within the group A only are given by the least squares equations

$$\left.\begin{aligned}(b_1)_A(C_{11})_A + (b_2)_A(C_{12})_A = (C_{y1})_A\\(b_1)_A(C_{12})_A + (b_2)_A(C_{22})_A = (C_{y2})_A\end{aligned}\right\} \dots\dots\dots\dots (8\cdot75)$$

and the sum of squares attributable to this regression is

$$(b_1)_A(C_{y1})_A + (b_2)_A(C_{y2})_A \dots\dots\dots\dots\dots (8\cdot76)$$

representing 2 degrees of freedom. The residual sum of squares within the group A is

$$(C_{yy})_A - (b_1)_A(C_{y1})_A - (b_2)_A(C_{y2})_A \dots\dots\dots\dots (8\cdot77)$$

and represents $n_A - 3$ degrees of freedom.

A regression may similarly be fitted within group B only; the sum of squares attributable to the regression is

$$(b_1)_B(C_{y1})_B + (b_2)_B(C_{y2})_B \dots\dots\dots\dots\dots (8\cdot78)$$

and is once more based on two degrees of freedom, while the residual sum of squares is

$$(C_{yy})_B - (b_1)_B(C_{y1})_B - (b_2)_B(C_{y2})_B \dots\dots\dots\dots (8\cdot79)$$

and is associated with $n_B - 3$ degrees of freedom.

The two separate regressions account between them for 4 degrees of freedom and the combined residual sum of squares is based on $n_A + n_B - 6$ degrees of freedom. If we fit an average "within groups" regression as in § 8·41 above, the regression sum of squares

$$b_1[(C_{y1})_A + (C_{y1})_B] + b_2[(C_{y2})_A + (C_{y2})_B]$$

(*cf*. Expression (*8·71*)) accounts for only 2 degrees of freedom, and the corresponding residual sum of squares represents $n_A + n_B - 4$ degrees of freedom. The sum of squares associated with the two degrees of freedom which are transferred to the residual when the average "within groups" regression is fitted represents any differences between the separate "within groups" regressions. If such differences are attributable only to chance fluctuations, then the sum of squares representing "differences between regressions" will estimate only the residual (error) variance, and the mean square should differ from the residual variance about the separate "within groups" regressions only because of sampling fluctuation. An *F*-test of the mean square representing differences between regressions against the residual mean square about the separate regressions within groups will thus indicate whether the differences between the separate regressions may or may not reasonably be ascribed to chance, i.e. whether or not the differences must be considered as significant.

Table 8·9

ANALYSIS OF VARIANCE FOR DIFFERENCES
BETWEEN REGRESSIONS

Source	Sum of Squares	Degrees of Freedom	Mean Square
Due to average "within groups" regression	(Expression *8·71*)	2	
Differences between regressions	(By subtraction)	2	**(1)**
Due to separate "within groups" regressions	(Expressions *8·76, 8·78*)	4	
Residual	(Expressions *8·77, 8·79*)	$n_A + n_B - 6$	**(2)**
Total ..	$(C_{yy})_A + (C_{yy})_B$	$n_A + n_B - 2$	

The Analysis of Variance table takes the form of Table 8·9. The mean square indicated by **(1)** is tested against that indicated by **(2)** by means of an

F-test; if the value of *F* obtained is found to be significant it is concluded that real differences in slope exist.

If significant differences between regressions are found then, as was pointed out in § 7·83, we cannot readily compare the groups except by specifying the levels of the "nuisance factors" at which the comparison is to be made; the adjusted difference in means is not particularly revealing. The existence of differences in regression slopes is itself, however, an indication of some difference between groups, and this conclusion alone may be of importance.

8·421   In the general case, when there are *k* nuisance factors, the procedure for comparing the "within groups" regressions is the same except that each regression sum of squares is associated with *k* degrees of freedom and there are therefore *k* degrees of freedom representing differences between regressions. Correspondingly, the residual sum of squares is based on $n_A + n_B - 2(k + 1)$ degrees of freedom.

REGRESSIONS AND FUNCTIONAL RELATIONSHIPS

8·5   A regression equation is a statistical relationship between observed values of two or more variables, and *no more than this*. This point should not be lost sight of in any discussion of regressions and functional relationships. Though a regression equation may be, and frequently is, used as an estimate of a functional relationship, the circumstances for such use must be closely defined, otherwise completely misleading results may be obtained. There is, for example, a class of problems in which regressions exist but there is no such thing as a functional relationship; the scatter about a fitted regression arises from real variation in the individuals studied, and is not the result of errors of observation or measurement. This is commonly the case in biometric and biological work, but is also sometimes true in industrial work, as is illustrated by the example discussed earlier on abrasion loss and hardness of rubber samples. The key word for this class of problems is "individuals"; where relationships are sought between concomitant observations on a series of separate individuals or items, it is usually inappropriate to envisage other than regression relationships. Where such relationships are the only relationships which can exist, regression equations may legitimately be used for purposes of description and prediction. More than one regression equation may be fitted to each set of data, since each variable may equally be considered as the "dependent" variable, but all regressions are equally valid and may be used as appropriate.

8·51   In most industrial and scientific work, however, a series of observations will represent a series of "states of nature" rather than a series of individuals

or separate items. It is common then to postulate or expect a functional
relationship between the quantities studied; examples of simple relationships
are Ohm's Law and the perfect gas laws, while more complex examples arise
in, for instance, reaction kinetics.

The conditions under which a regression equation may be used to estimate
a functional relationship, when one exists, are specified from the manner in
which the equation is derived. The least squares equations giving the
coefficients are those which minimise the sum of squares of deviations of
observed values of the "dependent" variable from the values predicted by the
regression, the dependent variable being invariably denoted above by y. The
assumption is thus that only errors in y need be considered; that it is the
observed value of y which deviates from the corresponding true value, and
not the value of any other variable. If this is in fact so, then the regression of
y on the "independent" variables is simultaneously the best estimate of the
underlying functional relationship. Only if all values of the independent
variables are determined without error, and the only variations which arise
are errors of measurement of values of the dependent variable, is the regression of the dependent variable on the independent variables the best estimate
of the functional relationship. In other circumstances the regression gives a
biased estimate of the true relationship, the bias depending on the errors of
measurement for the independent variables and the ranges covered by these.
The regression may still be used for prediction of "observed" values from
observed values (*cf.* § 7·3) if the observations on which it is based may be
considered as a random sample of possible observations, but is otherwise of
little value.

8·52 In practice it is not necessary to insist too rigorously on the absence
of errors in the measured values of the independent variables; provided that
these are small compared with the ranges covered, and with the errors in the
dependent variable, the regression equation gives a reasonably satisfactory
estimate of the functional relationship. These conditions are most likely to
be met in controlled experiments, where wide ranges can usually be covered
and the values of the independent variables can be set with a high degree of
accuracy. Thus, wherever possible, functional relationships should be estimated from the results of controlled experiments rather than from accumulated uncontrolled observations. It is also, of course, possible to arrange in a
controlled experiment for the orthogonality of the separate effects, which is
an added advantage.

8·53 Where controlled experiments cannot be carried out, or where for
other reasons the conditions for use of a regression equation cannot be
satisfied, other methods must be used to estimate a functional relationship,

and these are, in general, outside the scope of this handbook. The simplest case is that of a multiple linear relationship, when the error variances for the independent variables are known. Let these be denoted by $\sigma_1^2, \ldots, \sigma_p^2$, there being N sets of observations. Then the usual least squares equations for the regression coefficients should be modified to

$$\left.\begin{aligned} b_1(C_{11} - N\sigma_1^2) + b_2C_{12} + \ldots + b_pC_{1p} &= C_{y1} \\ b_1C_{12} + b_2(C_{22} - N\sigma_2^2) + \ldots + b_pC_{2p} &= C_{y2} \\ \cdots\cdots\cdots\cdots\cdots\cdots\cdots\cdots\cdots\cdots\cdots\cdots\cdots \\ b_1C_{1p} + b_2C_{2p} + \ldots + b_p(C_{pp} - N\sigma_p^2) &= C_{yp} \end{aligned}\right\} \ \ldots\ldots(8\cdot8)$$

i.e. each sum of squares should be "corrected" for the extra variation attributable to error. The result is a generalisation of that given in § 7·6. Where only the *ratios* of the error variances are known, no generalisation of the result [§ 7·6] for the two-variable case is available, but the relationship may be estimated by an iterative method given in [8·6]. No generalisation to the multivariate case is available of Bartlett's method [§ 7·62] of estimating a linear functional relationship when no error variances are known.

The estimation of curvilinear functional relationships when all variables are measured with error is more difficult, and there is a further difficulty in that (taking the bivariate case for an example), even if y is measured without error, the regression of x on y is not readily obtainable for use as an estimate of the functional relationship. In the bivariate case, a functional relationship of known form may be estimated given one of the error variances or the ratio of the two error variances; the appropriate least squares equations can always be set up. These will not, however, be linear, and an iterative method of solution will be necessary. Multivariate curvilinear relationships introduce still further complexity; given the error variances for the independent variables, or the ratios of all error variances, solutions can in general be obtained, but the exercise is not one to be recommended. Here, if nowhere else, the reader should seek expert advice.

CORRELATION

8·6 Relationships between several variables can, like relationships between two variables, be described both by regression coefficients and by correlation coefficients. Details of the complex of "partial correlation coefficients," and the somewhat cumbersome notation with which they are burdened, are given, for example, in [8·7]; since they are of little practical value, they are not discussed here. It is noted, however, for the benefit of the reader who may come across them elsewhere, that each correlation coefficient is associated with a reduction in a particular sum of squares. Thus $r_{3y.12}$, the partial correlation coefficient between y and x_3 for x_1 and x_2 fixed, may be defined by

$$\frac{\text{Residual sum of squares of } y \text{ after taking out regression on } x_1, x_2, x_3}{\text{Residual sum of squares of } y \text{ after taking out regression on } x_1, x_2}$$

$$= 1 - r^2_{3y.12} \dots \dots (8 \cdot 9)$$

The most useful of the correlation coefficients associated with multiple regression is the Multiple Correlation Coefficient, usually denoted by R. It measures the overall extent of association between values of the dependent variables and the corresponding values of the independent variables and is defined by

$$R^2 = \frac{\text{Sum of squares due to multiple regression}}{\text{Total sum of squares of } y\text{-values about their mean}} \dots (8 \cdot 91)$$

so that the final residual sum of squares is $(1 - R^2)$ times the original sum of squares.

REFERENCES

[8·1] WOOLF, B. "Computation and Interpretation of Multiple Regressions," *Jour. R.S.S.*, Series B, XIII, 1, 100 (1951).

[8·2] Box, G. E. P. "Multi-factor Designs of First Order," *Biometrika*, **39**, 49 (1952).

[8·3] Box, G. E. P., and WILSON, K. B. "On the Experimental Attainment of Optimum Conditions," *Jour. R.S.S.*, Series B, XIII, 1, 1 (1951).

[8·4] FISHER, R. A., and YATES, F. *Statistical Tables for Biological, Agricultural and Medical Research* (fifth edition). Oliver and Boyd (Edinburgh and London, 1957).

[For other tables giving ξ_1–ξ_6, for $n = 3(1)52$, see *Biometrika Tables for Statisticians*, Vol. I. Cambridge University Press (1954).]

[8·5] FISHER, R. A. *Statistical Methods for Research Workers* (twelfth edition). Oliver and Boyd (Edinburgh and London, 1954).

[8·6] QUENOUILLE, M. H. *Associated Measurements*. Butterworth (London, 1952).

[8·7] YULE, G. U., and KENDALL, M. G. *Introduction to the Theory of Statistics*. Griffin (London, 1945).

APPENDIX 8A

FITTING OF MULTIPLE AND CURVILINEAR REGRESSIONS BY THE METHOD OF LEAST SQUARES

(a) Multiple regressions

8A·1 A linear dependence of a variable y on variables $x_1, \dots, x_p$ may be written as

$$y = b_0 + b_1 x_1 + \dots + b_p x_p \dots \dots \dots (8A \cdot 1)$$

For sets of values satisfying this relationship exactly,

$$y - b_0 - b_1 x_1 - \dots - b_p x_p = 0 \dots \dots \dots (8A \cdot 11)$$

For any set of values $x_{1i}, \ldots, x_{pi}$ of the "independent" variables $x_1, \ldots, x_p$ we may derive an "expected value" Y_i of the "dependent" variable y from the relationship

$$Y_i = b_0 + b_1 x_{1i} + \ldots + b_p x_{pi} \ldots\ldots\ldots\ldots(8A\cdot12)$$

Observations obtained in practice will be more or less scattered about an exact relationship. To each observed set of values $x_{1i}, \ldots, x_{pi}$ will correspond an expected value Y_i of the dependent variable y, but the observed value y_i of y will not, in general, be equal to Y_i. The difference between the observed and expected values of y will be

$$(y_i - Y_i) = (y_i - b_0 - b_1 x_{1i} - \ldots - b_p x_{pi}) \ldots\ldots(8A\cdot13)$$

The values of the constants $b_0, \ldots, b_p$ are as yet unknown. The problem is to derive those values for the constants which will give rise to the least disagreement, overall, between observation and expectation. As a measure of the overall disagreement we take

$$Q = \Sigma_i(y_i - Y_i)^2 \ldots\ldots\ldots\ldots\ldots\ldots(8A\cdot14)$$

i.e. the sum of squares of the deviations of observed values of the dependent variable from those expected. In fitting by the method of least squares we aim to choose $b_0, \ldots, b_p$ so as to minimise Q. This may be done by the methods of the differential calculus; the partial derivatives of Q with respect to $b_0, \ldots, b_p$ are each equated to zero, giving a set of simultaneous equations for the desired values of $b_0, \ldots, b_p$.

We have that

$$Q = \Sigma(y - b_0 - b_1 x_1 - \ldots - b_p x_p)^2 \ldots\ldots\ldots(8A\cdot2)$$

where, for convenience, we have dropped the subscript i and the summation is understood to be over the n sets of observations $i = 1, \ldots, n$. Differentiating with respect to b_0 and equating to zero:

$$\frac{\partial Q}{\partial b_0} = -2\Sigma(y - b_0 - b_1 x_1 - \ldots - b_p x_p) = 0$$

i.e.

$$nb_0 = \Sigma y - b_1 \Sigma x_1 - \ldots - b_p \Sigma x_p$$

or

$$b_0 = \bar{y} - b_1 \bar{x}_1 - \ldots - b_p \bar{x}_p \ldots\ldots\ldots\ldots(8A\cdot21)$$

For $k \neq 0$:

$$\frac{\partial Q}{\partial b_k} = -2\Sigma x_k(y - b_0 - b_1 x_1 - \ldots - b_k x_k - \ldots - b_p x_p) = 0$$

i.e. $b_0 \Sigma x_k + b_1 \Sigma x_1 x_k + \ldots + b_k \Sigma x_k^2 + \ldots + b_p \Sigma x_p x_k = \Sigma y x_k \ldots(8A\cdot22)$

Now $b_0 = \bar{y} - b_1 \bar{x}_1 - \ldots - b_p \bar{x}_p$, from Equation $(8A\cdot21)$.

Hence, eliminating b_0, Equation $(8A\cdot22)$ becomes

$$b_1 \Sigma x_k(x_1 - \bar{x}_1) + \ldots + b_k \Sigma x_k(x_k - \bar{x}_k) + \ldots + b_p \Sigma x_k(x_p - \bar{x}_p)$$
$$= \Sigma x_k(y - \bar{y}) \ldots\ldots\ldots(8A\cdot23)$$

Now $\Sigma x_k(x_1 - \bar{x}_1) \equiv \Sigma(x_k - \bar{x}_k)(x_1 - \bar{x}_1)$;

the difference between the two expressions is $\bar{x}_k \Sigma(x_1 - \bar{x}_1)$, which is identically zero from the definition of $\bar{x}_1$. A similar modification may be made to

S

the other summations involved in Equation $(8A\cdot23)$, which thus becomes

$$b_1\Sigma(x_1 - \bar{x}_1)(x_k - \bar{x}_k) + \ldots + b_k\Sigma(x_k - \bar{x}_k)^2 + \ldots$$
$$+ b_p\Sigma(x_p - \bar{x}_p)(x_k - \bar{x}_k) = \Sigma(y - \bar{y})(x_k - \bar{x}_k)$$
$$(k = 1, \ldots, p)$$

or, more concisely

$$b_1C_{1k} + \ldots + b_kC_{kk} + \ldots + b_pC_{pk} = C_{yk} \quad \ldots\ldots(8A\cdot24)$$
$$(k = 1, \ldots, p)$$

where C_{1k} denotes $\Sigma(x_1 - \bar{x}_1)(x_k - \bar{x}_k)$, etc.

Equation $(8A\cdot24)$ represents in fact a set of p simultaneous equations for the regression coefficients $b_1, \ldots, b_p$. Written out in more detail these take the form

$$\left.\begin{array}{l} b_1C_{11} + b_2C_{12} + b_3C_{13} + \ldots + b_pC_{1p} = C_{y1} \\ b_1C_{12} + b_2C_{22} + b_3C_{23} + \ldots + b_pC_{2p} = C_{y2} \\ b_1C_{13} + b_2C_{23} + b_3C_{33} + \ldots + b_pC_{3p} = C_{y3} \\ \cdots\cdots\cdots\cdots\cdots\cdots\cdots\cdots\cdots\cdots\cdots \\ b_1C_{1p} + b_2C_{2p} + b_3C_{3p} + \ldots + b_pC_{pp} = C_{yp} \end{array}\right\} \quad \ldots(8A\cdot25)$$

These equations, together with Equation $(8A\cdot21)$, give the least squares estimates of the constants in the regression equation representing the dependence of y on $x_1, \ldots, x_p$. For a regression on one variable only ($p = 1$) they reduce to those derived in Appendix 7A.

(b) Curvilinear regressions

8A·2 The equation to be fitted may be written as

$$y = b_0 + b_1x + b_2x^2 + \ldots + b_px^p \quad \ldots\ldots\ldots\ldots(8A\cdot3)$$

Since observed values will not usually satisfy this exactly, we must, as for a multiple regression, choose values of the b's which will minimise

$$Q = \Sigma(y_i - Y_i)^2$$

which in this instance is

$$Q = \Sigma(y - b_0 - b_1x - b_2x^2 - \ldots - b_px^p)^2 \ldots\ldots(8A\cdot31)$$

Differentiating with respect to b_0 and equating to zero, we obtain

$$\frac{\partial Q}{\partial b_0} = -2\Sigma(y - b_0 - b_1x - b_2x^2 - \ldots - b_px^p) = 0$$

i.e.

$$nb_0 = \Sigma y - b_1\Sigma x - b_2\Sigma x^2 - \ldots - b_p\Sigma x^p$$

or

$$b_0 = \bar{y} - b_1\bar{x} - b_2\overline{x^2} - \ldots - b_p\overline{x^p} \quad \ldots\ldots\ldots\ldots(8A\cdot32)$$

The notation $\overline{x^2}$ is used to denote the mean value of x^2, and so on. For $k \neq 0$:

$$\frac{\partial Q}{\partial b_k} = -2\Sigma x^k(y - b_0 - b_1x - b_2x^2 - \ldots - b_px^p)$$

i.e. $\quad b_0\Sigma x^k + b_1\Sigma x \cdot x^k + b_2\Sigma x^2 \cdot x^k + \ldots + b_p\Sigma x^p \cdot x^k = \Sigma yx^k \quad \ldots(8A\cdot33)$

Using Equation $(8A\cdot32)$ to eliminate b_0, we derive

$$b_1\Sigma x^k(x - \bar{x}) + b_2\Sigma x^k(x^2 - \overline{x^2}) + \ldots + b_p\Sigma x^k(x^p - \overline{x^p}) = \Sigma x^k(y - \bar{y})$$

and hence, since $\Sigma x^k(x - \bar{x}) = \Sigma(x^k - \overline{x^k})(x - \bar{x})$, etc.:

$$b_1\Sigma(x - \bar{x})(x^k - \overline{x^k}) + b_2\Sigma(x^2 - \overline{x^2})(x^k - \overline{x^k}) + \ldots$$
$$+ b_p\Sigma(x^p - \overline{x^p})(x^k - \overline{x^k}) = \Sigma(y - \bar{y})(x^k - \overline{x^k})\ldots\ldots(8A\cdot34)$$

Equations $(8A\cdot32)$ and $(8A\cdot34)$ are exactly equivalent to Equations $(8A\cdot21)$ and $(8A\cdot24)$, with the powers $x^1, \ldots, x^p$ of the independent variable x taking over the roles of the independent variables $x_1, \ldots, x_p$ in the multiple regression. Thus, a curvilinear regression giving the dependence of y on the successive powers $x^1, \ldots, x^p$ of x is fitted precisely as if it were a multiple regression on p independent variables $x_1, \ldots, x_p$, with $x_1 = x^1$, $x_2 = x^2$, etc.; each power of x entering into the fitted equation is treated as if it were a separate independent variable. The result is in fact implicit in the derivation of the least squares equations; in deriving these we seek to minimise Q with respect to variations in the regression coefficients $b_0, \ldots, b_p$, and the observed values of the powers of x (or of the separate independent variables in a multiple regression) are then merely constants which may be labelled arbitrarily—provided we use the appropriate numerical value it does not matter whether we denote this by x_r or x^r.

APPENDIX 8B

SOLUTION OF THE LEAST SQUARES EQUATIONS

Estimation of regression coefficients

8B·1 The least squares equations for the estimation of the regression coefficients in a multiple regression of a variable y on the p variables $x_1, \ldots, x_p$ were derived in Appendix 8A; they are

$$\left.\begin{array}{l} b_1C_{11} + b_2C_{12} + \ldots + b_pC_{1p} = C_{y1} \\ b_1C_{12} + b_2C_{22} + \ldots + b_pC_{2p} = C_{y2} \\ \cdots\cdots\cdots\cdots\cdots\cdots\cdots\cdots \\ b_1C_{1p} + b_2C_{2p} + \ldots + b_pC_{pp} = C_{yp} \end{array}\right\} \ldots\ldots(8B\cdot1)$$

where $C_{11} = \Sigma(x_1 - \bar{x}_1)^2$, $C_{12} = \Sigma(x_1 - \bar{x}_1)(x_2 - \bar{x}_2)$, etc. The notation is convenient for emphasising the general similarity in form of these coefficients, but for illustration of methods of solution is much less convenient; a notation is then required which enables us to distinguish specific coefficients more readily.

The equations for a regression on four variables may be written as

$$\left.\begin{array}{l} az_1 + bz_2 + dz_3 + gz_4 = A \\ bz_1 + cz_2 + ez_3 + hz_4 = C \\ dz_1 + ez_2 + fz_3 + iz_4 = F \\ gz_1 + hz_2 + iz_3 + jz_4 = J \end{array}\right\} \ldots\ldots\ldots(8B\cdot2)$$

where $z_1, \ldots, z_4$ are the four unknowns represented by $b_1, \ldots, b_4$ elsewhere, and $a \equiv C_{11}$, etc. The method of solution will be illustrated in terms of the four equations (8B·2), but no difficulty will be encountered in extending the methods to other numbers of equations and unknowns. The arrangement of the letters used to represent the coefficients should be particularly noted, as this helps in the use of the scheme for fewer unknowns and in showing the extension to larger numbers of unknowns. The pattern is symmetric about the diagonal elements a, c, f, j, and is built up by adding columns successively from the left, thus:

$$
\begin{array}{c|c|c|c|c|c|c|c}
a & b & d & g & k & p & \cdot & \cdot \\
  & c & e & h & l & q & \cdot & \cdot \\
  &   & f & i & m & r & \cdot & \cdot \\
  &   &   & j & n & s & \cdot & \cdot \\
  &   &   &   & o & t & \cdot & \cdot \\
  &   &   &   &   & u & \cdot & \cdot \\
  &   &   &   &   &   & \cdot & \cdot \\
\end{array}
$$

The spaces below the diagonal are filled in such a way as to complete the symmetry. Advantage is taken of this symmetry in the method given below for solution of the equations.

The form of the computation is set out below, followed by an explanation.

Table 8B·1

SOLUTION OF LINEAR EQUATIONS

						S	
a	b	d	g	A	(A)	s_1	
b	c	e	h	C	(C)	s_2	
d	e	f	i	F	(F)	s_3	
g	h	i	j	$\mathcal{J}$	$(\mathcal{J})$	s_4	
						S	
$\mathbf{a}$	$\mathbf{b}$	$\mathbf{d}$	$\mathbf{g}$	$\mathbf{A}$		$\mathbf{s_1}$	$\mathbf{a^{-1}}$
	$\mathbf{c}$	$\mathbf{e}$	$\mathbf{h}$	$\mathbf{C}$		$\mathbf{s_2}$	$\mathbf{c^{-1}}$
		$\mathbf{f}$	$\mathbf{i}$	$\mathbf{F}$		$\mathbf{s_3}$	$\mathbf{f^{-1}}$
			$\mathbf{j}$	$\mathbf{J}$		$\mathbf{s_4}$	$\mathbf{j^{-1}}$
z_1	z_2	z_3	z_4				

The quantities $a, b, \ldots, j$ and A, C, F and $\mathcal{J}$ are first written out in a rectangular array and an "S check" column is added on the right. The elements in this column are simply the sums of the successive rows of coefficients, e.g.

$$s_1 = a + b + d + g + A$$

and are included solely to provide a running check on the computation. A second array of numbers denoted by bold sanserif type is now calculated row by row from the first array in accordance with the following scheme.

*Row 1**

Enter, in the positions shown, $a = \sqrt{a}$ and a^{-1}, then calculate and enter $b = ba^{-1}$, $d = da^{-1}$, $g = ga^{-1}$, $A = Aa^{-1}$, and $s_1 = s_1a^{-1}$ in succession.
Confirm S check:

$$a + b + d + g + A = s_1$$

Row 2

Enter $c = \sqrt{(c - b^2)}$, then c^{-1}, followed by $e = (e - bd)c^{-1}$, $h = (h - bg)c^{-1}$, $C = (C - bA)c^{-1}$, and $s_2 = (s_2 - bs_1)c^{-1}$ in succession.
Confirm S check:

$$c + e + h + C = s_2$$

Row 3

Enter $f = \sqrt{(f - d^2 - e^2)}$, then f^{-1}, followed by $i = (i - dg - eh)f^{-1}$, $F = (F - dA - eC)f^{-1}$, and $s_3 = (s_3 - ds_1 - es_2)f^{-1}$.
Confirm S check:

$$f + i + F = s_3$$

Row 4

Enter $j = \sqrt{(j - g^2 - h^2 - i^2)}$, then j^{-1}, followed by $J = (J - gA - hC - iF)j^{-1}$ and $s_4 = (s_4 - gs_1 - hs_2 - is_3)j^{-1}$.
Confirm S check:

$$j + J = s_4$$

The unknown z's are now obtained in succession as follows:

$$z_4 = Jj^{-1}$$
$$z_3 = (F - iz_4)f^{-1}$$
$$z_2 = (C - hz_4 - ez_3)c^{-1}$$
$$z_1 = (A - gz_4 - dz_3 - bz_2)a^{-1}$$

The z's are entered in the positions indicated and a final check is obtained by substituting them in the equations. The calculated values A, C, F and J of the right-hand sides of the equations should agree closely with the actual values A, C, F and J.

In practice it will be found that the above routine is much simpler than it at first appears, since it follows a regular and easily remembered pattern.

The method is illustrated in the following example, taken from § 8·25. The regression coefficients describing the dependence of the flow rate of sulphate of ammonia on the three independent variables initial moisture content, length/breadth ratio and percent impurity are the solutions of the following equations:

$$\left. \begin{array}{r} 2{,}052{\cdot}98z_1 + 49{\cdot}15z_2 + 782{\cdot}12z_3 = -257{\cdot}59 \\ 49{\cdot}15z_1 + 12{\cdot}46z_2 + 13{\cdot}50z_3 = -11{\cdot}72 \\ 782{\cdot}12z_1 + 13{\cdot}50z_2 + 577{\cdot}25z_3 = -141{\cdot}37 \end{array} \right\} \quad \ldots (8B{\cdot}3)$$

* For convenience in printing the symbol a^{-1} will be used for $1/a$ throughout.

It is preferable, however, to arrange for the coefficients to be all of the same order of magnitude, as there will otherwise be some loss of accuracy in solving the equations. If, instead of length/breadth ratio, we use 10(length/breadth ratio) as our second independent variable, the equations become:

$$\left.\begin{array}{l} 2{,}052{\cdot}98z_1 + \ \ 491{\cdot}50z_2 + 782{\cdot}12z_3 = -\ 257{\cdot}59 \\ \ 491{\cdot}50z_1 + 1{,}246{\cdot}00z_2 + 135{\cdot}00z_3 = -\ 117{\cdot}20 \\ \ 782{\cdot}12z_1 + \ \ 135{\cdot}00z_2 + 577{\cdot}25z_3 = -\ 141{\cdot}37 \end{array}\right\} \ \dots\!(8B{\cdot}31)$$

These are the equations which will be solved. We have in effect multiplied the second column of coefficients in Equations $(8B{\cdot}3)$ by ten, so that the z_2 satisfying the new equations will be one-tenth of that satisfying the old, and have followed this by multiplying by ten the whole of the second equation, which has no effect on the solutions. Adjustment of a set of equations to bring the coefficients to a common order of magnitude may thus be achieved either by adjusting the scales of the variables or, more usually in practice, by multiplication by convenient factors of particular rows or columns of the matrix of coefficients.

The calculation of the solutions of Equations $(8B{\cdot}31)$ is set out in Table 8B·2.

Table 8B·2

SOLUTION OF EQUATIONS $(8B{\cdot}31)$

					S	
2,052·98	491·50	782·12	−257·59	(−257·59)	3,069·01	
491·50	1,246·00	135·00	−117·20	(−117·20)	1,755·30	
782·12	135·00	577·25	−141·37	(−141·37)	1,353·00	
					S	
45·3098	10·8475	17·2616	−5·6851		67·7339	0·0220703
	33·5906	−1·5554	−1·6532		30·3822	0·0297702
		16·6393	−2·7530		13·8864	0·0600987
−0·04882	−0·05688	−0·16545				

The solutions to Equations $(8B{\cdot}31)$ are thus found to be

$$z_1 = -\ 0{\cdot}04882; \quad z_2 = -\ 0{\cdot}05688; \quad z_3 = -\ 0{\cdot}16545 \quad ..(8B{\cdot}4)$$

The solutions to Equations $(8B{\cdot}3)$ are thus, to four-decimal accuracy:

$$z_1 = -\ 0{\cdot}0488; \quad z_2 = -\ 0{\cdot}5688; \quad z_3 = -\ 0{\cdot}1655 \quad \dots\!(8B{\cdot}41)$$

The reader may readily verify that the S checks are a good deal less satisfactory in the direct solution of Equations $(8B{\cdot}3)$ than they are in the solution of Equations $(8B{\cdot}31)$.

Depending on the calculating machine used, it may sometimes be more convenient to divide by a, c, etc., than to multiply by their reciprocals a^{-1}, c^{-1}, etc. More often than not, however, the choice between the two alternatives is a matter of personal preference.

Inversion of matrices

8B·2   If all that is required is the estimation of the regression coefficients, the method described above is most rapid and convenient. However, as was mentioned in § **8·241**, it is usually preferable to solve the equations indirectly by first calculating from the "matrix" of coefficients on the left-hand sides of the equations a second matrix, called the "reciprocal matrix." This reciprocal matrix may be defined as follows.

Suppose that instead of solving the set of equations (*8B·2*) the following four sets of equations are solved:

$$(1)\ (2)\ (3)\ (4)$$

$$
\begin{array}{l}
aZ_1 + bZ_2 + dZ_3 + gZ_4 = 1\ \ 0\ \ 0\ \ 0 \\
bZ_1 + cZ_2 + eZ_3 + hZ_4 = 0\ \ 1\ \ 0\ \ 0 \\
dZ_1 + eZ_2 + fZ_3 + iZ_4 = 0\ \ 0\ \ 1\ \ 0 \\
gZ_1 + hZ_2 + iZ_3 + jZ_4 = 0\ \ 0\ \ 0\ \ 1
\end{array}
$$

$$\dots\dots(8B\cdot5)$$

These sets of equations have the same coefficients on the left-hand side as (*8B·2*), but the elements A, C, F and J on the right-hand side are replaced for the first set by 1, 0, 0, 0 (the elements of column (1)), for the second set by 0, 1, 0, 0 (the elements of column (2)), and so on for the third and fourth sets.

It will be found that if the solutions of the first set of equations are denoted by $Z_1 = A'$, $Z_2 = B'$, $Z_3 = D'$, and $Z_4 = G'$, then the solutions of the second set can be written $Z_1 = B'$, $Z_2 = C'$, $Z_3 = E'$, and $Z_4 = H'$, where Z_1 of the second set is the same as Z_2 of the first set, and so on. The four sets of solutions may be arranged in a table as follows:

	Z_1	Z_2	Z_3	Z_4
(i)	A'	B'	D'	G'
(ii)	B'	C'	E'	H'
(iii)	D'	E'	F'	I'
(iv)	G'	H'	I'	J'

The matrix

$$
\begin{array}{cccc}
A' & B' & D' & G' \\
B' & C' & E' & H' \\
D' & E' & F' & I' \\
G' & H' & I' & J'
\end{array}
$$

is called the reciprocal (or inverse) of the matrix

$$
\begin{array}{cccc}
a & b & d & g \\
b & c & e & h \\
d & e & f & i \\
g & h & i & j
\end{array}
$$

and the process of calculating one from the other is referred to as matrix inversion. If, as is the case for Equations (*8B·2*), the matrix of coefficients for the left-hand side of the equations is symmetrical, then so will be its reciprocal matrix. The solution of any set of equations like $(8B\cdot2)$ with elements A, C, F and $\mathcal{J}$ on the right-hand side can be obtained immediately from the reciprocal matrix as follows:

$$\left.\begin{aligned} z_1 &= A'A + B'C + D'F + G'\mathcal{J} \\ z_2 &= B'A + C'C + E'F + H'\mathcal{J} \\ z_3 &= D'A + E'C + F'F + I'\mathcal{J} \\ z_4 &= G'A + H'C + I'F + \mathcal{J}'\mathcal{J} \end{aligned}\right\} \quad \dots\dots\dots(8B\cdot6)$$

The calculation of the reciprocal matrix is particularly useful because the elements of the matrix are proportional to the variances and covariances of the estimates, which are usually required in any case. Thus by solving the least squares equations using the reciprocal matrix, quantities required to give the standard errors and degree of correlation between the estimates are also obtained.

The calculation of the reciprocal matrix can best be set out as in Table $8B\cdot3$.

Table 8B·3

CALCULATION OF RECIPROCAL MATRIX

					S	
	a	b	d	g	s_1	
	b	c	e	h	s_2	
	d	e	f	i	s_3	
	g	h	i	j	s_4	
					S	
s_8	$A'a$	$B'b$	$D'd$	$G'g$	s_1	a^{-1}
s_7	B'	$C'c$	$E'e$	$H'h$	s_2	c^{-1}
s_6	D'	E'	$F'f$	$I'i$	s_3	f^{-1}
s_5	G'	H'	I'	$\mathcal{J}'j$	s_4	j^{-1}
	s_1	s_2	s_3	s_4		

The matrix to be inverted is written down together with the sums s_1, s_2, s_3 and s_4 of the rows, which are entered on the right of the matrix in the column marked S. For a reason to be explained later, the same values s_1, s_2, s_3 and s_4 are copied immediately below where the last row G', H', I', $\mathcal{J}'$ of the reciprocal matrix is due to appear. The triangular array a, b, d, etc., is next written down, following exactly the procedure already described in § $8B\cdot1$ for the solution of linear equations. In fact, this first stage in the calculation is identical with that in § $8B\cdot1$ but with the elements A, C, F and $\mathcal{J}$ omitted. The S check is applied as each row is computed, exactly as before. From the elements of this triangular array the elements of the reciprocal matrix may be obtained immediately. These are calculated in order from right to left, starting at the bottom row. As each row is completed it is checked by calculating the sum of products of the elements of the row with s_1, s_2, s_3 and s_4, which have been placed below the matrix for this purpose. It will be seen from Equations $(8B\cdot5)$, which define the reciprocal matrix, that the sum of products between any row or column of the original matrix and the corresponding row or column of the reciprocal matrix must be unity, while the sum of products of any row or column in the original matrix with any other row or column in the reciprocal matrix must be zero. It follows that the sum of products of any row of the reciprocal matrix with the row of elements s_1, s_2, s_3 and s_4 must be equal to unity if the calculation is correct. Therefore as each row of the reciprocal matrix is derived this check is carried out. The sums of products of the check are entered as s_5, s_6, s_7 and s_8 in a column on the left. The calculation follows an easily remembered routine as follows.

Row 4

Enter in turn the following elements:

$$J' = j^{-1}j^{-1}$$
$$I' = (-J'i)f^{-1}$$
$$H' = (-J'h - I'e)c^{-1}$$
$$G' = (-J'g - I'd - H'b)a^{-1}$$

Check:

$$G's_1 + H's_2 + I's_3 + J's_4 = 1$$

Row 3

Copy I' in its other position, and then enter:

$$F' = (f^{-1} - I'i)f^{-1}$$
$$E' = (-I'h - F'e)c^{-1}$$
$$D' = (-I'g - F'd - E'b)a^{-1}$$

Check:

$$D's_1 + E's_2 + F's_3 + I's_4 = 1$$

Row 2

Copy E' and H' in their other positions, and then enter:

$$C' = (c^{-1} - H'h - E'e)c^{-1}$$
$$B' = (-H'g - E'd - C'b)a^{-1}$$

Check:

$$B's_1 + C's_2 + E's_3 + H's_4 = 1$$

Row 1

Copy B', D' and G' in their other positions, and then enter:

$$A' = (a^{-1} - G'g - D'd - B'b)a^{-1}$$

Check:

$$A's_1 + B's_2 + D's_3 + G's_4 = 1$$

The reader will experience no difficulty in applying the method to matrices in which the number of rows or columns is greater or less than four. The following example shows the inversion of the 3×3 matrix of the left-hand side of the equations given in § 8B·1.

Table 8B·4

INVERSION OF MATRIX OF COEFFICIENTS OF EQUATIONS (8B·3l)

				S
2,052·98	491·50	782·12		3,326·60
491·50	1,246·00	135·00		1,872·50
782·12	135·00	577·25		1,494·37
45·3098	10·8475	17·2616		73·4190
	33·5906	−1·5554		32·0354
		16·6393		16·6394

				S
1·00000	0·0109306	−0·00027775	−0·0141604	0·0220703
1·00000	−0·00027775	0·0089401	0·0016725	0·0297702
1·00002	−0·0141604	0·0016725	0·0361185	0·0600987
	3,326·60	1,872·50	1,494·37	

The reciprocal matrix is thus found to be

$$10^{-4} \times \begin{bmatrix} 10\cdot931 & -2\cdot777 & -14\cdot160 \\ -2\cdot777 & 8\cdot940 & 1\cdot672 \\ -14\cdot160 & 1\cdot672 & 36\cdot119 \end{bmatrix}$$

The check given confirms that the calculation has been completed satisfactorily.

The reciprocal of the matrix of coefficients of Equations $(8B\cdot3)$ is

$$10^{-3} \times \begin{bmatrix} 1\cdot093 & -2\cdot777 & -1\cdot416 \\ -2\cdot777 & 89\cdot401 & 1\cdot672 \\ -1\cdot416 & 1\cdot672 & 3\cdot612 \end{bmatrix}$$

To compensate for the multiplication of coefficients by ten to give Equations $(8B\cdot31)$ we must multiply similarly the elements of the reciprocal matrix.

APPENDIX 8C

CALCULATIONS FOR EXAMPLE 8·2:
EFFICIENCY OF A WATER-GAS PLANT

Fitting of the regression equation

8C·1 The data for this example are given in Table 8C·1; for convenience (air/steam ratio)^2 is denoted by z rather than by x^2.

From these we find that:

Σy^2	$= 203{,}198$
Correction for mean $= (2{,}132)^2/27$	$= 168{,}349$
$\Sigma(y - \bar{y})^2 = C_{yy}$	$= 34{,}849$
Σxy	$= 4{,}178\cdot68$
Correction for means $= (2{,}132 \times 48\cdot80)/27$	$= 3{,}853\cdot39$
$\Sigma(x - \bar{x})(y - \bar{y}) = C_{xy}$	$= 325\cdot29$
Σx^2	$= 92\cdot0574$
Correction for mean $= (48\cdot80)^2/27$	$= 88\cdot2015$
$\Sigma(x - \bar{x})^2 = C_{xx}$	$= 3\cdot8559$

With a calculating machine of $10 \times 10 \times 20$ capacity, particularly one of the electrical models designed for automatic squaring, it is convenient to calculate Σy^2, $2\Sigma xy$ and Σx^2 simultaneously, setting y and x at opposite ends of the setting register.

Table 8C·1

MONTHLY COKE USAGE, AIR/STEAM RATIO AND (AIR/STEAM RATIO)² FOR A WATER-GAS PLANT

Month	Coke Usage (working units) (y)	Air/Steam Ratio (x)	(Air/Steam Ratio)² (z)
1	120	2·11	4·45
2	122	2·29	5·24
3	128	2·32	5·38
4	124	2·31	5·34
5	118	2·25	5·06
6	114	2·22	4·93
7	119	2·20	4·84
8	149	2·41	5·81
9	141	2·19	4·80
10	86	2·06	4·24
11	78	1·99	3·96
12	31	1·62	2·62
13	51	1·59	2·53
14	72	1·70	2·89
15	51	1·76	3·10
16	53	1·33	1·77
17	50	1·23	1·51
18	34	1·40	1·96
19	68	1·38	1·90
20	70	1·96	3·84
21	49	1·47	2·16
22	50	1·42	2·02
23	66	1·33	1·77
24	46	1·65	2·72
25	40	1·26	1·59
26	51	1·61	2·59
27	51	1·74	3·03
Sum ..	2,132	48·80	92·05

Proceeding similarly, we derive:

$$C_{zy} = 1{,}215{\cdot}99$$
$$C_{zz} = 51{\cdot}2192$$
$$C_{xz} = 14{\cdot}0118$$

$$\bar{y} = 78{\cdot}96 \quad \bar{x} = 1{\cdot}807 \quad \bar{z} = 3{\cdot}409$$

The least squares equations for the regression of y on x and z are:

$$\left.\begin{array}{l} 3 \cdot 8559 b_1 + 14 \cdot 0118 b_2 = 325 \cdot 29 \\ 14 \cdot 0118 b_1 + 51 \cdot 2192 b_2 = 1{,}215 \cdot 99 \end{array}\right\} \quad \cdots\cdots\cdots (8C \cdot 1)$$

Since there are only two equations, they can be solved directly [§ 8·24] to give

$$b_1 = \frac{(51 \cdot 2192 \times 325 \cdot 29) - (14 \cdot 0118 \times 1215 \cdot 99)}{(3 \cdot 8559 \times 51 \cdot 2192) - (14 \cdot 0118)^2}$$

$$= -\frac{377 \cdot 12}{1 \cdot 1656} = -323 \cdot 54 \quad \cdots\cdots\cdots\cdots\cdots (8C \cdot 2)$$

and

$$b_2 = \frac{(3 \cdot 8559 \times 1215 \cdot 99) - (14 \cdot 0118 \times 325 \cdot 29)}{(3 \cdot 8559 \times 51 \cdot 2192) - (14 \cdot 0118)^2}$$

$$= \frac{130 \cdot 84}{1 \cdot 1656} = 112 \cdot 25 \quad \cdots\cdots\cdots\cdots\cdots\cdots (8C \cdot 3)$$

The fitted regression equation is thus

$$(y - 78 \cdot 96) = -323 \cdot 54(x - 1 \cdot 807) + 112 \cdot 25(z - 3 \cdot 409)$$

i.e.
$$y = 280 \cdot 9 - 323 \cdot 54x + 112 \cdot 25z$$
$$= 280 \cdot 9 - 323 \cdot 54x + 112 \cdot 25x^2 \quad \cdots\cdots\cdots\cdots (8C \cdot 4)$$

This represents a parabola with a minimum at an air/steam ratio of

$$x = \frac{323 \cdot 54}{2 \times 112 \cdot 25} = 1 \cdot 44$$

Analysis of Variance

8C·2   The sum of squares attributable to the curvilinear regression is

$$b_1 C_{xy} + b_2 C_{zy} = (-323 \cdot 54 \times 325 \cdot 29) + (112 \cdot 25 \times 1{,}215 \cdot 99)$$
$$= 31{,}251$$

The sum of squares attributable to a linear regression on x only is

$$(C_{xy})^2 / C_{xx} = (325 \cdot 29)^2 / 3 \cdot 8559$$
$$= 27{,}442$$

Thus the Analysis of Variance for the significance of the $z\ (= x^2)$ term is that given in Table 8C·2.

The sums of squares "Addition due to x^2 term" and "Residual" are both obtained by difference from the other (known) values.

The F-ratio for the significance of the parabolic term is $3{,}809/150 = 25 \cdot 4$, with degrees of freedom 1 and 24. From Table D we see that the additional effect is significant at the 0·01 probability level.

Standard Errors

8C·3   The variances and covariance of the regression coefficients b_1 and b_2 are obtained from the elements of the inverse of the matrix of sums of squares

Table 8C·2

ANALYSIS OF VARIANCE FOR SIGNIFICANCE OF
PARABOLIC TERM

Source	Sum of Squares	Degrees of Freedom	Mean Square
Addition due to x^2 term ..	3,809	1	3,809
Due to linear regression ..	27,442	1	27,442
Total due to parabolic regression	31,251	2	—
Residual	3,598	24	150
Total ..	34,849	26	—

and products. For a regression on two variables (which we have here denoted by x and z) it may be shown that the inverse matrix is

$$\frac{1}{\varDelta} \begin{bmatrix} C_{zz} & -C_{zx} \\ -C_{zx} & C_{xx} \end{bmatrix}$$

where $\varDelta = C_{xx}C_{zz} - (C_{xz})^2$, a quantity which has already been used in
deriving the regression coefficients. The multiplication by $1/\varDelta$ is understood
to mean multiplication of each element of the matrix by this factor.

Thus
$$V(b_1) = \frac{150 \times 51\cdot2192}{1\cdot1656} = 6{,}591$$
$$V(b_2) = \frac{150 \times 3\cdot8559}{1\cdot1656} = 496$$
and
$$\text{cov } (b_1 b_2) = -\frac{150 \times 14\cdot0118}{1\cdot1656} = -1{,}803$$
.......(8C·5)

We may note in passing that the t-value measuring the significance of b_2 is
given by

$$t = \frac{112\cdot25}{\sqrt{496}} = 5\cdot04$$

which is the square root of the F-ratio of 25·4 obtained in § 8C·2 above. The
standard errors of the estimates are

$$S.E.(b_1) = 81\cdot2 \qquad S.E.(b_2) = 22\cdot3 \ldots\ldots\ldots\ldots(8C·6)$$

but because of the high correlation between the estimates these give little
information on the precision of estimates obtained from the regression
equation.

Prediction using the regression equation

8C·4   The regression equation is

$$y = 280 \cdot 9 - 323 \cdot 54x + 112 \cdot 25x^2$$

or, in the form in which it is originally derived,

$$(y - \bar{y}) = - 323 \cdot 54(x - \bar{x}) + 112 \cdot 25(x^2 - \overline{x^2})$$

Let Y_i denote the regression estimate corresponding to a value x_i of x. Then the uncertainty in Y_i is measured by a variance.

$$V(Y_i) = V(\bar{y}) + 6{,}591(x_i - \bar{x})^2 + 496(x_i^2 - \overline{x^2})^2 - 3{,}606(x_i - \bar{x})(x_i^2 - \overline{x^2})$$
$$= 5 \cdot 56 + 6{,}591(x_i - 1 \cdot 807)^2 + 496(x_i^2 - 3 \cdot 409)^2$$
$$- 3606(x_i - 1 \cdot 807)(x_i^2 - 3 \cdot 409) \ldots \ldots \ldots (8C \cdot 7)$$

This expression is a quartic in x_i and may be calculated as such; a series of values at equally spaced intervals may, for example, be built up using the constant fourth difference. For calculation of single values of $V(Y_i)$ it is, however, more convenient to use the form given above than to attempt rearrangement.

A short table of predicted values showing also $V(Y_i)$ and the 95% confidence limits for Y_i is given below. The confidence limits are derived using the appropriate t-multiplier for 24 degrees of freedom, i.e. 2·064.

Table 8C·3

VALUES PREDICTED USING THE REGRESSION EQUATION

x_i	Y_t	$V(Y_i)$	95% Confidence Limits	
			Lower	Upper
1·0	69·6	166·08	43·0	96·2
1·1	60·8	92·30	41·0	80·6
1·2	54·3	47·15	40·1	68·5
1·3	50·0	22·68	40·2	59·8
1·4	48·0	12·14	40·8	55·2
1·5	48·2	9·96	41·7	54·7
1·6	50·6	11·77	43·5	57·7
1·7	55·3	14·37	47·5	63·1
1·8	62·2	15·78	54·0	70·4
1·9	71·4	15·20	63·4	79·4
2·0	82·8	13·00	75·4	90·2
2·1	96·5	10·77	89·7	103·3
2·2	112·4	11·27	105·5	119·3
2·3	130·6	18·46	121·7	139·5
2·4	151·0	37·49	138·4	163·6
2·5	173·6	74·70	155·8	191·4

The limits derived above are shown graphically in Figure 8·7. They describe only the uncertainties of the regression estimates and take no account of the further scatter of individual results. The uncertainty of a further individual result is obtained by adding to $V(Y_i)$ the residual variance of 150 found earlier. For example, the observed coke usage at an air/steam ratio of 1·7 would be expected, with 95% confidence, to be within the limits

$$55·3 \pm 2·06\sqrt{(150 + 14)}$$

i.e.   28·9 and 81·7

Such limits would be used in applying the regression equation as a check on the future performance of the plant.

CHAPTER 9

FREQUENCY DATA AND CONTINGENCY TABLES

IN the majority of examples discussed in this handbook the data have consisted of observations that, apart from the rounding off, were measured on a continuous scale. The present chapter is concerned with data that occur as frequencies—the numbers of times certain events have happened, or counts of objects—and are therefore bound to consist of integers 0, 1, 2, 3, etc.

The binomial distribution

9·1 Since the Binomial Distribution was discovered through the study of games of chance, it will be appropriate to introduce it by considering the following problem: "Five 'poker' dice are thrown: what is the probability that the number of aces will be five, four, three, two, one, or zero?"

The probability that the number of aces is five is the product of the probabilities that each die shows an ace, i.e.

$$\tfrac{1}{6} \times \tfrac{1}{6} \times \tfrac{1}{6} \times \tfrac{1}{6} \times \tfrac{1}{6} = (\tfrac{1}{6})^5$$

provided that the dice are unbiased and that the events are *independent*, i.e. that the way one die falls does not influence the way another die falls.

The probability that four *specified* dice show aces and the remaining one "not-ace" is:

$$\tfrac{1}{6} \times \tfrac{1}{6} \times \tfrac{1}{6} \times \tfrac{1}{6} \times \tfrac{5}{6} = (\tfrac{1}{6})^4(\tfrac{5}{6})$$

The die which does not show the ace may, however, be any one of the five dice, so that the probability that the number of aces is four is $5(\tfrac{1}{6})^4(\tfrac{5}{6})$.

The probability that three specified dice show aces and the remaining two not-ace is $(\tfrac{1}{6})^3(\tfrac{5}{6})^2$. But the three showing aces may be any three out of the five, and the number of ways of choosing three out of five is:

$$\frac{5!}{2!\,3!} = \frac{5.4.3.2.1}{2.1.3.2.1} = 10$$

Hence the probability of three aces is $10(\tfrac{1}{6})^3(\tfrac{5}{6})^2$.

The remaining probabilities may be calculated in the same way (Table 9·1).

The probabilities are in fact the successive terms of the binomial expansion of $(\tfrac{1}{6} + \tfrac{5}{6})^5$.

In the general case, if

$$\mathfrak{p} = \text{probability that an event will happen}$$
$$\mathfrak{q} = 1 - \mathfrak{p} = \text{probability that it will not happen}$$

T

Table 9·1

THROWS OF FIVE POKER DICE

Number of Aces	Probability	Numerical Value of Probability
5	$(\frac{1}{6})^5$	0·00013
4	$5(\frac{1}{6})^4(\frac{5}{6})$	0·00321
3	$10(\frac{1}{6})^3(\frac{5}{6})^2$	0·03215
2	$10(\frac{1}{6})^2(\frac{5}{6})^3$	0·16075
1	$5(\frac{1}{6})(\frac{5}{6})^4$	0·40188
0	$(\frac{5}{6})^5$	0·40188
Total ..	—	1·00000

then the probability that it will happen a times, and fail to happen b times in n trials, where $n = a + b$, is:

$$P = \frac{n!}{a!\,b!}\ \mathfrak{p}^a\mathfrak{q}^b \quad \dots\dots\dots\dots\dots(9\cdot1)$$

which is the general term of the binomial expansion of

$$(\mathfrak{p} + \mathfrak{q})^n$$

The distribution defined by such a sequence of probabilities is accordingly known as the Binomial Distribution.

Mean and variance of the binomial distribution

9·11 If the distribution of a is given by the terms of the binomial expansion of $(\mathfrak{p} + \mathfrak{q})^n$ the mean or expected value of a is given by:

$$\mu = n\mathfrak{p} \quad \dots\dots\dots\dots\dots\dots (9\cdot2)$$

This can readily be seen from the example of the dice. Since in a very large number of throws the number of aces must average one-sixth of the number of dice thrown, the average number of aces *per set of five dice* must be $5 \times \frac{1}{6}$, i.e. $n\mathfrak{p}$, where $n = 5$ and $\mathfrak{p} = \frac{1}{6}$.

It will be noticed that although a is always a whole number, its mean value in a very long series of trials, i.e. its expected value, is not necessarily a whole number.

The variance of a is the mean of the square of the deviations from the mean. It can be shown that if a is distributed in the binomial distribution given by terms of the expansion of $(\mathfrak{p} + \mathfrak{q})^n$, then the variance of a is given by:

$$\sigma^2 = n\mathfrak{p}\mathfrak{q} \quad \dots\dots\dots\dots\dots (9\cdot3)$$

This is also the variance of b.

The binomial distribution differs from the Normal distribution, not only because it is discontinuous, but also because, unless n is large, it can be very markedly asymmetrical when either $\mathfrak{p}$ or $\mathfrak{q}$ is small. Nevertheless, provided n is large and neither $\mathfrak{p}$ nor $\mathfrak{q}$ is small, that is provided both a and b are large, sufficiently accurate tests of significance can be made by treating a as though it were a Normal variate with mean and variance given by the above formulae. These tests, based on "large sample" theory, are illustrated in the succeeding section, and are followed by the exact tests suitable for "small" samples.

An example on accident rates

9·12   The data in Table 9·2 below show the number of lost-time accidents to women and men in an I.C.I. factory over a period of many years. To tell whether one sex is more prone to accidents than the other, it would be natural to express these figures as rates per thousand "man-hours" worked. However, if the hours of work a day and number of days worked a year are taken to be the same for the two sexes, and if there have been no violent fluctuations in the numbers employed, virtually the same conclusions will be drawn if we calculate the accident rate per hundred persons. The number employed will conveniently be taken as an average over the period of observation, say the average of the numbers on the payroll at the beginning of each year of the period.

Table 9·2

ACCIDENTS IN AN I.C.I. FACTORY

	Number of Accidents	Average Number Employed	Rate per Hundred
Women	$a = 48$	246	19·5
Men	$b = 127$	578	22·0
Total	$n = 175$	824	21·2

The rate for men is apparently higher, but it is necessary to apply a statistical test to decide whether the difference between the two rates really is greater than can reasonably be attributed to chance.

The proportion of women employed is:

$$\mathfrak{p} = 246/824 = 0·2985$$

and of men:

$$\mathfrak{q} = 578/824 = 0·7015$$

$$\overline{1·0000}$$

If men and women were equally prone to accident, the *expected number* of accidents to women would be:

$$n\mathfrak{p} = 175 \times 0.2985 = 52.24$$

and to men:
$$n\mathfrak{q} = 175 \times 0.7015 = 122.76$$

$$\overline{175.00}$$

The expected number is, of course, a mathematical concept, since there cannot be 0·24 of an accident. With a total of 175 it is clear that the number of accidents to women and men respectively could not be more strictly proportional to the average numbers employed than 52 : 123. A small variation either way can be attributed to chance, and it only remains to decide whether the numbers 48 : 127 deviate from the expected numbers more than would often happen by chance.

The variance of the binomial distribution is:

$$n\mathfrak{p}\mathfrak{q} = 175 \times 0.2985 \times 0.7015 = 36.65$$

The standard deviation is the square root of the variance, viz. 6·05. The observed deviation from expectation (ignoring sign) is:

$$|\, 48 - 52.24 \,| = 4.24$$

The deviations in the two classes are, of course, equal in magnitude but opposite in sign.

The ratio of observed deviation to standard deviation is:

$$u = 4.24/6.05 = 0.70$$

Provided the numbers in either class are not too small, the binomial distribution approximates to the Normal distribution, and the above ratio may therefore be referred to a table of the Normal distribution (Table A) to judge its significance. More briefly, it may be considered significant if it exceeds 2, this being the two-sided Normal deviate corresponding to a level of significance of approximately 0·05. It is obvious that, in the present example, the deviation is not significant: the probability of encountering a deviation from expectation (in either direction) larger than 0·70 times the standard deviation is about 0·48, a probability so large that there is no reason, *on the evidence of these figures alone*, for claiming that the rates are different for the two sexes.

An alternative approach

9·13 The following method, although mathematically equivalent and necessarily leading to the same conclusion, provides an alternative way of looking at the same problem.

The proportion of women employed is, as we have already seen:

$$\mathfrak{p} = 0.2985$$

The proportion of accidents which happen to women is:
$$p = 48/175 = 0·2743$$
If men and women are equally prone to accident, these two proportions should be the same, and the question resolves itself into: "Is p significantly different from $\mathfrak{p}$?"

As already stated, the variance of a or b in a binomial distribution is $n\mathfrak{pq}$, from which it follows that the variance of p $(= a/n)$ or of q $(= b/n)$ is:
$$\mathfrak{pq}/n = (0·2985)(0·7015)/175 = 0·0011966$$
Hence standard deviation $= 0·0346$.
But $$|p - \mathfrak{p}| = |0·2743 - 0·2985| = 0·0242$$
The ratio of the deviation of p to its standard deviation is:
$$u = 0·0242/0·0346 = 0·70$$
This is the same ratio as was obtained before and leads to the same assessment of the significance.

Precision of the estimate of a proportion

9·14 In some problems we are concerned, not with testing whether an observed proportion differs significantly from a hypothetical value $\mathfrak{p}$, but merely in estimating $\mathfrak{p}$ and determining the accuracy of our estimate. It is obvious that p, the observed proportion in the sample, is the best estimate of $\mathfrak{p}$, the true proportion in the Universe. It is, however, impossible to state the true variance of p, since we do not know the values of $\mathfrak{p}$ and $\mathfrak{q}$ to insert in the formula for the variance $\mathfrak{pq}/n$. In such cases we shall not be seriously in error if we use the *estimates p* and q for insertion in the formula, i.e. if we take the variance to be pq/n.

Let us suppose (in order to work with the same figures as before) that a Public Opinion survey has shown that 48 persons in a random sample of 175 persons answered "Yes" to a certain question. Then the estimate of the proportion in the population who would answer "Yes" is:
$$p = 48/175 = 0·2743$$
The estimated variance of p is accordingly:
$$pq/n = (0·2743)(0·7257)/175 = 0·0011375$$
Estimated standard deviation $\qquad = 0·0337$
The estimated standard deviation can be used for setting limits to $\mathfrak{p}$. Thus the 95% confidence limits are:
$$0·2743 \pm 1·96 \times 0·0337 = 0·208 \text{ to } 0·340$$
Hence it can be asserted, with 95% confidence, that the proportion in the population lies between 21% and 34%.

Exact method

9·15 The methods described above depend on the substitution for the discontinuous binomial distribution of a continuous Normal distribution with the same mean and variance, and will be reasonably accurate only when neither a nor b is small. If either a or b is less than 15, the Normal approximation will be unsatisfactory. In Quality Control work the number of defective articles in a sample is often as small as two or three, and in such cases the mechanical application of the above methods will lead to grossly misleading conclusions.

An exact test of significance is always provided by the sum of the appropriate number of terms of the binomial distribution, as the following example will illustrate.

9·151 A person claiming "clairvoyant" powers offers to predict the fall of a die. In five successive attempts he is right three times. Discuss the strength of the evidence in favour of his claim. The Null Hypothesis to be tested is that his "predictions" are pure guesses. On this hypothesis, the probability of guessing right is exactly $\frac{1}{6}$. The probabilities of any number of correct guesses from 0 to 5 in five attempts are given by the terms of the expansion of $(\frac{1}{6} + \frac{5}{6})^5$, and in fact have already been worked out in Table 9·1. If any result is to be judged significant, then so must any greater number of correct guesses. The significance of his result is therefore judged by the probability of guessing right three, four, or five times in the five attempts, i.e.

$$P = 0{\cdot}03215 + 0{\cdot}00321 + 0{\cdot}00013 = 0{\cdot}03549$$

The probability of getting by chance a result as good as or better than he actually achieved is approximately 0·035 and according to the usual convention is sufficiently small for the result to be judged significant. However, in view of the extravagance of the claim, perhaps a much *higher* level of significance (i.e. a much smaller value of P) should be demanded.

9·152 Let us now consider a more practical problem. A sample of 25 articles is drawn at random from a bulk or from a day's production, etc., and three of them are found to be defective (or underweight, or possessing some other relevant characteristic). We wish to draw conclusions about the proportion of defective articles in the bulk. In this and the following example we assume that the sample is only a small fraction of the bulk (lot or consignment) being sampled, certainly not more than a fifth. In other words, we must reasonably be able to treat the bulk as an infinite Universe in comparison with the sample. The best estimate of proportion defective is, of course:

$$p = 3/25 = 0{\cdot}12$$

If the true proportion defective is $\mathfrak{p}$, the probability of encountering 3 *or fewer* defectives in a sample of 25 is the sum of the last four terms of the binomial expansion of $(\mathfrak{p} + \mathfrak{q})^{25}$, i.e.

$$P = \frac{25!}{3! \ 22!} \ \mathfrak{p}^3 \mathfrak{q}^{22} + \frac{25!}{2! \ 23!} \ \mathfrak{p}^2 \mathfrak{q}^{23} + 25 \mathfrak{p} \mathfrak{q}^{24} + \mathfrak{q}^{25}$$

For any chosen level of significance, say $P = 0·025$, it is possible to solve this equation and find a value of $\mathfrak{p}$ such that the 3 defectives in 25 are just on the borderline of being significantly *too few*. For any larger value of $\mathfrak{p}$ the result would be significant, and for any smaller value not significant. In other words, the value of $\mathfrak{p}$ given by this equation sets an upper limit beyond which one can state, with reasonable confidence, that the true value of $\mathfrak{p}$ does not lie. Similarly the probability of encountering 3 *or more* defectives in a sample of 25 is given by the sum of the first twenty-three terms of the same binomial expansion:

$$P = \mathfrak{p}^{25} + 25\mathfrak{p}^{24}\mathfrak{q} + \frac{25!}{23!\,2!}\,\mathfrak{p}^{23}\mathfrak{q}^2 + \cdots + \frac{25!}{3!\,22!}\,\mathfrak{p}^3\mathfrak{q}^{22}$$

Putting $P = 0·025$ we can solve this equation to find a value of $\mathfrak{p}$ such that 3 defectives in 25 are just on the borderline of being significantly *too many*. This value of $\mathfrak{p}$ sets a lower limit, below which one can state, with reasonable confidence, that the true value of $\mathfrak{p}$ does not lie.

Evidently the solution of these equations would be troublesome, and it was for this reason that Table F (Confidence Limits for mean μ of the Binomial and Poisson Distributions) was calculated. The table is used when either a or b is less than 15, and the smaller of the two numbers is always denoted by a. It is entered for a and for p, the observed proportion, interpolating if necessary with respect to p. Thus to find the 95% confidence limits we enter with $a = 3$ and $P = 0·025$ and find:

p	Lower	Upper
0·2	0·650	7·21
0·1	0·634	7·96

Simple linear interpolation between $p = 0·1$ and $p = 0·2$ gives the limits corresponding to $p = 0·12$, the observed proportion defective.

p	Lower	Upper
0·12	0·637	7·81

These are the limits of the *expected* number defective (i.e. of $n\mathfrak{p}$) in a sample of twenty-five, and the limits of $\mathfrak{p}$ are accordingly:

$$0·637/25 = 2·55\%$$
$$7·81/25 = 31·2\%$$

Hence it can be stated that the percentage defective in the bulk from which the sample was drawn is not less than 2·55% nor greater than 31·2%. The extraordinarily low accuracy of determination of $\mathfrak{p}$ will be noted. Evidently a much larger sample than twenty-five would be necessary to obtain useful information about $\mathfrak{p}$. This point is often overlooked by those responsible for drafting sampling clauses in specifications.

9·153 A manufacturer has to meet a specification which lays down that 200 articles shall be drawn at random from the lot, or consignment, and that the lot shall be rejected if there are more than 3 defective articles in the sample. He wants to be sure that not more than 10% of the lots he submits shall be rejected. Assuming that he can manufacture under controlled conditions, to what level must he reduce his Process Average (= average percentage defective)?

A lot will be rejected if $a = 4$ or more. The observed proportion defective when $a = 4$ and $n = 200$ is $p = 4/200 = 0·02$. The lower confidence limit for $\mu = np$ is found from the table against $a = 4$, under $P = 0·1$. It is hardly necessary to interpolate for p: when the observed proportion is very small it will be sufficient to read from the bottom line corresponding to $p = 0$, giving the value 1·74. Hence the process average must not be permitted to exceed $\mathfrak{p} = 1·74/200 = 0·87\%$ defective.

9·154 Discuss the protection given to the consumer by the specification of the above example.

The upper $P = 0·1$ limit corresponding to $a = 3$, $p = 0$, is 6·68. Hence even if the percentage defective in a lot were as high as 3·34%, the consumer would still run a one-in-ten risk of accepting it.

The Poisson distribution

9·2 When the n of the binomial distribution is very large and the $\mathfrak{p}$ very small, the terms of the binomial, from the last backwards, tend to the values:

$$e^{-\mu}, \ e^{-\mu}\mu, \ e^{-\mu}\mu^2/2!, \ e^{-\mu}\mu^3/3!, \ e^{-\mu}\mu^4/4!, \ . \ . \ .$$

the general term being

$$e^{-\mu}\mu^a/a!$$

where $\mu = n\mathfrak{p}$,

$e =$ base of natural logarithms.

These are the probabilities that the event will happen respectively 0, 1, 2, 3, 4, . . . times, and the general term is the probability that it will happen a times. This distribution is known as the Poisson Distribution.

The mean and variance of the Poisson distribution can be found from those of the binomial distribution by putting $n\mathfrak{p} = \mu$ and letting $\mathfrak{p}$ tend to zero and $\mathfrak{q}$ to unity:

$$\text{Mean} \quad = n\mathfrak{p} \qquad = \mu$$
$$\text{Variance} = n\mathfrak{p}\mathfrak{q} \to n\mathfrak{p} = \mu$$

The parameter μ therefore represents both the mean and the variance of the distribution.

The Poisson distribution may be considered as a convenient approximation to the binomial distribution when n is very large compared with a. We were in effect using the Poisson distribution in the examples of §§ **9·153** and **9·154**, when we read the limits of expectation appropriate to $p = 0$. It is also the distribution which will be followed if the events are independent and there is no absolute upper limit to a, or at least if the upper limit is obviously very large though not exactly known. The following example will illustrate this.

Example: Density of particles in a dusty gas

9·21 In using an ultramicroscope to count the number of suspended particles in a dusty gas, it is obviously impossible to count more than a few at a time, because they are in motion. The device is adopted of illuminating the field of the microscope by a flash of light and adjusting the volume of the field so that only a very few particles are seen simultaneously. By making a sufficiently large number of counts, in successive flashes of light, it is possible to determine the average number in the field, and hence the number per cubic centimetre, to any desired degree of accuracy.

The data in Table 9·3 show the number of occasions on which the number of visible particles equalled 0, 1, 2, 3, . . . out of a total of 143 occasions.*

Table 9·3

FREQUENCIES OF 0, 1, 2, 3, . . . PARTICLES

Number of Particles Seen in Field	Number of Occasions	Total Number of Particles Seen	Expected Number of Occasions
0	34	0	34·10
1	46	46	48·88
2	38	76	35·04
3	19	57	16·74
4	4	16	6·00
5	2	10	1·72
> 5	0	0	0·51
Total ..	143	205	142·99

* Data kindly supplied by Mr. E. H. M. Badger, Gas Light and Coke Company.

It can be understood why the conditions of the experiment are such as to make it likely that the distribution will follow the Poisson law. The total number n of particles in the gas is many millions. The probability $\mathfrak{p}$ that any particular particle will be in the field at a given instant is exceedingly small, but with so many particles available we shall expect to see a few. The total number of particles seen is 205, and the mean number per occasion is therefore $205/143 = 1·4336$.

Using this as our estimate of μ, we find that the probabilities that the field will contain $0, 1, 2, 3, \ldots$ particles are given by:

$$e^{-1·4336} = 0·23845$$
$$e^{-1·4336}(1·4336) = 0·34184$$
$$e^{-1·4336}(1·4336)^2/2 = 0·24503, \text{ etc.}$$

The expected number of occasions (out of 143) on which the field should contain $0, 1, 2, 3, \ldots$ particles is found by multiplying these probabilities by 143, and is given in the last column of Table 9·3. It is seen that the observed frequencies follow the expectations given by the Poisson law rather closely.

The variance* of the number of particles on one occasion is μ. The variance of the mean number on 143 occasions is therefore $\mu/143$. To obtain an estimate of the variance we insert the estimate of μ, giving:

$$1·4336/143 = 0·010025$$

The standard deviation of the estimate of μ $(= 1·4336)$ is therefore $\sqrt{0·010025} = 0·1001$.

To find the number of particles per cubic centimetre, we must divide by the volume of the illuminated field. The standard deviation of the number of particles per cubic centimetre will of course be found by dividing the above standard deviation by the same factor. Alternatively we may note that the coefficient of variation is $0·1001/1·4336 = 7·0\%$.

Using the one-in-forty limits, i.e. the 95% confidence limits corresponding to $1·96$ standard deviations, we may therefore say that it is reasonably certain that the result will be correct to within $\pm 14\%$.

---

* The variance of the distribution may also be estimated from the sum of the squares of the observations according to the method of Appendix 3C. The estimate of variance is found to be $1·3318$. This is a little smaller than the mean $(1·4336)$, but the difference is not significant. When the variance estimated in this way differs significantly from the mean one must abandon the hypothesis that the distribution follows the Poisson law. An estimated variance significantly too small might be due to a tendency to miss some particles when the number seen is large: an excessive estimated variance would usually indicate lack of uniformity in the dust-gas mixture. In either case the experimental technique is at fault. When the technique is satisfactory, it is better to use the mean as the estimate of variance than to estimate the latter from the sum of squares.

The χ^2 distribution

9·3 In the succeeding examples use will be made of a criterion which has not yet been mentioned specifically. It will now be defined.

Let a sample of ϕ quantities, u_1, u_2, . . . , u_ϕ, be drawn at random from a Normal Universe with zero mean and unit standard deviation. Then χ^2 is the sum of squares of these ϕ quantities:

$$\chi^2 = u_1{}^2 + u_2{}^2 + \ldots + u_\phi{}^2$$

If we continue drawing samples, each of ϕ quantities, from the same Universe, we can build up the distribution of the resulting values of χ^2 in the form of a histogram. As the number of samples tends to infinity, the histogram tends to a smooth distribution, which is called the χ^2-distribution. Clearly the form of the distribution depends on ϕ, which is referred to as the Number of Degrees of Freedom.

The table of χ^2 (Table B) shows the values of χ^2 corresponding to various levels of significance and to values of ϕ from 1 to 30. An approximate formula is given for values of ϕ exceeding 30. Thus for $\phi = 8$ and level of significance $P = 0·01$ the table gives $\chi^2 = 20·1$. This means that the probability that a χ^2 with 8 degrees of freedom will exceed 20·1 is just one in a hundred.

It is of interest to note that χ^2 is related to the bottom row of the table of F (Table D), where the number of degrees of freedom of the second estimate of variance is infinite. F is in fact χ^2 divided by the number of degrees of freedom. Thus from the table of F, for $P = 0·01$, $\phi_1 = 8$, $\phi_2 = \infty$, we obtain $F = 2·51$, which is the result of dividing 20·1 by 8.

When there is only one degree of freedom, χ^2 is simply the square of a Normal deviate with mean zero and standard deviation unity. Thus the values of χ^2 in the top line of the table are simply the squares of the Normal deviates for the same levels of significance:

$$\chi^2 = 1·96^2 = 3·84 \text{ for } P = 0·05, \text{ etc.}$$

Two useful properties of χ^2 follow directly from its definition. The first is that the sum of a χ^2 with ϕ_1 degrees of freedom and a χ^2 with ϕ_2 degrees of freedom is a χ^2 with $\phi_1 + \phi_2$ degrees of freedom. The second is that ϕ is the average or expected value of a χ^2 with ϕ degrees of freedom.

Single classification: More than two classes

Equal expectations

9·41 The data below show the number of times piston rings failed on each of four steam-driven compressors during a period of some years.

Assuming, as was approximately the case, that the compressors were used equally, we shall want to know if we can draw the conclusion that there are real differences between them in respect of piston-ring failure—whether, for

Table 9·4

FAILURE OF PISTON RINGS ON STEAM-DRIVEN COMPRESSORS

Compressor No. ...	1	2	3	4	Total
Failures	46	33	38	49	166

example, the fact that compressor No. 2 had the smallest number of failures really means that there is something about this machine which reduces the probability of failure, or whether, on the contrary, the differences between these numbers can reasonably be ascribed to chance.

If all four compressors are identical and subject to identical treatment, the probability that the next failure will be on No. 1 (or on any one of the four compressors) is $p = 0·25$. The expected number of failures on No. 1 compressor out of a total of $n = 166$ is therefore $np = 166 \times 0·25 = 41·50$, and of course this is also the expected number of failures on any other compressor.

Here, as before, the "expected number" is a mathematical concept—there cannot be 0·5 of a failure. The total of 166 cannot be distributed more equally between the four machines than 42 : 42 : 41 : 41, in some order. The question to be answered is: "Do the data deviate from equal numbers sufficiently to cause us to reject the hypothesis that the machines are behaving identically, and to admit the alternative hypothesis that there are real differences?"

The criterion used to measure and to test the significance of the deviations from expectation is:

$$\chi^2 = \Sigma \frac{(\text{Deviation})^2}{\text{Expectation}}$$

The computation of χ^2 may be set out as in Table 9·41.

Table 9·41

CALCULATION OF χ^2: EQUAL EXPECTATIONS

Compressor No. ..	1	2	3	4	Total
Failures observed ..	46	33	38	49	166
Failures expected ..	41·50	41·50	41·50	41·50	166·00
Deviation	+ 4·50	− 8·50	− 3·50	+ 7·50	0·00
(Deviation)^2	0·488	1·741	0·295	1·355	3·879
Expected value					

$$\chi^2 = 3·879$$

Notice that if the deviations are recorded with sign, they are checked by adding to zero.

It is apparent from the way of calculating χ^2 that it is a general measure of deviation from expected values, being large when the deviations are large. Moreover it can be shown that if the expectations are not too small in number (say not less than five) the quantity just calculated is distributed, to a very close approximation, like the χ^2 defined in § **9·3**. To judge the significance, it is therefore only necessary to refer to the χ^2 table, and see if the calculated χ^2 is larger than the value tabulated for the 0·05 or 0·01 level of significance.

To enter the table one needs to know ϕ, the number of degrees of freedom. This is always the number of *independent* deviations. Although there are four deviations, the method of calculation implies that their total is identically zero. Hence there are only three independent deviations, since when any three are known the fourth can be determined. The number of degrees of freedom is accordingly $\phi = 3$.

Entering the table with $\phi = 3$ and making a rough interpolation, we find that the significance of the calculated χ^2 is $P = 0·28$.

It appears that even if the probabilities of failure were equal in all four compressors, the chances of getting as large a value of χ^2 or larger are 28 in 100. There is, then, no reason for believing that the compressors differ in respect of probability of failure and there is no point in looking for explanations of the apparent differences.

Alternative method of calculating χ^2

9·411   A shorter method of calculating χ^2 is provided by the formula:

$$\chi^2 = \frac{\Sigma a^2}{n\mathfrak{p}} - n$$

$$= \frac{46^2 + 33^2 + 38^2 + 49^2}{41·50} - 166 = 3·880$$

However, the other method has the distinct advantage of showing the contributions to χ^2 made by each class. The exceptional classes are then indicated, as will be shown more clearly in the next example.

Unequal expectations

9·42   In the more general case, the expectations in the different classes are unequal. In Table 9·42 is shown another classification of the 175 accidents in an I.C.I. factory. The sections have been arranged in order of decreasing rate per hundred, although this step is not essential to the subsequent computation.

There appear to be large differences between the rates in different sections, but as the numbers in several sections are quite small it is necessary to apply a test of significance.

Table 9·42

ACCIDENTS CLASSIFIED BY SECTIONS

Section	Average Number Employed	Number of Accidents	Rate per Hundred	Expected Number	Deviation	Contribution to χ^2
Samplers ..	21	11	52·38	4·46	+ 6·54	9·59**
By-products ..	22	10	45·45	4·67	+ 5·33	6·08*
Laggers ..	18	6	33·33	3·82	+ 2·18	1·24
Fitters.. ..	103	29	28·16	21·88	+ 7·12	2·32
Fitters (Labs.)	106	26	24·53	22·51	+ 3·49	0·54
Riggers ..	21	5	23·81	4·46	+ 0·54	0·07
Refinery ..	145	33	22·76	30·80	+ 2·20	0·16
Laboratories ..	66	14	21·21	14·02	− 0·02	0·00
Conversion ..	153	29	18·95	32·49	− 3·49	0·37
Elect. and Inst.	89	8	8·99	18·90	− 10·90	6·29*
Day Gang ..	45	3	6·67	9·56	− 6·56	4·50*
U.S. plant ..	35	1	2·86	7·43	− 6·43	5·56*
Total ..	824	175		175·00	0·00	36·72
General Rate..			21·238			

$$\chi^2 = 36·72$$

The general rate for the whole works is $175/824 = 21·238$ per hundred average employed. The expected number of accidents in any section (fourth column) is simply the average number employed multiplied by the general rate ($\div$ 100), e.g. for Samplers it is:

$$21 \times 0·21238 = 4·46, \text{ etc.}$$

In the fifth column are shown the deviations from expectation, e.g. for Samplers:

$$11 - 4·46 = + 6·54$$

As a check, the sum of this column must be zero.

In the last column are shown the contributions to χ^2:

$$(\text{Deviation})^2/\text{Expectation} = 6·54^2/4·46 = 9·59, \text{ etc.}$$

The total is $\chi^2 = 36·72$

The number of degrees of freedom, as in the previous example, is one less than the number of classes:

$$\phi = 12 - 1 = 11$$

Reference to Table B shows that the probability of encountering as large a value of χ^2 or larger due to chance is less than 0·001. The differences between rates are therefore certainly significant.

In order to pick out the sections with rates which differ significantly from the general rate, we may regard each contribution as a χ^2 of one degree of freedom, to a first approximation. Clearly there is an error in this assumption, because if each contribution were a χ^2 of one degree of freedom, their sum would be a χ^2 of 12 degrees of freedom, although, as we have already noted, the sum has only 11 degrees of freedom. The effect of this assumption is therefore slightly to overestimate the significance; but this is not a serious matter, since the borderline cases can be checked by the exact method of § 9·15.

The 0·05 and 0·01 levels of χ^2 with one degree of freedom are respectively 3·84 and 6·63. Individual contributions passing these levels are marked in the table with one and two asterisks respectively. Five sections show significant deviations, of which Day Gang is the least significant.

If we exclude the five significant sections and calculate χ^2 for the remaining seven, by exactly the same process as was used for the whole twelve, we get:

$$\chi^2 = 3·29$$
$$\phi = 6$$

If we include Day Gang with these seven, we get, for testing the differences between eight sections:

$$\chi^2 = 8·65$$
$$\phi = 7$$

It was noted in § 9·3 that the expected value of χ^2 of ϕ degrees of freedom is ϕ. If Day Gang is excluded, the variation as measured by χ^2 is a little less than expected, whereas if Day Gang is included, the variation is a little more than expected, although the χ^2 still does not approach anywhere near significance. It is therefore doubtful whether Day Gang should be regarded as significantly different from the other seven non-significant sections. Of the remaining sections, it is reasonably safe to conclude that Samplers and By-products show significantly high rates and Electrical and Instrument and U.S. Plant show significantly low rates. Further investigation would therefore be directed to explaining the peculiarities of these four sections, and no time would be lost in looking for "causes" of the apparent differences between the other sections.

It will be observed that the most significant sections are not necessarily those which show greatest deviation from the general mean rate. A section rate may show a large deviation from the general rate and yet, being based on small numbers, may fail to reach significance. In the present example, Electrical and Instrument shows stronger evidence of departing from the general rate than Day Gang, although the latter has apparently the lower rate. This illustrates how the statistical investigation modifies and corrects general impressions.

It may also be noticed that χ^2 has been calculated in spite of the general rule which says that the approximation is not reliable when any expected value is less than five [§ 9·41]. This rule need not be applied too rigidly:

when there are many degrees of freedom it does not matter if a few of the expectations are a little below five; but if any doubt is felt, it is always possible to test individual comparisons by the exact method described in § 9·15.

Alternative method of calculating χ^2

9·421 The value of χ^2 may also be found by a short method which is a generalisation of § **9·411**. Multiply the number of accidents by the corresponding rate in each class, and add. This is done in a single continuous operation on the calculating machine, without writing down individual products:

$$11 \times 52\cdot38 + \ldots + 1 \times 2\cdot86 = 4,496\cdot41$$

Divide by the general rate:

$$4,496\cdot41 \div 21\cdot238 = 211\cdot72$$

Subtract total accidents: 175

Then $\chi^2 = 36\cdot72$, as before.

The disadvantage of this method is that it does not show the individual contributions to χ^2 and therefore fails to direct attention to the more significant classes.

CONTINGENCY TABLES

Example of a 4 × 3 table

9·51 The data in Table 9·51 show the numbers of time piston rings have failed in each leg (North, Centre, and South) of four compressors at an I.C.I. factory.

Table 9·51

PISTON-RING FAILURES IN FOUR COMPRESSORS

Comp. No.	Leg			Total
	North	Centre	South	
1	17	17	12	46
2	11	9	13	33
3	11	8	19	38
4	14	7	28	49
Total ..	53	41	72	166

The four compressors are apparently identical and are orientated the same way in the Compressor House. Each leg consists of two cylinders arranged vertically: the lower cylinder deals with the first stage of compression, and the upper cylinder with the second stage. The South leg is, in every case, adjacent to the drive. Since the machines are apparently identical, it is legitimate to subtotal the data vertically and to use these subtotals to decide whether one leg is generally more likely to fail than another. The horizontal subtotals would be used for comparing compressors and have, in fact, already been treated in § 9·41.

A table of frequency data which can be subtotalled in two directions is known as a Contingency Table. In particular, the example given is known as a 4 × 3 contingency table to denote that there are 4 rows × 3 columns of data.

The data should provide answers to the following questions:
 (i) How does the probability of failure differ in the different compressors?
 (ii) How does the probability of failure differ in the different legs?
 (iii) Is the answer to (ii) generally true of all the compressors, or do the different compressors behave differently?

It is evident on reflection that it is the third question which must be answered first because, if the compressors do not behave in a similar way, no general statement about compressors of this type can be valid.

Examination of the data suggests that compressors 2, 3, and 4 are similar (each has most failures in the South leg and fewest in the Centre leg), while compressor No. 1 appears to be anomalous in having fewest failures in the South leg. The statistical treatment will be directed to confirming or rejecting this impression.

In the first instance we are not concerned with whether the differences between the compressor subtotals or between the leg subtotals mean anything, but taking these subtotals as given, we ask whether there is any evidence that the proportion of failures in any leg differs significantly in the different compressors.

The proportion of failures in the North leg over all compressors is:
$$53/166$$
If the proportion of North leg failures were the same for all compressors, the expected number of failures in the North leg of No. 1 compressor would be:
$$46 \times 53/166 = 14 \cdot 687$$
The argument may be put in a slightly different way. The probability of a failure in some North leg is estimated at:
$$53/166$$
The probability of failure in some leg of No. 1 compressor is estimated at:
$$46/166$$
If these events are independent (i.e. if the compressors behave in the same way), the probability of a failure in the North leg of No. 1 is the product of these two probabilities:
$$(53/166) \times (46/166)$$

X

The expected number of failures in the North leg of No. 1 out of a total of 166 failures is therefore:

$$(53/166) \times (46/166) \times 166 = 14\cdot687, \text{ as before.}$$

In Table 9·52 are shown the expected number of failures in each leg of each compressor:

Table 9·52

EXPECTED NUMBER OF PISTON-RING FAILURES

No.	North	Centre	South	Total
1	14·687	11·361	19·952	46·000
2	10·536	8·151	14·313	33·000
3	12·133	9·386	16·482	38·001
4	15·645	12·102	21·253	49·000
Total ..	53·001	41·000	72·000	166·001

Here again the expected number is a mathematical fiction. Obviously the number of failures in the North leg of No. 1 cannot be closer to expectation than 15, and of course, because of chance fluctuations, the numbers will generally not even be as close as this. The statistical test must decide whether, on the whole, the data deviate from expectation by more than can reasonably be ascribed to chance.

The criterion χ^2 is calculated by the same method as in the earlier examples. For the first "cell" of the table we have:

Number observed	=	17
Number expected	=	14·687
Deviation from expectation	=	+ 2·313
Contribution to χ^2 = (deviation)²/expectation =		0·364

The full calculation is set out in Table 9·53. It will be noticed that the vertical and horizontal subtotals of the deviations are all zero. This provides a check.

The number of degrees of freedom is equal to the number of *independent* deviations. It is evident, from the method of computing the deviations, that not more than six of them could be assigned arbitrarily. If we know any two in the first row, we also know the third, since their sum is zero. Similarly any two in the second row will determine the third, and any two in the third row will determine the third. When the deviations in three rows are determined, so are the deviations in the fourth row, because vertical subtotals are also zero. Hence number of degrees of freedom $\phi = 6$. In general, the number of degrees of freedom for a $j \times k$ table is $(j - 1)(k - 1)$.

Table 9·53

PISTON-RING FAILURES: COMPUTATION OF χ^2

No.	North	Centre	South	Total	
1	17	17	12	46	
	14·687	11·361	19·952	46·000	
	+ 2·313	+ 5·639	− 7·952	0·000	
	0·364	2·799	3·169		6·332
2	11	9	13	33	
	10·536	8·151	14·313	33·000	
	+ 0·464	+ 0·849	− 1·313	0·000	
	0·020	0·088	0·120		0·228
3	11	8	19	38	
	12·133	9·386	16·482	38·001	
	− 1·133	− 1·386	+ 2·518	− 0·001	
	0·106	0·205	0·385		0·696
4	14	7	28	49	
	15·645	12·102	21·253	49·000	
	− 1·645	− 5·102	+ 6·747	0·000	
	0·173	2·151	2·142		4·466
Total ..	53	41	72	166	
	53·001	41·000	72·000		
	− 0·001	0·000	0·000		
	0·663	5·243	5·816		11·722

$$\chi^2 = 11·722$$

It will be found, by reference to the table of χ^2, that the 0·10 and 0·05 levels for 6 degrees of freedom are respectively 10·6 and 12·6. According to the usual convention, the χ^2 for the present example does not reach significance, although since it passes the 10% level one can admit that there is some rather weak evidence that the compressors are not all behaving alike.* The

---

* If required, the value of P measuring the significance of the result can be found with the aid of the Nomogram at the end of this book. The deviations of the calculated value of χ^2 from the tabulated values for $P = 0·10$ and 0·05 respectively are found thus:

P	= 0·10		0·05
χ^2	= 10·6	11·7	12·6
Deviations	1·1	0·9	
Deviations × 5	5½	4½	

Then on the 0·10 and 0·05 arms of the nomogram we can mark off − 5½ and + 4½ respectively, and join with a straight-edge. The intersection gives $P = 0·07$ as the probability that χ^2 will exceed 11·7.

biggest contribution to χ^2, amounting to more than half the total, comes from No. 1 compressor. If one were asking specifically whether this compressor differed from the remaining three, one would compare the data for No. 1 with the data obtained by subtotalling Nos. 2, 3, and 4, as shown in Table 9·54:

Table 9·54

PISTON-RING FAILURES: No. 1 COMPARED WITH THE REST

Comp. No.	North	Centre	South	Total
1	17	17	12	46
2 + 3 + 4	36	24	60	120
Total ..	53	41	72	166

The χ^2 for this table can be calculated by the same method as was used for the whole table. Since it is a 2×3 table, there will be $(2 - 1)(3 - 1) = 2$ degrees of freedom.

$$\chi^2 = 8{\cdot}760, \phi = 2$$

This value of χ^2 passes the 0·025 level, showing fairly conclusively that No. 1 is different. On the other hand, the differences between the remaining compressors are tested for significance by applying the χ^2 test to Table 9·55:

Table 9·55

PISTON-RING FAILURES: COMPRESSORS Nos. 2, 3, AND 4

Comp. No.	North	Centre	South	Total
2	11	9	13	33
3	11	8	19	38
4	14	7	28	49
Total ..	36	24	60	120

For this table we find:

$$\chi^2 = 3{\cdot}106, \phi = 4$$

so there is evidently not the slightest reason for believing that these three compressors are not all alike.

The conclusion that No. 1 is exceptional would have been on a firm logical foundation if the decision to compare it with the other three had been made *before examining the data*, i.e. if the comparison had been made because, for example, Nos. 2, 3, and 4 were of the same model but No. 1 of a different model. In the present case, however, the comparison was made only because it was suggested by the data themselves. As has often been pointed out, the danger of this procedure is that even when the data do not, as a whole, show significant departure from the hypothesis we are testing, we can usually discover some particular comparisons which are significant. In fact, one would expect to find that one-twentieth of all possible comparisons pass the one-in-twenty (0·05) level of significance. The present example should be contrasted with the previous example [§ **9·42**]. There the total χ^2 was indubitably significant, and one had no hesitation in picking out the classes showing significant departure from the general mean. Here the total χ^2 is not significant, although it approaches significance, and one must therefore be very cautious before claiming significance for any special comparisons suggested by the data themselves.

An interesting situation arises if a plausible explanation for the anomalous behaviour of No. 1 is advanced *after examining the data*. A strict logician would probably not admit that this could affect the issue, but it must be conceded to common sense that the evidence would be strengthened if it could be shown, *a posteriori*, that No. 1 differed from the other three in a way in which the other three did not differ among themselves.

Summarising the conclusions, we may say that there is no evidence that the proportions of failures in the three legs differ in compressors Nos. 2, 3, and 4, but that there is some evidence that the proportions in No. 1 are anomalous, and that this evidence would be correspondingly strengthened if a plausible explanation of the anomaly were found. These conclusions accord with the general impressions noted at the beginning of the discussion, but the statistical test shows that less weight should be given to the apparent anomaly of No. 1 than most investigators would probably give it if they relied solely on an inspection of the figures.

We may now turn to a consideration of the marginal subtotals. The differences between compressors have already been tested in § **9·41**. The procedure for testing the differences between legs will depend on whether we do or do not choose to accept the conclusion that No. 1 is anomalous. In the latter case we shall simply apply the method of § **9·41** to the lower marginal subtotals of Table 9·51, and find $\chi^2 = 8·831$, $\phi = 2$.

In the former case we shall use the subtotals 36 : 24 : 60, obtained by excluding No. 1, and find $\chi^2 = 16·800$, $\phi = 2$.

In either case the χ^2 is significant, so we may conclude that the probability of failure is not the same in the three legs. The second χ^2 is the more significant because the exclusion of the possibly anomalous compressor permits the differences between legs to show up more clearly on the others.

Since the three legs are clearly proved to be different, one may complete the analysis by testing comparisons between any two, by the method of

§ 9·1. It will be found that the evidence for a difference between North and Centre is very weak, but that the failure rate for South is certainly higher than for the other two.

The 2 × k contingency table

9·52 When a contingency table contains only two rows or two columns, there are a number of short methods for calculating χ^2. One such method is illustrated in [9·1], Example 11. These special methods are not exemplified here, because one may always use the general method given in the example of the 4 × 3 table above.

Three-dimensional contingency tables

9·53 Tables of frequency data may have a triple or multiple classification. Thus the full data on piston-ring failure would show a classification under four machines, three legs, and two stages (high-pressure and low-pressure) and would therefore be a 4 × 3 × 2 contingency table. Such examples may be treated by an extension of the methods already explained, which the reader should have no difficulty in making if he has understood the principles.

The 2 × 2 contingency table

9·54 The distribution of the χ^2 calculated from the data is fairly close to the χ^2 defined in § 9·3 and tabulated in the table of χ^2, provided the expected values are not too small. The working rule is that for the test of significance to be reasonably accurate no expectation should be less than five. There is however one exceptional case, the 2 × 2 table, where a mechanical application of the χ^2 test can sometimes lead to seriously misleading results.

Table 9·6 shows the number of defective and effective articles in two samples, one taken before and one after the introduction of a modification intended to improve the process of manufacture. The proportion of defective articles has clearly fallen, and it is desired to test whether this apparent decrease is significant.

Table 9·6

DEFECTIVE AND EFFECTIVE ARTICLES IN TWO SAMPLES

	Defective	Effective	Total
Before	18	162	180
After	4	96	100
Total ..	22	258	280

Calculating the deviations from expectations in the usual way, we shall find that they are all equal in magnitude, but two are positive and two negative. For the top left cell we have:

$$
\begin{aligned}
\text{Number observed} &= 18 \\
\text{Number expected} = 22 \times 180/280 &= 14\cdot143 \\
\text{Deviation from expectation} &= 3\cdot857
\end{aligned}
$$

Now the χ^2 for a 2×2 table has only one degree of freedom and is therefore simply the square of a Normal deviate. This suggests that instead of finding χ^2, an exactly equivalent test would be provided by comparing the deviation from expectation with its standard deviation. The variance of the number in any cell is given by the formula:

$$
\begin{aligned}
\text{Variance} &= \frac{\text{Product of marginal subtotals}}{\text{Grand total cubed}} \\
&= \frac{180 \times 100 \times 22 \times 258}{280^3} \\
&= 4\cdot654
\end{aligned}
$$

The standard deviation, being the square root of the variance, is therefore 2·157.

The significance of the ratio

$$
u = \frac{\text{Observed deviation}}{\text{Standard deviation}} = \frac{3\cdot857}{2\cdot157} = 1\cdot788
$$

may therefore be judged by reference to a table of the integral of the Normal curve. The ratio u is the square root of the χ^2 of one degree of freedom, which would have been found by the usual method.

When we examine the ratio, we perceive one of the reasons why this, or the equivalent χ^2 test, is not a very good approximation. The data always consist of whole numbers, and therefore when the marginal subtotals are given, the possible deviations are in steps of unity. The smallest possible deviation is $-0\cdot143$, for the table:

14	166	180
8	92	100
22	258	280

Other possible deviations belong to the sequence:

$$\ldots, -2\cdot143, -1\cdot143, -0\cdot143, +0\cdot857, +1\cdot857, +2\cdot857, +3\cdot857, \ldots$$

What we are doing is to replace a series of discrete values by a continuous distribution. On this convention a number like 3·857 really stands for a continuum of numbers from $(3\cdot857 - 0\cdot5)$ to $(3\cdot857 + 0\cdot5)$.

Since the probability P, which measures significance, is supposed to tell us the probability of getting a deviation *as big as* or bigger than the one observed, we expect to get a closer approximation if in calculating the ratio we use a deviation just half a unit smaller than the one observed. Thus:

$$u = (3{\cdot}857 - 0{\cdot}5)/2{\cdot}157 = 3{\cdot}357/2{\cdot}157 = 1{\cdot}556$$

From the table of the Normal integral (Table A) we find that this corresponds to a probability of $P = 0{\cdot}06$. This is the probability of finding a deviation as large as the one actually observed, or larger, in the direction *favourable to the second sample*. If we are sure that the modification cannot make matters worse, and are merely asking whether it effects an improvement, this is the appropriate measure of significance. If however we were asking whether the proportions defective were different in the two samples, we should have to take into account the possibility of a deviation in the opposite direction, and accordingly assess the significance as:

$$P = 2 \times 0{\cdot}06 = 0{\cdot}12$$

It may be noted that this is the level of significance obtained if we calculate χ^2 after diminishing each deviation by half a unit: χ^2, being a square, cannot distinguish between deviations in the two directions. The conclusion is that there is some weak evidence that the modification has effected an improvement, but that the evidence is not strong enough for us to regard the question as settled beyond reasonable doubt.

The exact test of the 2 × 2 table

9·541 The significance of a 2×2 contingency table may be determined exactly by a treatment given in [9·1], § 21·02. Applying this method to the example above, we find:

$$P = 0{\cdot}0554$$

Without applying the correction of half a unit, we should find the significance, corresponding to $u = 1{\cdot}788$, to be $P = 0{\cdot}037$. With the correction, the significance, as we have seen, is $P = 0{\cdot}060$. It is evident that the correction improves the approximation, although in the present example it overcorrects.

The exact probabilities are given in [9·2], Table 38, for marginal numbers up to 15; in other cases the exact treatment may involve some lengthy calculations, and a third method, which is quite accurate, is available [9·3], Table VIII.

However, in the vast majority of cases encountered in chemical and industrial research, the approximate method, *with the correction of half a unit*, gives a sufficiently accurate measure of significance. The only case where one may be in doubt is where one expectation is rather small and *both* margins are very unbalanced (i.e. one subtotal is more than three times the other in both margins). An example of such a table is:

10	50	60
20	220	240
30	270	300

Even here one does not have to worry if, by the simple method, the result is strongly significant or not at all significant: it is only in borderline cases that one might prefer to recalculate the significance by one of the more exact methods cited above.

The continuity correction applied to other cases

9·542 The device of subtracting 0·5 from the deviation—the so-called Correction for Continuity—may be used in all cases where there is only one degree of freedom. It could, for instance, have been used in the example of the binomial distribution [§ **9·12**]: the deviation would be taken as 3·74 instead of 4·24. The only reason why it was not introduced at that point in the discussion is that when $a < 15$, an exact test of significance is available by the use of Table F, while for large values of a the effect of the correction becomes progressively less important.

Notice that continuity corrections are *never* applied in the general case where there is more than one degree of freedom.

General considerations on frequency data

9·6 In conclusion, it is worth while to emphasise that although valid conclusions can always be drawn from frequency data by applying the correct tests of significance, yet the results of these tests are generally of a low order of accuracy. It is usually better to avoid having to present the data as a contingency table if there is any reasonable alternative. Two examples will make this clear.

9·61 If we use, in measuring a machine-made article, gauges set to upper and lower tolerances, we can classify the members of a sample into three classes—undersize, within tolerance, and oversize. Comparing samples from, say, six different machines, we may therefore present the results in a 6 × 3 contingency table. However, more precise comparisons can be made if we have the actual measurements and use the methods described in Chapter 6. Admittedly, in practice this higher precision may be offset by the fact that direct measurement takes more time than applying "go" and "not-go" gauges, but if this consideration is advanced, a statistician should be consulted so that the relative costs per unit of information can be determined.

9·62 In some cases, one classification of the contingency table may be on a qualitative scale. Thus we may be subjecting test-pieces to rough treatment and classifying them at the end of the test (preferably by comparison with a scale of examples) into undamaged, slightly damaged, damaged, very badly damaged, and completely disintegrated, respectively. Instead of using contingency table methods, it will often be found more profitable simply to score these five grades as 0, 1, 2, 3, and 4, and to treat the data by Analysis of Variance as though the score x were a continuous measurement. It is perhaps rather surprising that the Analysis of Variance can be employed on data which depart so violently from the Normal distribution, but it is a fact that the methods remain very nearly correct provided we have suitably chosen our qualitative scale, i.e. provided there is not a large excess of test-pieces at either end of the scale.

REFERENCES

[9·1] FISHER, R. A. *Statistical Methods for Research Workers* (twelfth edition). Oliver and Boyd (Edinburgh and London, 1954).

[9·2] PEARSON, E. S., and HARTLEY, H. O. *Biometrika Tables for Statisticians*, Vol. 1. Cambridge University Press, 1954.

[9·3] FISHER, R. A., and YATES, F. *Statistical Tables for Biological, Agricultural and Medical Research* (fifth edition). Oliver and Boyd (Edinburgh and London, 1957).

CHAPTER 10

CONTROL CHARTS*

QUALITY control charts are graphs on which the quality of the
product is plotted as manufacture is actually proceeding. By
allowing corrective action to be taken at the earliest possible
moment the charts help to ensure the manufacture of a uniform
product which complies with specification.

Introduction

10·1 Control charts are a very useful statistical tool for analysing data
obtained during production or research investigations on a plant where a large
number of individual readings (say 50 or more) may be obtained. The subject
known as Quality Control is simply the use of control charts as part of a continuous inspection system where readings are plotted on charts as manufacture
proceeds. It must be emphasised, however, that control charts may be used
for statistical analysis of data in many types of problems and are not confined
to the use normally associated with Quality Control.

A control chart is a chart on which the values of the quality characteristic
being analysed are plotted in sequence. The chart consists of a central line
and two pairs of limit lines spaced above and below the central line. These
are usually termed the Inner and Outer Control Limits. The distribution
of the plotted values in relation to the control limits provides valuable
statistical information on the quality characteristic being studied.

The control chart may take a variety of different forms; what is suitable
for one process may not be suitable for another, and a detailed knowledge of
the process is required before successful application of control charts can be
made. By and large, each process has to be dealt with on its own merits, but
there are a number of common elements and principles that govern the
construction and application of control charts. This chapter will be concerned mainly with the basic principles; the detailed explanations and the
examples are confined to the control of the average quality and the variability
of a process where the criterion of quality is a continuous measure. This is
usually referred to as "the control of variables," and it represents the most
common application in the chemical industry. Other applications are mentioned in § **10·6**, and detailed accounts of these will be found in the references
cited.

---

* This chapter employs the notation which is becoming standardised in Quality
Control work and differs in minor respects from the notation employed in the
other chapters.

General purpose of control charts

10·2 A set of data obtained under plant research or production conditions usually consists of measurements of a quality characteristic such as weight, a dimension, moisture content, concentration, etc. Control charts enable one to test whether a set of data is statistically uniform or statistically controlled, i.e. whether the data are consistent with the hypothesis that they are random values from the same Universe or whether changes in level and variability have taken place. Variation in the values of the quality characteristic under examination is bound to occur. If this variation arises solely from a constant system of chance causes, then the data are said to be Statistically Uniform or Homogeneous and the variation is said to be Statistically Controlled: in other words, the data belong to the same Universe. If the variation is and remains statistically controlled, valid predictions may be made about further data from the same source, and further statistical tests may be safely carried out. Deductions may also be made with the knowledge that conclusions drawn will apply to future data. Such assurance is invaluable in deciding whether the values of the quality characteristic will comply with a specification which may have been laid down, or in helping to determine the extent of the variation which may be expected from the process. The magnitude of this variation may decide that action should be taken to reduce it. In an experiment the lack of statistical uniformity in the readings may seriously limit the conclusions which may be drawn from the results.

Types of variation

10·3 The variation which arises in the values of a quality characteristic may be considered as being due to causes of two main kinds:

(i) *Chance causes*. These are innumerable causes, each of which exercises a small effect on the total variation. They are permissible variations which cannot be identified, either because of lack of knowledge or because such identification would be uneconomic. They are inherent in the production system and cannot be reduced or eliminated without modification in the system itself. Examples of chance causes are small variations in reaction conditions, small variations in quality of raw materials, etc.

(ii) *Assignable causes*. These are causes which can be identified and which it is usually economically worth while to discover and eliminate. They arise from sudden or abnormal variation in properties of raw materials or reaction conditions or from mechanical faults. In a manufacturing process they cause difficulties during production and interfere with smooth running. When they are present on a plant, the plant is not operating as efficiently as it might. Assignable causes of variation may operate during a laboratory experiment or test as well as on a plant and may vitiate the results accordingly.

The two terms are only relative, and chance causes may be assigned with the acquisition of more knowledge. The purpose of control charts is to test when variation ceases to arise solely from a constant system of chance causes and when assignable causes intervene. If assignable causes of variation can be shown to be present in a set of data which is being analysed, the data are not statistically uniform and their value so far as drawing conclusions is concerned is restricted. Further statistical analysis of the data should be undertaken with care. The indication of the presence of assignable causes may, however, be valuable as a first step in an investigation to improve a process, a method of analysis, etc.

In research work in the laboratory, where conditions are carefully controlled, it may usually be assumed that no assignable causes of variation have intervened during the experiments. Such an assumption, however, cannot safely be made in regard to data obtained under plant conditions, whether the data are part of a research investigation or a production investigation. Even under laboratory conditions much will depend on the class of work being done, and the investigator himself will have to decide whether he is justified in treating his data as statistically uniform. If he has enough results he can easily check the point by means of control charts or he can apply the more sensitive tests described in Chapter 6. The latter technique may be used when the results are too few for control-chart analysis.

Analysis of data by control charts

10·4 In the analysis of data by control charts, as in many other statistical techniques, a hypothesis is first postulated and then tested. The hypothesis to be tested in this case is that the data are statistically uniform and that a constant system of chance causes only is responsible for variation. If this is so, the data must comply with certain statistical requirements. If they do comply, there is no reason to believe that the data are not statistically uniform. If they do not comply, the hypothesis is disproved and assignable causes of variation are present. The data cannot then be regarded as having been drawn at random from the same Universe, and further statistical deductions must be undertaken with caution.

The procedure to be followed in analysing data by means of control charts is set out more fully later and illustrated by the use of an example in Appendix 10A. It is also given in several publications on the subject [10·1]–[10·6]. The main steps to be taken are briefly as follows. Fuller details are given when dealing with control charts for production control, usually termed Quality Control.

10·41 Set out the individual readings in the order in which they were obtained and divide them into a number of Rational Sub-groups or samples.

Rational sub-groups are groups *within* which there is reason to believe that only chance causes of variation have operated but *between* which assignable causes may have operated. Thus a sub-group may be the results obtained on one batch of raw material. Data from different plants, machines, or experiments could clearly not be combined to form a rational sub-group. If a group of 100 readings were available and there were no clear indication from the process as to how the rational sub-groups should be taken, a convenient division would be into 20 sub-groups or samples each containing 5 readings. This sample size is convenient to handle and sufficiently large for most purposes. The 100 readings need not all be consecutive. It is often convenient during a manufacturing process to take readings in groups of 5, the groups being taken at frequent intervals.

10·42   From the data estimate the process average and the standard deviation, which measures the inherent variation of the process. The best estimate of this standard deviation is obtained from the variance within samples as described in Chapter 3. If the samples contain less than 12 individuals, the average sample range may be used to provide an estimate of the Universe standard deviation [10·7] and [10·8].

10·43   Construct one control chart for sample averages and another for sample ranges. Plot these values for the samples. If no points fall outside the outer control limits there is no reason to think that the data are not statistically uniform, i.e. no assignable causes of variation have intervened during the acquisition of the data. Predictions may then be safely made about the data, and other statistical techniques such as tests of significance may be employed and deductions drawn.

Control charts for process control
10·5   This use of control charts is now widely known under the title of Quality Control. Control charts, when used as part of a process-testing system, provide a continuous graphical record of the quality characteristic being charted. The results of measurements are recorded in the order in which they are obtained and as soon as they are obtained. Samples consisting of groups of say 5 consecutive readings are taken from the production system not at random but in a purposive order, viz. the order of production. Control charts then test whether the samples meet the criteria associated with samples drawn at random from the same Universe. If they do, then clearly the order of taking the samples did not affect the sampling results and the product did not appear to change with time. Therefore there is reason for believing that the production system is in a state of statistical control. The charts simply show whether the data are statistically uniform or not. They may be uniform and at the same time show very wide variation which may

make them of little value. It must not therefore be assumed that because statistical uniformity has been established the data are satisfactory in all other respects.

Control charts are most easily applied where measurements may be made on discrete units taken from the producing system. This is the reason why they have been widely used in light engineering work for inspecting the output of machine-tool processes. In the chemical industry the procedure is not usually so straightforward. Sampling problems are more complex, and the method and frequency of sampling may have to be carefully investigated before control charts can be introduced. Batch processes are frequently employed for the manufacture of bulk chemicals, and in such processes every batch is sampled and tested. A batch may take only a few hours or several days to manufacture, and frequently analytical tests on a batch to assess its quality take a long time. It follows that charts for batch processes are more suitable for long-term control and less suitable for day-to-day or hour-to-hour control as in highly repetitive or continuous processes.

A chart consisting of the individual batch results is usually required, and in many cases this is sufficient. Charts of averages and ranges of consecutive groups of 4 or 5 batches are useful additions for the more established manufactures.

The main purposes of control charts for batch processes are:

(a) To give a clear picture of the performance of the process.

(b) To indicate whether the process is under control and, if not under control, to indicate the extent of the departure from control.

(c) To indicate what the process is capable of doing if operated under conditions of statistical control.

Most chemical processes at some stage involve filling, packing, and weighing operations. For these operations control charts are ideally suited, and it is thought that their introduction to many weighing operations would be well worth while, especially as a first step on plants where they have not previously been used.

A valuable application is in the testing of raw materials, where the charts can be used to provide evidence of the variation in quality of the materials being supplied [10·9]. From these charts compliance with specification may be judged, and it may be ascertained whether the supplier can produce to limits close enough to ensure that practically all his raw material conforms to specification. Furthermore, control charts enable raw materials from various suppliers to be compared and the most uniform source selected for future purchases. The use of charts to check raw materials may enable a customer to draw a distinction between variation which arises from his production process and that introduced by defective raw materials, and "trouble-hunting" may be reduced in consequence. Control charts are primarily producers' tools, however, and suppliers of raw materials should be encouraged to use control charts themselves, if these can be applied to the processes they employ.

Taking of samples

10·51   The principles of sampling are discussed in detail in Chapter 11. For processes where individuals may be selected, e.g. bags or containers for control of weight, it is sufficient to take say 5 individuals in sequence from a conveyor. Samples should not be taken at absolutely regular intervals in case there is some assignable cause of variation operating with a periodicity which coincides with the interval between the taking of successive samples. The proportion to be sampled will depend on the degree of control shown and on the factors dealt with in Chapter 11.

Construction of control charts

10·52   The same procedure briefly outlined in § **10·41** is followed when constructing charts for process control, but the subject will be dealt with more fully here. Order is of the greatest importance, and results must be analysed and plotted in the order in which they are obtained. It is also important to take measurements at that point in the process at which any action consequent on points falling outside the control limits would rectify the trouble in the shortest possible time.

Variation in a given quality characteristic is bound to occur, and hence it is not sufficient only to specify the average value. Some measure of the dispersion about this average is necessary if the uniformity of the characteristic is to be studied. As has been pointed out in Chapter 3, the standard deviation is the best measure of dispersion, and the average value and the standard deviation provide a great deal of information about the quality characteristic in question: in fact, if the distribution of the individual values is Normal, they define it fully.

Estimation of a Universe average $\bar{X}$, and Universe standard deviation σ

10·521   Unless the Universe average and standard deviation have been defined in a specification or are known from previous experience, it is necessary as a first step to obtain sufficient readings to enable good estimates of these parameters to be made. We require an estimate of the standard deviation which measures the inherent variation of the producing system, and 50–100 readings should be suitable for this purpose. Divide the readings into rational sub-groups or samples, each containing 4–6 readings, bearing in mind the points made in § **10·41**.

   (*i*)   *Universe average* ($\bar{X}$)

      The estimate is simply the arithmetic mean of the 50–100 individual readings.

(*ii*) *Universe standard deviation* (σ)

This may be estimated by any of the following methods:

(*a*) Variance within samples.

(*b*) The average sample standard deviation $\bar{s}$.

(*c*) The average sample range $\bar{w}$.

Method (*a*) gives σ direct and provides the most accurate estimate. Methods (*b*) and (*c*) require the use of tables given at the end of this Handbook and in [10·1]. If the sample size is less than 12, the value of σ can be estimated quite accurately from the average sample range $\bar{w}$, i.e. by Method (*c*), provided the number of samples is greater than 10. In this chapter, therefore, the use of $\bar{w}$ only is illustrated. By the use of sample range the arithmetic is reduced and all calculations are made extremely simple.

Drawing limit lines

10·522 In order to obtain the maximum amount of information from the charts, two should be plotted, one on which the sample averages $\bar{x}$ are recorded and the other on which sample ranges w are recorded.

(*i*) *Chart for sample averages*

The drawing of the limit lines for sample averages is based on the following principles. It has been shown in Chapter 3 that if individual observations from the same Universe are distributed round the Universe average $\bar{X}$ with a standard deviation of σ, then the averages of samples, each containing n individuals drawn at random from that Universe, are distributed round $\bar{X}$ with a standard deviation of $\sigma/\sqrt{n}$. If the distribution of individuals is Normal, the distribution of sample averages is also Normal. If the distribution of the individuals is not Normal, the distribution of sample averages approaches Normality as n increases. Even when n is as small as 4 or 5, provided the distribution of the individuals is not extremely asymmetrical, the distribution of the sample averages will be closely Normal.

Thus it will be seen that by taking averages of samples of n individuals instead of the individuals themselves, the probabilities associated with the Normal distribution curve may be used. These have been fully worked out, and provided always the data belong to the same Universe, i.e. are statistically uniform or controlled, only 1 sample mean in 40 will on the average lie above the limit $\bar{X} + 1{\cdot}96\sigma/\sqrt{n}$ and 1 in 40 below the limit $\bar{X} - 1{\cdot}96\sigma/\sqrt{n}$, that is 1 in 20 will lie outside the limits $\bar{X} \pm 1{\cdot}96\sigma/\sqrt{n}$. These limits are referred to as the 1 in 40 or 0·025 limits. Further only 1 sample mean in 1,000 will lie above the limit $\bar{X} + 3{\cdot}09\sigma/\sqrt{n}$ and 1 in 1,000 below the limit $\bar{X} - 3{\cdot}09\sigma/\sqrt{n}$, i.e. 1 in 500 outside $\bar{X} \pm 3{\cdot}09\sigma/\sqrt{n}$. These limits are known as the 1 in 1,000 or 0·001 limits. Lines drawn at a

U

distance of $1·96\sigma/\sqrt{n}$ above and below $\bar{X}$ provide the Inner Control Limits. Lines drawn at a distance of $3·09\sigma/\sqrt{n}$ above and below $\bar{X}$ provide the Outer Control Limits. Table G at the end of the volume enables limit lines to be drawn for various values of n.

Since with statistical control only 1 sample mean in 20, on average, lies outside the inner control limits, the occurrence of a point outside these limits may be regarded as a warning of possible lack of statistical control, i.e. that an assignable cause of variation has intervened. A point outside the outer control limits is very strong evidence of lack of statistical control and calls for action to discover the assignable cause of variation and eliminate it.

B.S. 600R: 1942 [10·1] recommends the use of both sets of limit lines, whereas B.S. 1008 [10·2] (which deals with American practice) refers to outer control limits only, spaced symmetrically above and below $\bar{X}$ at a distance of $3\sigma/\sqrt{n}$. These limits are, of course, almost identical with the outer control limits of British practice. It is relevant to point out that the choice of these outer control limits to indicate a variation which should not be allowed to pass is justified on the grounds that practical experience has shown that the presence of a point outside them is a very useful guide to action. When points have fallen outside them trouble has been experienced and detected on investigation, and its elimination has proved economically worth while. The fact that control limits correspond to definite probabilities derived from the Normal distribution curve may be of value when interpreting the charts, but too much attention should not be paid to the precise probability values associated with the particular multiple of the standard deviation adopted. This is especially so for sample ranges, to which reference is made below.

Experience may show that for some processes the outer control limits or Action Limits should be spaced at a distance of less than $3·09\sigma/\sqrt{n}$ from $\bar{X}$, and this will have to be left to the judgment of the user of the charts. In batch processes in the manufacture of dyestuffs, for example, it has been found more convenient to use 1 in 400 outer control limits, i.e. lines spaced at $2·81\sigma/\sqrt{n}$ from $\bar{X}$. The inner control limits are as above, viz. 1 in 40.

The foregoing remarks have dealt with the general case, but if the sample size is less than 12 the control limits can be calculated direct from $\bar{w}$ by the use of Table G.

(ii) *Chart for sample ranges*

Tables G·1 and G·2 for drawing limit lines for sample ranges have been drawn up on the assumption that the distribution of the individual observations is approximately Normal. Experience in practice has shown that the assumption of Normal distribution of individuals and the use of the limit lines recommended in [10·1] are justified when considering sample ranges and enable the dispersion within a sample to be studied and controlled. If the distribution of individuals is not Normal, the probabilities associated with multiples of the standard deviation of the range will differ from those on which Tables **G·1** and **G·2** are based, but this will not invalidate the use of the outer control limits as action limits.

As before, provided $\bar{w}$ enables a good estimate of σ to be obtained, the limits may be calculated direct from $\bar{w}$ by the use of Table **G·2**.

Plotting the points

10·523 After the limit lines have been drawn, the points for the samples which have been used to derive $\bar{X}$ and σ may be plotted. It is advisable to plot both charts on one piece of paper, with one chart under the other, and to cover as long a period of time as possible to show up trends. The points for sample averages may be distinguished from sample ranges by using dots for the former and circles for the latter. It may well happen that the points show lack of statistical control for either or both the charts, with one or more points outside the outer control limits. This shows that assignable causes of variation have intervened during the acquisition of the initial data. Any sample which shows lack of control in relation to sample range should be discarded if it is desired to know the inherent variation of the process, and the value of σ should be recalculated. It is, of course, advisable to try to locate and eliminate the cause of the trouble which led to the sample value being out of control. New control lines should be drawn and the procedure repeated until all the remaining points come within the control limits on the ranges chart. Whether a sample showing an average value out of control with its range under control is discarded or not will depend on the purpose for which the chart is being used. If no specification exists for the process and it is desired to know the best that can be expected, samples showing lack of control on sample averages would also be discarded. If an average has been specified for the process, the calculated limit lines could be drawn round the specified average without reference to the average $\bar{X}$ achieved during the trial period.

If the points derived in the trial period or from past production data show a state of statistical control, the charts can be put into use and test results for the process recorded as they come along. Provided the points lie within the inner control limits, production is statistically controlled and the product is as uniform as the process is capable of making it. Points outside the inner control limits are regarded as a warning that assignable causes of variation may be present, and a further sample should be taken to see whether the

warning is confirmed. Points outside the outer control limits should be
regarded as justifying action to find the assignable cause and to eliminate it.

Interpretation of control charts

10·53 Lack of control as exhibited by the two control charts may be
interpreted by reference to Figures 10·1–10·3. Figure 10·1 shows two
distribution curves with different Universe averages, $\bar{X}_1$ and $\bar{X}_2$, but the same
standard deviation, $\sigma_1 = \sigma_2$.

The distribution curves are of the same shape, but No. 2 is displaced to the
right of No. 1—in other words, the average has shifted. This state of affairs
would be reflected in the control charts by the sample averages being out of
control while the sample ranges were under control. This is a common occurrence in practice, and means that the system is inherently capable of operating
under control but that some factor or factors have caused the average to shift.
A mechanical example would be a control chart for a weighing machine where
the sample average shifted owing to material sticking in the pan.

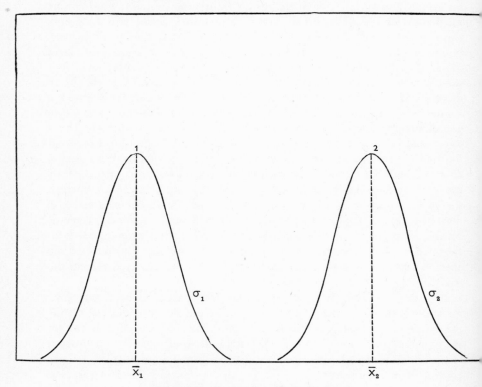

Fig. 10·1. Lack of control of averages

Figure 10·2 corresponds to the condition of lack of control on the chart for ranges while sample averages are under control. This is a more fundamental lack of control and suggests something inherently wrong with the system. A mechanical example would be that no sticking was occurring in the weighing-machine pan but bearings were loose or knife-edge movement was taking place. In practice the conditions suggested by Figure 10·2 would probably result in a state of affairs present in Figure 10·3. Figure 10·3 corresponds to the conditions of lack of control for sample averages and sample ranges, and might correspond in the above example to both sticking of material and worn machine parts. These illustrations represent a special case, and in general, lack of control may imply many Universes.

When examining the range chart for lack of control, too much attention should not be paid to points outside the lower limits unless an investigation is in hand to determine the conditions under which some samples were more uniform than others. For routine work the lower limits may be omitted entirely.

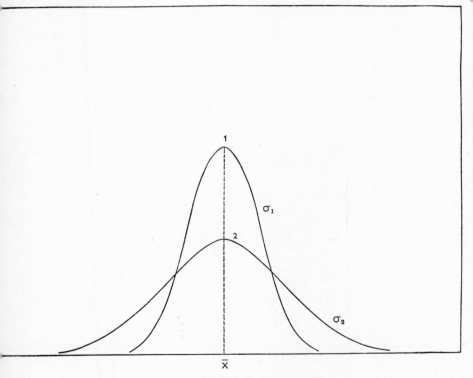

Fig. 10·2. Lack of control of ranges

The two charts should be examined together if it is hoped to form an opinion of the kind of trouble to look for when lack of statistical control is evident. Experience in repetitive processes, such as machine-tool production, filling of containers, weighing of bags, etc., has shown that if sample averages are statistically uncontrolled while sample ranges are under control, as in Figure 10·1, there is evidence of setting errors, faulty operation, or tool wear. The implication is that the producing system is inherently capable of statistically controlled operation within certain limits about the desired average but some external factor or factors are causing the average to shift. If ranges are out of control as well as sample averages, as shown in Figure 10·3, it would suggest more fundamental trouble such as worn or loose mechanical parts.

It is unlikely in chemical processes that such a clear distinction between "setting errors" and "machine errors" can be drawn; there are so many possible causes of changes both in mean and in variation that it is not possible to generalise. Interpretation of the charts will clearly depend in a large measure on a knowledge of the process and the chemical factors involved.

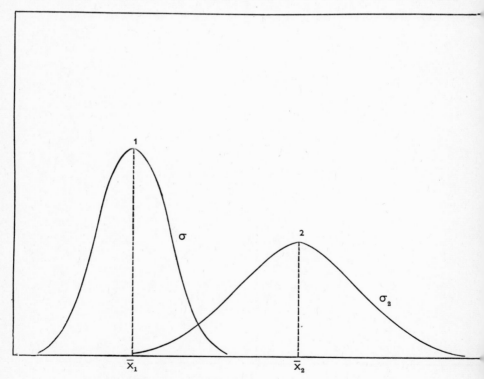

Fig. 10·3. Lack of control of averages and ranges

Level of control

10·54 It must not be thought that because a process is under control it is necessarily operating satisfactorily. A plant may be manufacturing a product most of which does not comply with specification, and yet the process may be under control. If such circumstances obtained, control would exist at too low a level. The level of control is often as important as the control itself. A process may be under control at the wrong level for the following reasons:

(i) The achieved average value of the quality characteristic does not coincide with the specified value;

(ii) The inherent variation of the producing system is too great, so that an excessive proportion of the product falls outside the specified limits, even when they are plotted round the achieved average;

(iii) Conditions (i) and (ii) may apply simultaneously.

The level of control in relation to the specified average may often be adjusted to suit, but if the level of control in relation to the specified limits about the average is too low, the specification cannot be met without alteration to the process, which may entail redesign of equipment or modification to the process recipe.

Compliance with specifications

10·55 The procedure given in the previous sections has been directed chiefly to discovering the inherent variation of the process and the fluctuations in the quality characteristic about its achieved average value. Such procedure determines what the process is doing, and is of value in fixing standards where none already exists. For many processes, however, specifications exist which define the average to be aimed at and also define the limits above or below the average which may only occasionally be exceeded, e.g. 1 in 1,000 samples. With this information it is possible to construct a chart for sample averages in which the central line is the specification average and on which, in addition to the control chart limit lines calculated from σ, specification limit lines are also included. If the specification allows a tolerance of $\pm b$ on the specified average for single tests, the specification limit lines are spaced at a distance of $b/\sqrt{n}$ above and below the aimed-at average for samples of n tests.

It is clear that if the product is to comply with the specification, $3{\cdot}09\sigma$ must be less than b. If $3{\cdot}09\sigma > b$, the producing system is incapable of manufacturing a product practically all of which will meet the specification. The remedy is either to increase b by widening the specification limits or to reduce σ by modifying the process.

If the producing system is under statistical control at the correct level, valid predictions may be made from the results of tests on small samples on the extent to which the whole product is meeting the specification and the proportion of the product which is failing to meet the specification. This aspect of predicting the limits within which various proportions of the total product must lie is one of the most valuable practical results arising from statistical control; but it is important to stress that unless statistical control is achieved, valid predictions relating to the whole future product cannot be made from the results of the tests on small samples. The accuracy of predictions made in the absence of a state of statistical control is largely fictitious unless 100% inspection is carried out, and even 100% inspection is not foolproof.

Further applications of control charts

10·6 In this section other types of control charts are indicated briefly and references where detailed treatments will be found are given.

So far we have dealt only with the control of quality when this may be represented by a continuous variable. Another important measure of quality which applies to a different type of manufacture is the proportion or number of defective items in a batch consisting of a number (usually large) of similar articles, for example a day's run in the manufacture of cartridge cases, nuts, bolts, or a particular component of a radio valve. In all such cases each article should pass a specification in order to be suitable for sale, or for use in a subsequent process. For instance, a component part of a valve has to satisfy a close specification for measurement, and when it fails to do so it is referred to as a "defective." A convenient measure of the quality of a batch of articles is then the "proportion defective." The higher the proportion defective, the greater the trouble experienced in the subsequent stages of the process.

Closely allied to "proportion defective" is another measure of quality referred to as the "number of defects"; this applies to products such as metal or plastic sheets, cloth, yarn, etc., where it is important that the number of defects per unit length or area of the material should be kept low.

Charts for "proportion defective" and "number of defects per unit" are based respectively on the binomial and Poisson distributions, which were dealt with in Chapter 9. Both types of chart are dealt with in a similar way; a sample from each batch is taken and examined in detail for the number of defectives or the number of defects as the case may be, and the results are plotted in chronological order. The samples from each batch are of the same size. The mean line on the chart is the average of previous manufacture, and the control limits corresponding to any required probability may be determined from Table F. For instance, if samples of 100 were taken from each batch and the average number of defectives were 5, then the number of defectives in a sample of 100 giving a lower confidence limit of 5 would be between 10 and 11. The upper inner control limit is then 10. Tables exist which will enable these limits to be obtained directly (see [10·1] and [10·4], where also a full discussion of these charts is given).

10·61 The following method is sometimes useful for controlling the proportion defective; it applies in those instances in which an article is defective if it fails to reach a certain specification based on a quantitative measurement. For example, a defective article may be one whose strength is below a certain specified level; it may not matter how high the strength is, provided the specified figure is exceeded. In a batch of such articles the strengths will vary from one individual to another, and will in fact have a certain distribution. Usually this distribution can be assumed to be Normal, or may be readily transformed into one that can be assumed to be Normal. Given the mean μ and the standard deviation σ we can then readily calculate the proportion expected below any specified value x_0. This proportion is obtained by first calculating $u = (\mu - x_0)/\sigma$ and referring to the appropriate entry in Table A. Conversely, given x_0 and σ we can calculate the value of μ for which the proportion less than x_0 is equal to a given value.

In practice μ and σ are not known and the estimates $\bar{x}$ and s obtained from a sample have to be used. The estimate of u is given by $(\bar{x} - x_0)/s$. This statistic is distributed as a "non-central t" which has been tabulated sufficiently for this purpose; in fact tables exist which give directly the control limits for u [10·1]. The proportion defective derived from the value of u is a more efficient estimate of the proportion defective in the batch than is the actual proportion defective in the sample.

10·62 In some high-speed processes such as the manufacture of tablets, where it is necessary to control the weight, the standard method of taking a sample and weighing *each individual* in the sample is too slow and cumbersome. In the manufacture of tablets departures from a standard weight may be caused by the slipping of the machine, or more likely by gradual changes in the bulk density or other properties of the granules. The only control required at this stage is to ensure that the machine is operating at the correct level, and this is best achieved by taking the total weight of a number of tablets, say 10 or 20.

The allowable variation in the weights of individual tablets is governed by an official specification, and this, together with a knowledge of the standard deviation σ within short runs on the machine, can be translated into limits of tolerance for the machine. In other words, the machine may be allowed to drift to an extent of $\pm \delta$ from a specified weight. The level of operation of the machine has to be estimated from a sample of the tablets, and this estimate is subject to error. We may then construct the control chart scheme on the following basis:

(i) We are prepared to take a chance β of failing to detect a change in level of $\pm \delta$.

(ii) We are prepared to take a chance α of adjusting the machine unnecessarily.

These two conditions (which really represent the operating characteristics of the scheme required [§ 5·21]), together with the value of σ, determine the number of tablets to be weighed in each sample and also determine the action limits [§ 5·46].

The risk β must be related to the frequency of taking the sample, and both of these will depend on the expected frequency and magnitude of changes in the mean weight of tablets delivered by the machine, these latter being determined from past experience. This is really the *prior distribution* which was discussed in relation to a similar type of problem in Chapter 5. The other risk α of adjusting the machine unnecessarily must be kept small, because more harm can be done by this type of wrong decision than is generally realised.

The process control then takes the form of weighing *in total* a sample of n tablets at the prescribed intervals, and adjusting the machine when the weight falls outside calculated limits L_1 and L_2. An occasional check or control chart on the standard deviation σ is usually desirable, and this is carried out by weighing individual consecutive tablets at longer intervals, e.g. every hour. This control of the standard deviation is done independently of the control of the level of operation of the machine.

The illustration sketched above is a particular case of "controlling to a specification" (see [10·4]).

10·63 It is worth mentioning here one further type of control chart that is applicable to processes where changes are gradual and for which testing is expensive. Samples are taken at roughly regular intervals, and control limits are calculated for these samples. If the result falls outside the limits, the appropriate action is taken; if the result falls within the limits, the result is combined with the previous one and compared with another set of control limits. The process can be repeated combining three, four or more of the past results if desired. This is, in effect, an application of a sequential test in reverse. Sequential tests are discussed in Chapter 11 and more fully in "Design and Analysis."

10·7 The above discussion does not exhaust the possible types of control charts that arise in practice. We emphasise that each process has to be examined in detail to find the best means of controlling the quality, and that each process must be dealt with on its own merits. It will rarely be found that a type of control used in one process can be used in another without at least some modification.

Careful consideration must be given in deciding at what stage or stages in the process the control should be applied and what particular measurements should be used. Ideally, the control should be applied at the earliest stage where defects or changes can be detected or prevented, or where corrective measures can be applied. The criterion for control need not necessarily be a measurement on the finished product; it can also be a measurement taken at an earlier stage that is known to be correlated with the measurement on the finished product. To find such a measure will require detailed examination of the process variables and may require specially planned experiments to establish the relationship. A control chart should be devised not only to suit the process, but must also be acceptable to the process chemist or engineer. It may well be worth using a criterion that is not quite 100% efficient if it is easier to operate, more acceptable to the process men, or falls more in line with the previous methods of control. A control chart must therefore not be regarded as an end in itself; it is an aid to judgment additional to (but not in place of) technical knowledge of the process.

Summary of the value of control charts and the advantages of a state of statistical control

10·8 (i) Test results can be clearly and concisely set out to provide information and a running commentary on production which a mass of tabulated data cannot convey.

(ii) Unless production is statistically controlled, the fact that tests on small samples comply with a given specification is no proof that the remainder of the product complies with the specification. With statistically controlled production the quality of the product which will be manufactured in the future can be accurately predicted.

(iii) Departures from statistically controlled production are shown up on a control chart, and steps can be taken to rectify the trouble so that a minimum quantity of reject material is manufactured. The supervisory staff can investigate production troubles armed with quantitative data and the knowledge of when the trouble occurred.

(iv) The quality of the product can be accurately specified, and it can be stated with what specification limits the product complies. If the process is in a state of statistical control, greater uniformity of the product cannot be achieved without changing the process itself. Hence it is known that the process is being operated as efficiently as possible as far as the particular quality characteristic is concerned.

(v) The control chart is indispensable if an attempt is being made to bring a process from an uncontrolled to a controlled state. It is also invaluable for assessing in quantitative terms the effect of modifications in operating methods or of changes in equipment. Unaided judgment cannot always decide whether a significant improvement has been made or not, and opinion frequently differs on whether a change in process or equipment has made any improvement or not. Control charts enable such differences of opinion to be resolved.

(vi) For any degree of certainty about predictions relating to the quality characteristics of a product the recording and analysis of test results by methods based on statistical principles, e.g. control charts, are the most economical. With the process in a state of statistical control, testing may be reduced to a minimum.

REFERENCES

[10·1] DUDDING, B. P., and JENNETT, W. J. *Quality Control Charts*. B.S. 600R: 1942. British Standards Institution (London, 1942).

[10·2] American Defence Emergency Standards: *Guide for Quality Control and Control Chart Method of Analysing Data*. (Reproduced by courtesy of the American Standards Association.) B.S. 1008 : 1942. British Standards Institution (London, 1942).

[10·3] DUNCAN, A. J. *Quality Control and Industrial Statistics*. R. D. Irwin Inc. (Illinois, 1952).

[10·4] DUDDING, B. P., and JENNETT, W. J. *Control Chart Technique when Manufacturing to a Specification*. B.S. 2564 : 1955. British Standards Institution (London, 1955).

[10·5] SIMON, L. E. *An Engineers' Manual of Statistical Methods*. John Wiley (New York, 1941), Chapman & Hall (London, 1941).

[10·6] SHEWHART, W. A. *Economic Control of the Quality of Manufactured Product*. Van Nostrand (New York, 1941).

[10·7] DAVIES, O. L., and PEARSON, E. S. "Methods of Estimating from Samples the Population Standard Deviation." *Journal of Royal Statistical Society Supplement*, **1**, 1 (1934), 76–93.

[10·8] PEARSON, E. S. "The Probability Integral of the Range in Samples of *n* Observations from a Normal Population." *Biometrika* offprint, Vol. XXXII, Pts. III and IV, April 1942, 302–10.

[10·9] Idem. *The Application of Statistical Methods to Industrial Standardisation and Quality Control* (B.S. 600 : 1935). British Standards Institution (London, 1935).

APPENDIX 10A
USE OF CONTROL CHARTS

10A·1 This appendix illustrates the use of control charts in a research investigation on a plant manufacturing a plaster. The investigation was concerned with the setting and hardening properties of the plaster.

The results have been set out in the following tables, which show how the Universe average and Universe standard deviation are estimated.

Table 10A·1. Measurements made on initial setting time v in minutes, and hardening rate u in arbitrary units.

Table 10A·2. Division of measurements into rational sub-groups or samples.

Table 10A·3. Control chart calculations for v.

Table 10A·4. Control chart calculations for u.

Table 10A·1
MANUFACTURE OF A PLASTER
(Measurements made on initial setting times v in minutes and hardening rate u in arbitrary units)

Run*	Batch	v	u	Run*	Batch	v	u
48	1	18¾	225	49	1	14¾	211
	2	22¼	222		2	17	211
	3	23½	263		3	18½	263
	4	23¾	278		4	20	253
	5	17¾	244		5	19½	238
	6	17½	270		6	21½	240
	7	17½	250		7	20½	255
	8	33¼	250		8	19	232
	9	29	204		9	18¼	238
	10	18	233		10	19	234
	11	17¼	288		11	14¾	208
	12	20¼	267		12	18½	218
	13	16½	260		13	19¾	227
	14	18	263		14	18¾	235
	15	21¼	244		15	20¼	244
	16	22½	213		16	18½	226
	17	21½	232		17	18	200
	18	21½	230		18	17	207
	19	21½	213		19	18½	200
	20	19	210		20	18	190
	21	11½	212		21	18½	187
	22	11½	229		22	18¼	176
	23	12½	240		23	19	183
	24	15¼	232		24	21	180
	25	12	225		25	17	192
	26	15½	220		26	15½	194
	27	13¾	246				
	28	16	202				

* A run represents a convenient number of batches for record and costing purposes.

Table 10A·1 (*continued*)

MANUFACTURE OF A PLASTER

(Measurements made on initial setting times v in minutes and hardening rate u in arbitrary units)

Run	Batch	v	u	Run	Batch	v	u
50	1	24	282	51	1	$17\frac{1}{4}$	260
	2	25	293		2	$20\frac{1}{2}$	287
	3	$25\frac{3}{4}$	276		3	$21\frac{1}{2}$	292
	4	$22\frac{3}{4}$	270		4	15	262
	5	$21\frac{1}{2}$	275		5	$15\frac{3}{4}$	254
	6	15	266		6	15	259
	7	18	296		7	$14\frac{3}{4}$	263
	8	19	290		8	14	262
	9	$15\frac{1}{2}$	256		9	$13\frac{1}{2}$	254
	10	16	236		10	21	256
	11	21	296		11	$20\frac{3}{4}$	268
	12	$16\frac{1}{2}$	307		12	$15\frac{1}{2}$	247
	13	$15\frac{1}{2}$	300				
	14	$15\frac{1}{2}$	306				
	15	18	317				
	16	$17\frac{1}{4}$	296				
	17	16	306				
	18	$15\frac{1}{2}$	281				
	19	$14\frac{1}{2}$	266				
	20	$15\frac{3}{4}$	276				
	21	16	271				
	22	15	277				
	23	15	224				
	24	$15\frac{1}{2}$	289				
	25	16	253				

Table 10A·2

DIVISION OF MEASUREMENTS INTO RATIONAL SUB-GROUPS OR
SAMPLES

(Based on Table 10A·1)

v		u	
No. of Sample	No. of Batch	No. of Sample	No. of Batch
1	48/1, 2, 3, 4	1	48/1, 2, 3, 4
2	48/5, 6, 7, 10	2	48/5, 6, 7, 8
Omitted	48/8, 9	3	48/9, 10, 11, 12
3	48/11, 12, 13, 14	4	48/13, 14, 15, 16
4	48/15, 16, 17, 18	5	48/17, 18, 19, 20
5	48/19, 20, 21, 22		
		6	48/21, 22, 23, 24
6	48/23, 24, 25, 26	7	48/25, 26, 27, 28
7	48/27, 28, 49/1, 2	8	49/1, 2, 3, 4
8	49/3, 4, 5, 6	9	49/5, 6, 7, 8
9	49/7, 8, 9, 10	10	49/9, 10, 11, 12
Omitted	49/11		
10	49/12, 13, 14, 15	11	49/13, 14, 15, 16
		12	49/17, 18, 19, 20
11	49/16, 17, 18, 19	13	49/21, 22, 23, 24
12	49/20, 21, 22, 23	Omitted	49/25, 26
13	49/24, 25, 26, 50/1	14	50/1, 2, 3, 4
14	50/2, 3, 4, 5	15	50/5, 6, 7, 8
15	50/6, 7, 8, 9		
		16	50/9, 10, 11, 12
16	50/10, 11, 12, 13	17	50/13, 14, 15, 16
17	50/14, 15, 16, 17	18	50/17, 18, 19, 20
18	50/18, 19, 20, 21	19	50/21, 22, 23, 24
19	50/22, 23, 24, 25	Omitted	50/25
20	51/1, 2, 3, 4	20	51/1, 2, 3, 4
21	51/5, 6, 7, 8	21	51/5, 6, 7, 8
22	51/9, 10, 11, 12	22	51/9, 10, 11, 12

Batches were omitted where knowledge of the process suggested that
assignable causes of variation had operated.

The calculations for the samples are summarised in Tables 10A·3 and 10A·4.

Note the reference to the units used in Table 10A·3.

Table 10A·3

ESTIMATES OF $\bar{V}$ AND σ_v

(Based on Tables 10A·1 and 10A·2)

(Units: Minutes except Col. (3), where unit is $\frac{1}{4}$ minute)

No. of Sample	No. in Sample n	Sums of Differences from 18 min. $+$	$-$	Average $\bar{v}$	Range w
(1)	(2)	(3)		(4)	(5)
1	4	65		22·1	5·00
2	,,		5	17·7	0·50
3	,,	0		18·0	3·75
4	,,	59		21·7	1·25
5	,,		34	15·9	10·00
6	,,		67	13·8	3·50
7	,,		42	15·4	3·25
8	,,	30		19·9	3·00
9	,,	19		19·2	2·25
10	,,	21		19·3	1·75
11	,,	0		18·0	1·50
12	,,	7		18·4	1·00
13	,,	22		19·4	8·50
14	,,	92		23·8	4·25
15	,,		18	16·9	4·00
16	,,		12	17·3	5·50
17	,,		21	16·7	2·50
18	,,		41	15·4	1·50
19	,,		42	15·4	1·00
20	,,	9		18·6	6·50
21	,,		50	14·9	1·75
22	,,		5	17·7	7·50
Totals ..	$N = 88$	$+ 324$ $- 337$ $- 13$		395·5	79·75
Average Values ..	$n = 4$	$- 13/88 = - 0·1$		18·0	3·63

From Col. (3), $\bar{V} = 18·0 - 0·1 \times \frac{1}{4}$ (min.) $= 18·0$ min.

From Col. (5), $\bar{w} = 3·63$, d_4 (Table G·1) $= 2·059$, $\sigma_v = \bar{w}/d_4 = 1·76$ min.

Table 10A·4
CONTROL CHARTS: ESTIMATES OF $\bar{U}$ AND σ_u
(Based on Tables 10A·1 and 10A·2)
(*Units: Arbitrary scale of hardness*)

No. of Sample	No. in Sample n	Sums of Differences from 250 +	Sums of Differences from 250 −	Average $\bar{u}$	Range w
(1)	(2)	(3)		(4)	(5)
1	4		12	247	56
2	,,	14		254	26
3	,,		8	248	84
4	,,		20	245	50
5	,,		115	221	22
6	,,		87	228	28
7	,,		107	223	44
8	,,		62	234	52
9	,,		35	241	23
10	,,		102	224	30
11	,,		68	233	18
12	,,		203	199	17
13	,,		274	181	11
14	,,	121		280	23
15	,,	127		282	30
16	,,	95		274	71
17	,,	219		305	21
18	,,	129		282	40
19	,,	61		265	65
20	,,	101		275	32
21	,,	38		260	9
22	,,	25		256	21
Totals ..	$N = 88$	+ 930 − 1,093 − 163		5,457	773
Average Values ..	$n = 4$	− 163/88 = −1·9		248·0	35·1
From Col. (3)	$\bar{U} = 250 - 1\cdot9 = 248\cdot1$ units				
From Col. (5)	$\bar{w} = 35\cdot1$, d_4 (Table G·1) $= 2\cdot059$, $\sigma_u = \bar{w}/d_4 = 17\cdot0$ units				

Y

Initial setting time v

10A·2 From Table 10A·3 it will be seen that estimates of the Universe average and standard deviation, etc. are:

$$\bar{V} = 18\cdot0 \text{ min.}, \ \sigma = 1\cdot76 \text{ min.}, \ \bar{w} = 3\cdot63 \text{ min., and } n = 4$$

1. *Control Limits for Sample Averages* (*see Table G at end of volume*)

    (*i*) *Inner Control Limits*

      These are $18\cdot0 \pm 1\cdot76 \times 0\cdot980$, or $18\cdot0 \pm 3\cdot63 \times 0\cdot476$
      $= 19\cdot7$ and $16\cdot3$ min.

    (*ii*) *Outer Control Limits*

      These are $18\cdot0 \pm 1\cdot76 \times 1\cdot545$, or $18\cdot0 \pm 3\cdot63 \times 0\cdot75$
      $= 20\cdot7$ and $15\cdot3$ min.

2. *Control Limits for Sample Ranges* (*see Table G·1 or G·2*)

    These are:

    (*i*) *Inner Control Limits*—Lower: $1\cdot76 \times 0\cdot59 = 1\cdot0$ min.
      Upper: $1\cdot76 \times 3\cdot98 = 7\cdot0$ min.

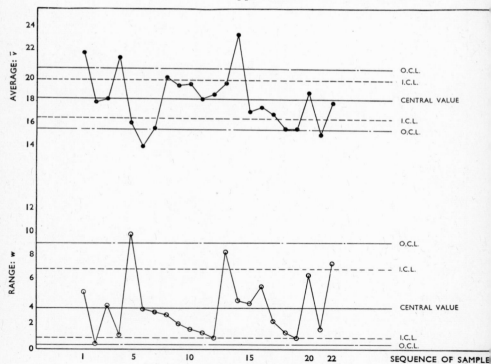

Fig. 10·4. Control charts. Initial set

(*ii*) *Outer Control Limits*—Lower: 1·76 × 0·20 = 0·4 min.

Upper: 1·76 × 5·31 = 9·3 min.

Central Value: 3·63 min.

Control charts for sample averages and ranges are plotted on Figure 10·4. It will be seen that the range for Sample 5 is outside the upper outer control limit and should therefore be omitted, as the purpose of the investigation was to determine the inherent variation of the process freed from the effect of assignable causes of variation. The assignable causes were identified in the investigation. It was found that Sample 13 was also out of control on ranges when the revised limits were calculated. When Samples 5 and 13 are omitted and $\bar{V}$ and σ recalculated, we have:

$$\bar{V} = 18\cdot0 \text{ min.}$$
$$\bar{w} = 3\cdot06 \text{ min.}$$
$$\sigma = 1\cdot49 \text{ min.}$$

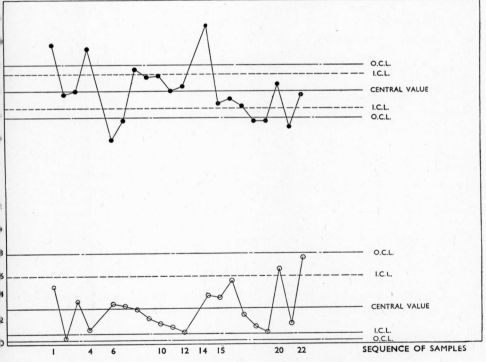

Fig. 10·5. Control charts. Initial set, samples 5 and 13 omitted

The revised limit lines are as follows:

Statistic	Control Chart Limits				
	Lower		Central Value	Upper	
	O.C.L.	I.C.L.		I.C.L.	O.C.L.
$\bar{v}$	15·7	16·5	18·0	19·5	20·3
w	0·3	0·9	3·1	5·9	7·9

In practice a small amount of preliminary calculation would show which samples should be discarded, and only the final limits and charts need be drawn. It will be seen from Figure 10·5 that sample ranges show good control but that sample averages show pronounced lack of control, and this is discussed below [§ **10A·4**].

Hardening rate u

10A·3 The control limits for u are as follows:

$$\bar{U} = 248 \cdot 1 \text{ units}$$
$$\bar{w} = 35 \cdot 1 \text{ units}$$
$$\sigma = 17 \cdot 0 \text{ units}$$

Statistic	Control Chart Limits				
	Lower		Central Value	Upper	
	O.C.L.	I.C.L.		I.C.L.	O.C.L.
$\bar{u}$	222	231	248	265	274
w	3	10	35	68	90

The control charts are given in Figure 10·6. Sample ranges show good control, whereas the sample averages show pronounced lack of control.

Interpretation of charts

10A·4 The charts show that in respect of initial setting time and hardening rate the process is inherently capable of being controlled with standard deviations of 1·49 min. and 17·0 units respectively. The sample averages, however, were not under control during the trials. This is the state of affairs illustrated in Figure 10·1.

Lack of control was due to the fact that no attempt was made during the trials to control the sample averages except within the specification limits. It will usually be found in investigations of this kind, where data are being obtained for a process where no control charts exist, that sample averages are out of control. If the quality characteristics had been plotted on charts during the plant trials they could have been brought under control. The research investigation discussed here has provided estimates of the variation to be expected from the process, and the next step would be to introduce the charts as part of the routine testing system to enable assignable causes of variation to be eliminated and to improve the uniformity of the product. The frequency of sampling would depend mainly on the degree of control achieved.

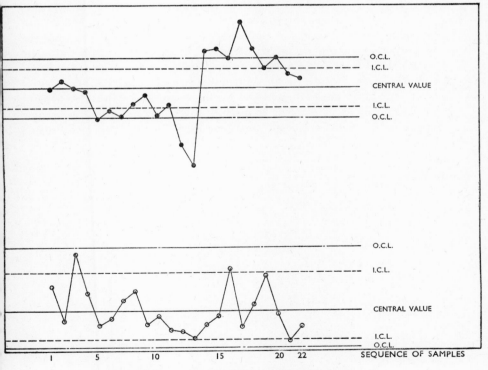

Fig. 10·6. Control charts. Hardening rate

From practical experience it has been found that if the plaster is to be satisfactory it should comply with the following requirements:

Initial setting time: Between 13 and 30 min., i.e. 21·5 min. $\pm$ 8·5 min.

Hardening rate: Between 168 and 308 units, i.e. 238 units $\pm$ 70 units.

If the plant is to be capable of making a product practically all of which complies with the above specification, we must have:

Initial setting time: 3·09σ less than 8·5 min.

but 3·09σ = 4·6 min., which is less than 8·5 min.

Hardening rate: 3·09σ less than 70 units

but 3·09σ = 53 units, which is less than 70 units.

Thus the required conditions are met and the specification limits lie outside the outer control limits, thus ensuring that if the process is operated under control practically all the product will meet the specification. It will be noted that the achieved averages ($\bar{V} = 18\cdot0$ min. and $\bar{U} = 248\cdot1$ units) differ from the specified averages. There would be no difficulty in adjusting the achieved averages to comply with the specification averages and thus in obtaining statistical control at the correct level. If it is desired to know the proportion of the product which will meet the specification, this can easily be calculated from Table A as shown in § 2·44.

It will be seen that the specification limits are well outside the outer control limits, and in such cases the averages could be allowed to shift a little without manufacturing reject material. In machine-tool processes where the machine might be "too good for the job," new outer control limits would be calculated [10·4].

CHAPTER 11

SAMPLING AND SPECIFICATIONS

To maintain a product at a consistently high level of quality a sampling inspection scheme may be employed. In such a scheme a sample is taken from each manufactured lot and tested; on the results of these tests the lot is either accepted or rejected. In this chapter the various considerations that are relevant to the selection of an efficient scheme are discussed.

Introduction

11.1 The term "sampling" is customarily taken as indicating the segregation of a small fraction from a large bulk of material in such a way that the characteristics of the bulk can be estimated by studying those of the sample. The object of this chapter is to discuss relationships between size of fraction and precision of estimation, taking into account the characteristics being studied and the nature of the material.

Sampling may be carried out, for instance, on a chemical product, such as a fertiliser, the characteristic to be determined being its nitrogen or potash content. If we require the average value for a lot of 100 bags, sampling might be carried out by extracting a suitable quantity from representative bags, mixing and analysing. If, however, the nitrogen or potash contents of individual bags are required, analyses must be carried out separately on samples drawn from different bags. Statistical treatment of the results is clearly different in the two cases. In other problems material may be defective in a way which it is impossible or inconvenient to measure, for example because of chips, scratches, breaks, or other qualitative imperfections. A proportion of the lot would then be inspected and the number of imperfections counted.

11·11 The results obtained on a sample are often compared with standard figures, such as those quoted in a relevant specification. In fact, much sampling is carried out to ensure that materials comply with specification requirements, although there are instances where tolerances are not imposed but where the characteristics must be known so that the material may be priced or used to the best advantage, e.g. coal and other minerals.

The fact that the results obtained on a sample are compared with a standard value implies that sampling has been carried out previously on similar material. In practice it is generally a continuing process, carried out on successive lots or batches, so that prior information on the mean, standard deviation, or average percent defective, is available. Such information is required in drawing up sampling plans. At the same time further information is continually accumulating, and may well be used in setting up standards, such as specification limits, for future use. Sampling and specifications cannot be considered independently, each having its influence on the other, and they are therefore discussed together in this chapter. Furthermore, no lot or batch should be regarded as an entirely separate entity, but should preferably be related to preceding or ensuing batches.

Random sampling and systematic sampling

11·2 A random sample is defined as a set of observations drawn from a Universe in such a way that every possible observation has an equal chance of being drawn at every trial. In this chapter the Universe is a lot or batch, each part or element of which should be equally likely to appear in the sample; this randomness is necessary in order to avoid possible bias.

The technique of obtaining a random sample obviously depends on the material being sampled and also on the particular properties that are being studied. If we are interested, for instance, in the weights of drums of material leaving a packing point, it is probably satisfactory to allow the check-weigher to go to the band conveyor at random intervals and each time take the first drum which comes along. If, however, we are interested in the condition of the paint film on the outside of the drum, there is a considerable risk that the man's choice may be influenced by the appearance of the drum, so that well-painted drums have a better (or possibly worse) chance of being chosen than badly painted drums. Such a sample would be said to be biased, and could not be regarded as a random sample. In spite of the bias for appearance, the sample might well be random for weight, as long as there was no connection between weight and appearance.

Practical considerations frequently make it difficult to obtain a truly random sample, but care should be taken to ensure that material from portions which do not come readily to hand stands a fair chance of being chosen. The judgment of the inspector or sampler may introduce a bias, and it may be considered desirable, in critical cases, to assign numbers to different portions of a lot and to select from these by a random method. In some instances practical considerations make it impossible to avoid bias, as for example in taking samples from sheets or rolls. They must then be taken from the ends or sides, but the amount of bias introduced should be determined initially, and at intervals, by thorough overall sampling of typical rolls or sheets, and correction applied in the case of subsequent samples.

It is common practice in sampling to work according to a systematic plan instead of in a truly random manner. Thus individual items or fractions may be taken at approximately equal intervals in time, in space, or by number. Such samples may frequently be perfectly satisfactory, but in their departure from the rules of random sampling they introduce a possibility of bias, and individual sampling schemes of this type should be carefully examined with this in mind. Three cases may be distinguished:

(i) The variations in the material are either completely random (i.e. the material is "controlled" in the sense used in Quality Control [Chapter 10]) or have a period short compared with the sampling interval. In this case the systematic sample will be to all intents and purposes a random sample.

(ii) The variations in the material have a period long compared with the sampling interval. In this case systematic sampling is generally satisfactory.

(iii) The variations have a period comparable with the sampling interval. In this case there is a danger of the sampling and the variations getting into step and thus introducing a bias.

Where sampling has to be carried out at equal intervals according to a systematic plan the position or time of the initial sample of the series should if possible be chosen in some random manner.

11·21 Statistical aspects of sampling are frequently concerned with relationships between sample size, lot size, and the accuracy with which the characteristics of the bulk should be estimated. The common assumption that a defined level of accuracy can only be attained by relating sample size to lot size is wrong, since truly random samples of the same size provide equally reliable estimates of bulk characteristics whatever the size of the lot when, as is generally the case, the sample is a small fraction of the lot.

However, when larger lots are being considered the amount at risk is greater, and a greater precision is therefore required, leading to an increased sample size. The indication is that the best sampling schemes are based on economic considerations, that is on minimum overall costs, following the principles already discussed in Chapter 5. As the information necessary to derive such schemes is not always available, only brief consideration will be given to them in this chapter. More attention will be devoted to schemes derived from consideration of defined risks of reaching wrong conclusions regarding the acceptance or rejection of a lot on the characteristics determined from a sample. The permitted risk of a wrong conclusion for a large lot will naturally be less than for a smaller lot. Manufactured lots of one product are generally of the same size, and so one set of defined risks can be adopted for this product.

If it is known or suspected that a lot is not uniform, it is advisable to divide it into approximately homogeneous sections, taking a random sample from each, i.e. to employ stratified sampling. The size of a lot is generally determined by the capacity of receptacles, storage facilities or transport arrangements. In theory, the optimum size is the largest which is likely to be homogeneous, depending on constancy of manufacturing conditions. The producer, knowing the order of manufacture, has the opportunity of building up homogeneous lots and of planning his sampling accordingly. The consumer, on the other hand, having no assurance that a lot can be regarded as uniform, may be faced with a heavy programme of stratified sampling, engendered by his lack of knowledge of order of manufacture. He may be able to establish that the production process is stable by applying Control Chart techniques to results obtained on a run of lots; but an alternative solution is that the producer should make his records available to the consumer and that they should be used as a basis for acceptance. In these circumstances the functional type of specification becomes redundant, but the methods of sampling, testing and recording should be carried out on an agreed basis and according to sound statistical principles.

In many instances a non-uniform lot can be made uniform by mixing and blending, and such operations are frequently included as part of normal production. Similarly, a number of samples drawn from different parts of the lot may be combined to form one large sample when the average quality only is being investigated. This presupposes, however, that variations in quality within the lot are of no consequence in the subsequent operation.

SAMPLING OF ATTRIBUTES

11·3 In Chapter 9 consideration was devoted to the binomial and Poisson distributions for treatment of data classified by frequency of occurrence or non-occurrence of certain events or attributes. Many sampling problems are concerned with data of this type, and the statistical theory developed previously is therefore applicable. As already indicated, the attribute may be a defect, such as a scratch or imperfection on a few members of a lot of nominally similar discrete articles, or a break in a thread, a crack in a piece of metal, a weaving fault in cloth, a bubble in a plastic sheet, an improperly soldered joint, etc. By examining a portion of a lot, the percentage or number of such attributes can be assessed and compared with a standard figure. Circumstances may also arise in which it is inconvenient or uneconomic to measure a dimension on each unit of a sample of similar articles, and they may then be classified as being greater or less than a certain fixed size by means of a gauge. Such a procedure is common in engineering industries, and the results may again be recorded as a percentage or count of defective articles.

In the last example the gauge defines a defect by fixing a measured and repeatable limit, but it is also necessary to set up similar inspection standards for many of the less definite examples quoted previously. While a break is either present or absent, a scratch, fault or crack may vary in size, and a decision has to be made as to the maximum size which does not render the articles or material unacceptable. Furthermore, standard defects may be required which can be constantly referred to, so that successive lots are subjected to inspection of the same rigour; this, however, is a problem of inspection rather than of sampling.

As a simple example consider the examination of a lot of discrete articles for the incidence of chips and breakages. A random sample ensures that repeat tests will provide the same results, within the limit of sampling error expressed by the binomial distribution [Chapter 9]. The examination is expected to reveal a small number of defective articles in the sample, and the result will be expressed as a percentage of defective articles. In the majority of instances the percentage will be small, so that the distribution of sampling errors will approximate to the Poisson type, for which there is a small chance of an occurrence in each of a large number of trials. The Poisson distribution is a sufficiently good approximation, in fact, when the percent defective is not more than 10%.

With defects such as breaks in thread, the result of an examination is expressed not as a percentage but as the number of faults in a certain length or area. These numbers are subject to the Poisson distribution, because there is a large, although indefinite, number of occasions on which the fault may occur, the probability of occurrence associated with each occasion being very small.

It should be noted that an implicit assumption has been made that a small number of defects is admissible. If not, then all the material must be examined and the question of sampling procedure does not arise.

Single sampling. Consumer's and producer's risks

11·31 The principles underlying the various methods of sampling for attributes may be expounded from a consideration of simple examples, although a complete theoretical treatment is outside the scope of this book; detailed treatment is given in [11·1] and [11·2]. Suppose in the first place that a sample of 100 pieces is being inspected and that it will be accepted if 2 or fewer defective articles are found and rejected if there are 3 or more. The Poisson distribution [§ 9·2] defines the probabilities with which 0, 1, 2, 3, ... defective articles will be found in the sample when the percentage in the lot is known; conversely, a specified number of defectives may arise, with different probabilities, from lots having different percentages of defective articles. Thus three or more defectives will be found with a probability of 0·1 when the proportion in the lot is such that the expected number in the sample is 1·10, a value obtained by entering Table F with $a = 3$, $p = 0$ (for the Poisson distribution) and the lower confidence limit for probability P of 0·1. In other words, if samples of 100 are taken from a number of lots all containing 1·10% defective articles, then one sample out of every ten is likely to contain 3 or more defectives and will be rejected. There is, however, no difference between the lots, and the producer, in adopting a sampling plan, undertakes a risk that it may reject some lots unjustifiably. This is known as the Producer's Risk. Table F also indicates that 2 or fewer defectives would be obtained with a probability of 0·1 when the expected number is 5·32. The consumer, therefore, also undertakes a risk of 0·1 that a lot containing 5·32% defectives will be accepted. Producer's and consumer's risks are seen to be the same as errors of the first and second kinds respectively [§ **5·43**.] Thus the producer's risk is the probability of asserting that there is a difference when none exists, which is an error of the first kind.

If a sample of 500 had been taken instead of 100, 9 or more defects would have been found with a probability of 0·1 when the average number in the lot was 5·43. The percentage of defective articles in the lot would then be 1·09%, and it will be seen, therefore, that in this particular illustration rejection with 3 defectives out of 100 or with 9 defectives out of 500 provides nearly the same producer's risk, 0·1, when the lot contains 1·1% defectives. The consumer's risks, however, are very different. Thus, the latter sampling plan would accept a sample containing 8 or fewer defects with a probability of 0·1 when the expected number is 13·0, equivalent to a percentage of 2·60% when the sample size is 500. The two plans will thus accept, with 0·1 probability, lots containing respectively 5·32% and 2·60% defective articles. Increasing the sample size has therefore made the inspection more efficient in the sense that an inferior lot is less likely to be accepted.

Attention need not be restricted to producer's and consumer's risks of 0·1, as the probabilities of accepting or of rejecting a lot containing any specified percentage of defective articles can be calculated, from the Poisson distribution, for a sampling plan defined by the sample size and the acceptable number of defective articles therein. Such calculations have, in fact, been made for the two sampling plans considered above, and the results are illustrated in Figure 11·1, which shows the relationship between the percentage of defective articles in the lot and the probability of acceptance.

Operating characteristic curve
11·32 The curves illustrated in Figure 11·1 are particular examples of Operating Characteristic Curves or Power Curves already considered in Chapter 5, but it is worth while recalling some of the points made there. The operating characteristic curve gives the probabilities of accepting or of rejecting lots containing specified percentages of defective articles when a defined sampling plan is employed. Any sampling plan has an Operating Characteristic associated with it, defined uniquely by either (1) specifying the sample size and the acceptable number of defective articles therein, or (2) choosing two points (p_1, a) and (p_2, β) where a is the probability of rejecting a batch in which the proportion of defective articles is p_1, and β is the

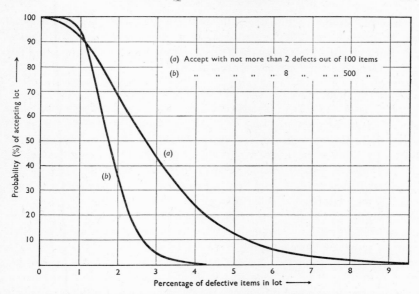

Fig. 11·1. Operating characteristic curves of two single sampling plans

probability of accepting a batch in which the proportion of defective articles is p_2, p_2 being greater than p_1. The argument in § **11·31** derives the second of these alternatives from the first. If p is less than p_1 the probability of rejection is less than α; similarly, if p is greater than p_2 the probability of acceptance is less than β. It is worth stressing that the curve for any given sampling plan is completely defined by two points only, and that when these are fixed the probabilities of accepting lots of differing qualities are also determined. The Operating Characteristic therefore contains complete information on the probable sentencing of a lot of any quality that may be presented. Furthermore, any two points may be chosen initially; thus curve (b) of Figure 11·1 is defined equally well by ($p_1 = 1\cdot1\%$, $\alpha = 0\cdot1$) and ($p_2 = 2\cdot0\%$, $\beta = 0\cdot35$) as by ($p_1 = 1\cdot1\%$, $\alpha = 0\cdot1$) and ($p_2 = 2\cdot6\%$, $\beta = 0\cdot1$).

The Operating Characteristic is of value in indicating the discriminatory power of a sampling plan. Thus, of the two plans illustrated in Figure 11·1, that with the larger sample size discriminates more effectively between good and inferior lots, as discussed in § **11·31**. However, the Operating Characteristic by itself provides no information on the quality of accepted material, but only indicates the probability of accepting a lot containing a specified proportion of defectives when such material is presented for inspection. If, in fact, the consumer's risk is $0\cdot1$ of accepting a lot containing $2\cdot6\%$ defectives, and 1% of the lots are of this quality, then $0\cdot1\%$ of the accepted material will be at this inferior level. The distribution of quality in production lots must be known, therefore, before the qualities of accepted and of rejected material can be determined. The overall costs of a sampling scheme can then be calculated as shown in Chapter 5 if the costs of inspection, of rejecting lots and of accepting inferior material are known.

Example of single sampling: Inspection of metal cups

11·33   The dimensions of a small metal cup were important from the point of view of its insertion into a cavity during an assembly operation. In parti-cular, it should be of the correct diameter, which could be checked most readily by means of maximum and minimum gauges. Producer and consumer in this case were part of the same organisation, and the cups were inspected in lots of 10,000 at the end of their manufacture before passing to the next stage. The consumer was of the opinion that lots containing 2·5% defectives or more might well entail too frequent stoppages of his assembly machines: the consumer's risk was chosen, therefore, with his consent, as a 0·1 proba-bility of accepting lots containing 2·5% defectives. As rejected lots would be scrapped, 100% inspection being uneconomic, the probability of rejecting a lot containing 0·5% defects was fixed at 0·025. With this information regarding producer's and consumer's risks, acceptance and rejection numbers may be found from Table F. The result is that a sample of 320 is inspected, accepted if there are 4 or fewer defects, and rejected if there are 5 or more. This result is readily obtained by trial from Table F. Thus the tabulated value for $a = 4$, $p = 0$, P (upper limit) $= 0·1$, is 7·99, i.e. with an average or expected number of defects of 7·99 the probability of obtaining 4 or fewer in one sample is 0·1. This, however, is postulated as the probability with which a lot containing 2·5% defects should be accepted, and the size of sample is therefore

$$\frac{7·99 \times 100}{2·5} = 320$$

Similarly, the tabulated value for $a = 5$, $p = 0$, P (lower limit) $= 0·025$, is 1·62, and as a lot containing 0·5% defects should be rejected with a probability of 0·025, the sample size is $1·62 \times 100/0·5 = 324$. The procedure, therefore, is to find from Table F acceptance and rejection numbers, the latter being necessarily one greater than the former, that lead to approximately the same sample size for the defined probabilities. There is no need to determine sample sizes with any great accuracy, and the size could well be 300 instead of 320 without any appreciable loss of discrimination. Thus, a lot con-taining 2·66% defectives would then be accepted with a probability of 0·1.

Inspection had previously been carried out on large samples from 366 different lots during a period of six months. No sample contained more than 1·2% defectives, so that for this series of lots there was virtually no risk of passing a lot containing 2·5% defectives, which would be unacceptable to the consumer. Provided that the conditions of manufacture remain unchanged and the overall quality of the product consequently unaltered, no sampling is required for the purpose of deciding whether a lot is satisfactory from the consumer's point of view. Sampling is, in fact, needed only to ensure that production remains controlled at the same level, and to detect any assignable causes of variation that might arise. For such purposes, which could be dealt with by a Control Chart system, the sample size could safely be reduced below that of 300 deduced above, and this matter is considered further in § **11·34**. The sample size of 300 was deduced by considering one lot as a separate entity, unrelated to previous or ensuing batches. Considerable advantage may be gained, however, by regarding the manufacture as a whole, particularly taking into account such objective information as is available.

11·331 In the example just considered, the distribution of percentage defectives between lots could be estimated from the information provided by the lots produced over a period of six months. This is the Prior Distribution, used in conjunction with the Operating Characteristic Curve, to assess completely a given sampling scheme, as described in § **5·2**. The Prior Distribution defines the proportion of lots of a given quality, and the Operating Characteristic the probability of rejection, from which the proportions of satisfactory batches which will be rejected and of faulty batches which will be passed may be calculated. Both are wrong decisions which will cost money either directly or indirectly. If these costs can be evaluated, then, together with the cost of sampling, the cost of the whole scheme can be found, which will form a basis for the derivation of the optimum size of sample.

A reasonable method of attack is by trial and error, starting with a few different sampling schemes and choosing that which provides minimum costs. Information on the costs of wrong decisions is frequently indefinite, so that calculation need not be pursued to the limit of precision. On the other hand, mathematical theory is available for many practical situations, but it is still far from complete, although developments may be expected. Useful publications have already been made by Barnard [11·3] following a more theoretical treatment by Wald [11·4].

In basing a scheme on defined consumer's and producer's risks, as discussed briefly in § **11·31**, considerable judgment is usually required, because in defining the level of risk a mental assessment is being made of the cost factors involved and of their probable effects. Mathematical theory is attempting to establish an objective quantitative basis instead of this subjective assessment.

Double and multiple sampling
11·34 A discouraging feature of sampling by attributes is the large sample size that is necessary to discriminate between lots containing even widely different percentages of defectives, such as $0·5\%$ and $2·5\%$. The amount of

inspection may be reduced by using Control Charts to establish statistical control and to ensure its maintenance by examining comparatively small samples. Other methods for reducing sample size may be illustrated by considering the plan for the inspection of cups, in which the sample size is 300.

If a lot of inferior quality is presented for inspection, the number of defects for rejection may be found when only a proportion of the sample has been examined. Inspection might then be stopped and the lot rejected, although the size of the sample examined is smaller than 300. It can also be shown that a lot of very good quality may be accepted legitimately when a relatively small sample has been examined, and the full sample of 300 will be needed only with lots of intermediate quality, more particularly those near the range 0·5% to 2·5% defectives associated with producer's and consumer's risks. It is reasonable, then, to adopt a Double Sampling Plan, examining a first sample in relation to assigned acceptance and rejection numbers, and a second only when a firm decision is not indicated by the first results. The advantage is that the total amount of inspection is less than with a Single Sampling Plan, since some lots should be accepted or rejected after inspecting the first sample.

The relative sizes of the first and second samples may be chosen in any convenient way; a ratio of 1 : 2 is generally satisfactory. In the example under discussion an acceptance number of 0 defectives in a first sample of 100 items corresponds to a 0·1 probability of accepting a lot containing 2·30% defectives. Similarly, a rejection number of 3 corresponds to a 0·025 probability of rejecting a lot containing 0·62% defectives. These probabilities, however, are only an approximation to the producer's and consumer's risks associated with the full Double Sampling Plan, in which a second sample of 200 is examined if there are 1 or 2 defectives in the first, and the lot is accepted if there are not more than 4 defectives in both samples combined. It may be shown, in fact, that this plan rejects lots with 0·5% defectives with a probability of 0·026, and accepts those with 2·9% defective with a probability of 0·1. The differences in risk levels introduced by subdividing the sample may well be greater in other instances, and those seeking further guidance are advised to study [11·2].

Inspection effort may be still further reduced by subdividing the sample into more than two parts and reaching a decision to accept, reject or continue inspection when each part has been examined. Such Multiple Sampling Plans call for careful recording of results, and to inspectors who are not fully aware of the statistical background they may appear to be indecisive in doubtful cases. If the inspection procedure is complicated or destructive, making it costly in relation to the selection of the sample, it would be preferable to proceed to the logical limit and to examine the accumulated results after the inspection of each individual piece, i.e. to employ Sequential Sampling.

Sequential sampling*

11·35 In sequential sampling the size of sample is not fixed in advance; a test is applied to the accumulated data after each article has been examined, and sampling is terminated as soon as this shows that a decision either to accept the lot or to reject it can be made with the required degree of certainty. The characteristics of a Sequential Plan, like those of plans involving Single or Double Sampling, are dependent on the producer's and consumer's risks, α and β, and on the fractions of defective articles, p_1 and p_2, associated with these risks. In general the values of p_1 and p_2 are sufficiently small to allow the Poisson approximation to the binomial distribution. Moreover, as mentioned previously, the number of defects or imperfections cannot always be represented by a proportion, because the sample size is not expressed in the same units as the number of defects. This applies to imperfections in cloth, wire, thread, sheet or other similar products, where a defect may occur with a very small probability on a large but indefinite number of occasions. Consequently in a defined area or length of product defects may occur with moderate frequency, e.g. there may be an average of two weaving faults per hundred yards of cloth. The distribution is then also of the Poisson type. For a Poisson distribution we use the letter m to denote either the average number of defects or the average number of defective items per unit inspected. In the latter sense it is the proportion of defectives, which has been denoted above by p. Thus

α is the risk of rejecting a lot in which m_1 is either the proportion of defectives or the number of defects per unit.

β is the risk of accepting a lot in which m_2 is either the proportion of defectives or the number of defects per unit ($m_2 > m_1$).

These four quantities must be chosen on economic grounds, and they define two points on the Operating Characteristic Curve, one by α and m_1, and the other by β and m_2.

The advantage of sequential sampling is that the total number of items inspected over a long run of lots is generally less than that in any other system for the same values of m_1, m_2, α and β. Nevertheless, attention should first be given to the size of the sample likely to be encountered. This will depend on the quality of material presented for inspection, very good or very poor lots needing relatively small samples to reach a decision. Maximum sample sizes normally occur with lots having a fraction of defectives intermediate between m_1 and m_2, but the amount of inspection will differ from lot to lot, even when they are of the same quality. Average sample sizes encountered with lots of quality m_1 and m_2 are respectively

$$\frac{(1-\alpha)h_1 - \alpha h_2}{s - m_1} \quad \text{and} \quad \frac{(1-\beta)h_2 - \beta h_1}{m_2 - s} \quad \ldots\ldots(11{\cdot}1)$$

---

* A fuller discussion of sequential tests will be found in *Design and Analysis*, Chapter 3.

z

where
$$h_1 = \frac{\ln\{(1-\alpha)/\beta\}^*}{\ln(m_2/m_1)}$$
$$h_2 = \frac{\ln\{(1-\beta)/\alpha\}}{\ln(m_2/m_1)}$$
$$s = \frac{m_2 - m_1}{\ln(m_2/m_1)}$$
$$\left.\rule{0pt}{60pt}\right\}\quad\dots\dots\dots\dots(11\cdot11)$$

The greatest average sample size occurs with lots having a quality close to $p = s$, and approximates to

$$h_1 h_2/s$$

For practical purposes it may be assumed that the amount of inspection required to reach a decision for any particular lot will not exceed three times the largest of the average sample sizes calculated above. If the result is regarded as excessive, a compromise must be worked out between degree of protection and amount of inspection by modifying the values of m_1, m_2, α or β. Average sample size will be reduced by increasing α or β or the interval between m_1 and m_2.

Having fixed reasonable values for m_1, m_2, α and β, a suitable test can be worked out which may be applied to the accumulated inspection results to indicate whether to accept the lot, to reject it, or to continue sampling. When n items have been inspected the greatest allowable cumulative number of defects for the lot to be accepted is d_1 and the smallest cumulative number for it to be rejected is d_2, where d_1 and d_2 are given by

$$d_1 = -h_1 + sn$$
$$d_2 = h_2 + sn$$
$$\left.\rule{0pt}{24pt}\right\}\quad\dots\dots\dots\dots\dots(11\cdot2)$$

and h_1, h_2 and s have the values defined above $(11\cdot11)$. Before inspection commences, values of d_1 and d_2 can be calculated for a series of values of n and a table drawn up of acceptance and rejection numbers corresponding to number of items inspected. As inspection of an actual sample proceeds, observed numbers of defects are compared with tabulated values, and a decision is taken to accept, to reject, or to continue sampling, depending on whether the observed number is not greater than d_1, not less than d_2, or intermediate between them. Alternatively, the straight lines represented by Equations $(11\cdot2)$ may be drawn on a graph on which points showing cumulative number of defects against number of items inspected are then plotted. Sampling is continued as long as the trace falls between the two lines but is terminated as soon as it crosses a line, the batch being accepted if it crosses the lower line and rejected if it crosses the upper line. It may sometimes be convenient to inspect items in groups instead of individually; this is a legitimate procedure, resulting only in slightly increased sample sizes.

---

* Table K (*Design and Analysis*) includes values of $\ln\{(1-\alpha)/\beta\}$ for various levels of α and β.

Example: Sequential inspection of drums

11·351 Drums for containing liquids, received in batches of approximately 500, are inspected visually for external defects, such as indentations, score marks, assembly faults, etc. As the inspection of each drum occupies a few minutes, available man-power limited the total amount of inspection, restricting the average sample size to about 30 or 40. A sequential scheme was clearly desirable, not only because the physical process of inspection would in any case select drums one by one in sequence, but also because such a scheme would provide the best protection for a defined total amount of inspection. Statistical investigations were directed, therefore, to finding a reasonable balance between average sample size and the risks involved, presenting alternative schemes to producer, consumer and inspector. The plan eventually chosen gave a 0·05 probability of rejecting a lot containing 1% defectives and a 0·1 probability of accepting a lot containing 8% defectives, so that $m_1 = 0·01$, $m_2 = 0·08$, $a = 0·05$, $\beta = 0·1$. Therefore from $(11·11)$:

$$h_1 = \frac{\ln(0·95/0·1)}{\ln(0·08/0·01)} = 1·0826$$

$$h_2 = \frac{\ln(0·9/0·05)}{\ln(0·08/0·01)} = 1·3900$$

$$s = \frac{0·07}{\ln(0·08/0·01)} = 0·0337$$

The average sample size expected with lots containing a fraction m_1 of defectives is therefore, from $(11·1)$:

$$\frac{0·95 \times 1·0826 - 0·05 \times 1·3900}{0·0337 - 0·01} = 40$$

Similarly, the average sample size expected with lots of quality m_2 is 25, and is 45 when $m = s$.

Adopting the graphical method for assessing inspection results, the equations of the two straight lines delimiting the zones of acceptance and rejection are, from $(11·2)$:

$$d_1 = -1·0826 + 0·0337n$$
and
$$d_2 = 1·3900 + 0·0337n$$

These are included in Figure 11·2, from which it will be noticed that the lower line meets the n-axis at a value of 32, so that at least 32 drums must be inspected before a lot can be accepted. Similarly, rejection can only occur when at least two drums have been examined.

The consumer would have preferred a scheme in which there was a 0·1 probability of accepting a lot containing 5% defectives (i.e. $m_2 = 0·05$), but the minimum sample size for acceptance would then have been 56, and the average sample size for lots of m_1 quality 83. These figures implied a greater inspection effort than could reasonably be undertaken, and the degree of

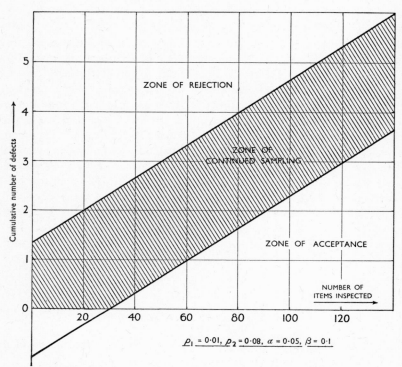

Fig. 11·2. Graphical assessment of sequential sampling.
Binomial distribution

protection was therefore relaxed, with the consumer's consent. Consideration of the costs consequent on this sampling scheme would have allowed a more precise definition of reasonable inspection effort, but the necessary information was not available.

Example: Inspection of plastic sheet

11·352 Minor imperfections are occasionally encountered in plastic sheet, but a batch in which their incidence is of the order of 1 per sheet should not be rejected. On the other hand, a frequency of 3 defects per sheet would be unacceptable to customers, and values for α and β of 0·05 and 0·01 were chosen as representing a reasonable quantitative interpretation of allowable risks. A sequential inspection scheme was therefore defined by the values

$$m_1 = 1, \quad m_2 = 3, \quad \alpha = 0.05, \quad \beta = 0.01$$

Formulae (11·1) indicate that the average sample sizes expected with lots of quality m_1 and m_2 are respectively 4·63 and 2·25.

The results of inspection were assessed by reference to Equations (*11·2*), which, for the example under consideration, are:

$$d_1 = - 4·15 + 1·82n$$
$$d_2 = \quad 2·72 + 1·82n$$

The values of d_1 and d_2 were calculated for successive integral values of n and rounded outwards to the nearest whole number, thereby providing values for the total cumulative number of defects at which a decision to accept or reject could be taken. Values for sample numbers 1 to 10 are included in Table 11·1.

Table 11·1

ACCEPTANCE AND REJECTION NUMBERS OF SEQUENTIAL
INSPECTION OF PLASTIC SHEET

Number of Items Examined	Maximum Total Number of Defects for Acceptance	Minimum Total Number of Defects for Rejection
1	—	5
2	—	7
3	1	9
4	3	10
5	4	12
6	6	14
7	8	16
8	10	18
9	12	20
10	14	21

It will be seen that the lot cannot be accepted until at least three sheets have been examined and that not more than one imperfection should have been observed on them.

11·353 Although the advantage of sequential sampling is that the total number of items inspected over a long run of lots is generally less than that in any other system with the same values of m_1, m_2, α and β, this economy may be obtained at the expense of a greater administrative effort in planning inspection procedures and in recording the result after inspecting each item. If the cost of obtaining the sample is large relatively to that of carrying out the inspection or test, there may be little economic advantage in employing sequential methods. It is also essential that the sample should be random, i.e. each item in the lot should have the same chance of appearing in the sample, and care must be taken to maintain this requisite when items are being selected and inspected one by one.

Preparing a plan for sampling for attributes

11·36 The factors that must be considered when choosing a plan for sampling
for attributes have already been considered in detail in Chapter 5. The
main considerations can be set out in the light of the detailed discussion
in the previous sections. In drawing up such a plan, decisions based on
technical or economic considerations must first be taken on the quality of
material which the consumer is prepared to accept and the quality which the
producer does not wish to be rejected, and on the associated probabilities.
In making these decisions, two points are being fixed on the Operating
Characteristic Curve, thus defining the sampling scheme as a whole. Initially,
therefore, attention may be restricted to fixed probability points, such as 0·1
for both α and β, knowing that the behaviour with respect to other probability
levels can be ascertained from the Operating Characteristic. Reasonable
values of m_1 and m_2 are then chosen, and the sample size is calculated which
will be related to the slope of the Operating Characteristic Curve when using
fixed values of α and β. Assigned values should be consistent with economic
considerations; for instance, if the consequences of accepting a lot of poor
quality or of rejecting a lot of good quality are serious or costly, the values of
m_1 and m_2 should be close together, thus giving a fairly steep operating
characteristic curve, and the requisite protection obtained at the expense of
large samples. If the scheme becomes too expensive because of the sample
size, the interval between m_1 and m_2 should be increased, but the scheme will
then be less discriminatory.

The economic balance between acceptance and rejection levels and amount
of sampling should be found by consultation between producer and consumer, and if possible by calculating costs consequent on the inspection
scheme. The choice of a fixed sample size or of a sequential scheme will be
indicated by the nature of the inspection problem, as discussed above. A
scheme involving a fixed sample size can be worked out in detail from Table
F for values of α and β of 0·005, 0·025 and 0·1; these should suffice for many
applications. Appropriate formulae for sequential plans are given above.

Sampling clauses in specifications

11·37 When sampling inspection is required to ensure compliance with
specification requirements, a clause to the effect that the proportion of
defective articles must not exceed a certain figure, e.g. 2%, is not operationally
practical. Thus it would require a very large sample to distinguish between
1·8% and 2%, and supplier and purchaser might well be involved in un-
resolvable arguments with batches of borderline quality. On the other hand,
a specification sampling clause defining the size of the sample and the allowable number of defective articles, particularly if it includes a statement of the
sampling risks involved, is unambiguous and readily put into operation.

Nevertheless, a requirement such as "no defective articles should be found in a sample of 10" provides very limited protection. Such a sampling scheme, in fact, accepts 10% of lots containing 21% of defectives, if they are presented for inspection, and rejects 10% of those containing 1%. While it may be satisfactory in restricted circumstances, such as checking that an established level of quality is being maintained, the consequent risks should be fully appreciated, and in general a larger sample would be preferred. Sequential schemes can be included in specifications by reference to a table of acceptance and rejection numbers, preferably including a statement of the consequent risks.

Sampling clauses in specifications generally legislate for all eventualities, including the possibility of inspecting very inferior lots. However, the producer may be able to demonstrate, by means of control charts, for instance, that his process is stable and that unacceptable lots are presented only very occasionally. A reduction in sample size is then justified, by mutual agreement, to such a level as to ensure only that stability is being maintained, as discussed in § **11·33**. If it were established that production was no longer stable, the larger sample size would be reinstituted to reject lots of unacceptable quality. The specification for such a scheme would include a clause to the effect that the smaller sample size would be permissible, provided that no rejections had taken place in a run of lots (e.g. the last twenty), and that the average percent defective was less than a specified figure.

SAMPLING OF VARIABLES

11·4 When the criterion on which the sample is judged is a measurement as distinct from an attribute, the data are treated by the methods described in Chapters 3–5. The measurement may be a dimension, or any mechanical, physical or chemical property; and the bulk of material may be in the form of discrete articles, a solid in lump or powder, a liquid or gas, or rolls, sheets or lengths of fabricated material. The object of sampling is to assess the mean value of the measurement and possibly its standard deviation.

The physical process of taking the samples will clearly depend on the type of material being dealt with, but the same statistical principles will apply whether the measurements comprise, for instance, the weights of pellets, the viscosity of oil, the ash content of coal, or the tensile strength of metal specimens. Further consideration need not be devoted, therefore, to the form of the material, except in so far as it may influence the statistical treatment.

Random sampling

11·41 If random samples of n articles or individual units are taken from the batch, then it was shown in § **3·71** that if μ is the average value of any property in the batch and σ is the standard deviation from article to article, the average value $\bar{x}$ of the property in the sample will vary round μ with standard deviation

$\sigma/\sqrt{n}$. It was also stated that, when the original distribution is not Normal, that of $\bar{x}$ rapidly approaches the Normal form as n is increased. Provided the original distribution is unimodal and not excessively skew, the distribution of $\bar{x}$ can be assumed to be Normal, even for sample sizes as small as 3. Thus, the limits for the value of μ at various probability levels can usually be determined with sufficient accuracy by establishing Confidence Limits [§ 4·21] $\bar{x} \pm u\sigma/\sqrt{n}$, the value of u for a given probability level being obtained from Table A. When σ is not known it has to be estimated from the sample, and the confidence limits are then $\bar{x} \pm ts/\sqrt{n}$, where the appropriate value of t is obtained from Table C.

Example: Sampling of fertiliser

11·411 A batch of fertiliser in bags had to be sampled for chemical estimation of certain constituents. A representative portion was withdrawn from each of eight bags selected at random and subjected to analysis; the results for the estimation of soluble phosphorus pentoxide were 6·34, 6·23, 6·47, 6·27, 6·43, 6·52, 6·25, 6·54. The mean of these results is 6·381 and the standard deviation 0·125; the standard error of the mean is therefore 0·044. As the standard deviation has been determined from the sample itself, confidence limits must be derived by employing a value of t from Table C, that for a probability of 0·025 with 7 degrees of freedom being 2·36. The 95% confidence limits for expressing the accuracy of the mean are therefore

$$6·381 \pm 2·36 \times 0·044$$

or $\qquad$ 6·485 and 6·277

11·412 If, in addition to the variation of the average value of the property in the sample, we consider also the errors in the determination of this property, two cases will arise. First, if the property is measured on each article n the sample separately and then averaged arithmetically, the variance of the resulting average will be $(\sigma_1^2 + \sigma_2^2)/n$, where σ_1 is the standard deviation among the articles in the batch and σ_2 is the standard deviation of the determination on the individual articles. If on the other hand the average is determined on the sample as a whole (e.g. finding the average weight of a number of pellets by weighing the whole sample and dividing by the number of pellets), then if σ_3 is the standard deviation of the determination on the whole sample (e.g. total weight of pellets), the standard deviation of the determination of the average will be σ_3/n, and therefore the total variance of the resulting average will be $(\sigma_1^2/n + \sigma_3^2/n^2)$. If the error in the determination is independent of the magnitude being determined, $\sigma_3 = \sigma_2$, and the direct determination on the whole sample will give the more accurate result. If on the other hand the error is proportional to the magnitude being determined (i.e. the coefficient of variation is constant), then $\sigma_3 = n\sigma_2$ and the variance given above reduces to $(\sigma_1^2/n + \sigma_2^2)$, so that the arithmetic average of determinations on individual articles will give the more accurate result, though it will of course involve more work.

A case of particular importance arises when the property measured is composition as determined by a chemical analysis. The sample as a whole may be ground (in the case of solids), thoroughly mixed, and divided before analysis. The process of mixing averages the composition over the n individual items and the analysis gives the average composition direct. Since the precision of the analysis is independent of the size of the original sample, the total variance will be $\sigma_1^2/n + \sigma_2^2$, where σ_2 is the standard deviation of the analytical method. In practice s will be used as an estimate of σ in the various cases discussed above.

A more complete account of investigations into sampling and testing errors is contained in *Design and Analysis*, Chapter 4.

Stratified sampling

11·42 When it is known or suspected that the average values of the properties of the material may not be the same in all parts of the bulk, stratified (or representative) sampling should be employed. The bulk to be sampled is divided into a number of real or imaginary sections, and the sample is made up by drawing an amount from each section proportional to its size. The portions should be drawn from the individual sections in a random manner and are known as *increments*. If the variation between the sections is considerable compared with the variation within the sections, it will be easily seen that, since each section is represented in the sample by its own increment, the composition of the sample will correspond more closely to that of the bulk than would be the case if each increment had been drawn at random from the bulk as a whole, which would probably result in some sections supplying a disproportionately large portion of the sample. Such a random sample would of course be unbiased in the sense that the average of a large number of such samples would tend to the average of the bulk; the sample mean would, however, have a higher standard deviation than that of the corresponding stratified sample.

Consider a batch of N articles divided up into a number of sub-groups containing respectively N_1, N_2, N_3, etc., articles. Consider some property whose average value (μ) for the whole batch we desire to measure, and let the average values of this property in the sub-groups be μ_1, μ_2, μ_3, etc., and the standard deviations of individual articles in the sub-groups be σ_1, σ_2, σ_3, etc. Then:

$$\mu = (N_1\mu_1 + N_2\mu_2 + N_3\mu_3 + \ldots)/N$$

From each sub-group several articles (n_1, n_2, n_3, etc., in number) are taken, the same proportion being taken from each group, that is, $an_1 = N_1$,

$an_2 = N_2$, etc., where a is a constant. Let the total number of articles in the sample be m, where $m = n_1 + n_2 + n_3$, etc. If $\bar{x}$ is the average value of the property in the sample it will vary round μ with a variance of $V(\bar{x})$ given by

$$V(\bar{x}) = (n_1\sigma_1{}^2 + n_2\sigma_2{}^2 + n_3\sigma_3{}^2 + \ldots)/m^2$$

If the sub-groups have the same standard deviation, $\sigma_1 = \sigma_2 = \sigma_3 = \ldots = \sigma$, and the above formula reduces to

$$V(\bar{x}) = \sigma^2/m \quad\ldots\ldots\ldots\ldots\ldots\ldots\ldots(11 \cdot 3)$$

It should be noted that the accuracy depends on the standard deviation within the sub-groups and not, as in the case of random sampling, on the standard deviation of the batch as a whole. The above reasoning may be applied when the material is a continuous medium, such as a powder or liquid, instead of being composed of discrete articles. If appreciable variations in the bulk are suspected, the bulk is divided into portions, the number of increments from each being proportional to its size. Since few materials can with certainty be regarded as homogeneous, stratified sampling should normally be used whenever a sample is taken in a number of increments that are to be mixed together before examination.

Example: Stratified sampling of pellets

11·421 A representative sample is to be taken from a consignment of 10 tins of pellets consisting of a mixture of sodium nitrite and ammonium chloride. This sample is to be used to determine the average chlorine content of the consignment. The pellets normally contain 29% of chlorine, and the variation from pellet to pellet in the same tin is known from previous work to correspond to a standard deviation of about 1·2% chlorine, the analytical error being negligible. How many pellets should be taken from each tin in order that the sampling error of the average for the consignment should have a standard deviation of less than 0·1% chlorine?

In this case we have $\sigma = 1 \cdot 2\%$, and $V(\bar{x})$ should not exceed $(0 \cdot 1)^2$.

From Formula (11·3) we have $V(\bar{x}) = \sigma^2/m$.

$$m = \sigma^2/V(\bar{x}) = (1 \cdot 2/0 \cdot 1)^2 = 144$$

The requisite accuracy would therefore be obtained by taking 15 pellets from each tin, making 150 in all. These would then be ground, mixed, subdivided, and analysed for chlorine.

If the standard error of analysis, σ_1, is appreciable, more than one analysis may have to be carried out. For n analyses

$$V(\bar{x}) = \frac{\sigma^2}{m} + \frac{\sigma_1{}^2}{n} = 0 \cdot 1^2$$

n and m may be readily chosen by trial. Several solutions may be possible, and the choice between them can be made on a cost basis.

It should be noted that in using Formula (11·3) we have made the tacit assumption that all the pellets are of the same weight and that therefore the arithmetic average of the compositions of the individual pellets is identical with the average composition by weight. Only when the distribution is very skew would this assumption materially affect the result, in which case a weighted average would have to be used.

Producer's and consumer's risks

11·43 Most sampling will be carried out to ensure compliance with specification requirements in which maximum or minimum values, or both, are specified. Sampling errors considered in relationship to these limits necessitate consideration of producer's and consumer's risks, already discussed in § **11·31** for sampling by attributes. Thus, consider an example in which the confidence limits are $\bar{x} \pm 3$ units, with a probability of 0·05 that the true value will lie outside this range. If test results fall just on one of the specified limits there is a 0·025 probability that the consumer will accept material in which the true value is 3 or more units on the wrong side of the specified limit, and conversely a similar probability that the producer will reject material the true value of which is 3 or more units on the right side of the specified limit. As in the former discussion, these probabilities are the consumer's and producer's risks. The practical result is that the sentencing of a lot is indeterminate when the true value is close to a specified limit, but that the sentencing, either acceptance or rejection, becomes more definite when the true value is remote from this limit. The Operating Characteristic Curve, showing the relationship between true value and probability of acceptance, is, in fact, a cumulative normal curve for samples of reasonable size. It is defined either by the midpoint, standard deviation and sample size, or by producer's and consumer's risks and the levels of quality associated with them.

The range of uncertainty for defined producer's and consumer's risks can be reduced by increasing the size of the sample, but this may be uneconomic when the majority of lots have mean values which are well removed from the specified limits. In these circumstances it would be profitable to adopt a double sampling plan, taking a second sample when the result of the first falls in the range of uncertainty. Economy of sampling would also be achieved by the use of control charts [§ **10·8**]. Whenever possible, the economics of a sampling scheme should be considered by reference to the distribution of quality of lots presented for inspection, and costs of inspection, rejection, and acceptance of inferior material.

Sequential sampling of variables

11·44 Instead of adopting a multi-sampling technique it may be more logical to employ sequential sampling, as discussed in § **11·35**. The results are then assessed after each observation, and a decision is reached to accept, reject, or continue sampling.

The sequential plan is defined in terms of five quantities, namely:

m_1, the average value for material which should not be rejected.

m_2, the average value for material of barely acceptable quality.

a, the producer's risk of rejecting material when in fact it has an average value m_1.

β, the consumer's risk of accepting material when in fact it has an average value m_2.

σ, the standard deviation.

When lots of worse quality than m_2 are presented the probability of acceptance will be less than β, and similarly lots of better quality than m_1 will be rejected with a probability less than a. The value of m_1 may be greater or less than m_2, depending on whether the specified limit is a minimum or maximum figure, and the difference between them, as well as the values of a and β, should preferably be decided from technical and economic considerations.

The above five quantities define the sequential scheme, but it is often preferable to consider it in relation to the Operating Characteristic Curve, which is fixed uniquely by two points, such as (m_1, a) and (m_2, β). The considerations in § 11·32, which deals with the Operating Characteristic Curve for inspection by attributes, frequently apply to the sampling of variables. Thus, attention may be restricted to the instances in which a and β have equal values of, say, 0·025, choosing m_1 and m_2 to be reasonably spaced on the curve. Average sample sizes can be calculated as shown later; if the scheme is considered too expensive, bearing in mind the costs of accepting inferior material and rejecting good material, the interval between m_1 and m_2 should be increased, thereby reducing the slope of the characteristic curve.

The size of sample required to reach a decision will depend chiefly on the quality of lots presented for inspection. Thus, small samples will suffice for lots of very good or of very bad quality, which will be quickly accepted or rejected; whereas lots of intermediate quality, particularly those with average values between m_1 and m_2, will require larger samples. Furthermore, samples of the same size will not, in general, be taken from lots of the same quality owing to sampling fluctuation; average sample sizes can, however, be calculated, the values for lots with mean values of m_1, m_2 and $(m_1 + m_2)/2$ being respectively

$$\frac{(1 - a)b - aa}{(m_2 - m_1)^2/2\sigma^2}, \quad \frac{(1 - \beta)a - \beta b}{(m_2 - m_1)^2/2\sigma^2} \quad \text{and} \quad \frac{ab}{(m_2 - m_1)^2/\sigma^2} \quad (11.4)$$

where $a = \ln [(1 - \beta)/a]$ and $b = \ln [(1 - a)/\beta]$.

Sample sizes greater than three times the largest of these values are unlikely to be encountered. If the amount of inspection appears to be excessive, necessitating a reduction in sample size, an increase should be made in a, β or the difference between m_1 and m_2, but there is then a greater risk of reaching wrong decisions. In the long run, sequential methods provide a valid basis for decisions with smaller samples than other procedures.

As the results become available one by one during sequential sampling, they may be assessed by reference to a table of acceptance and rejection values prepared beforehand from the formulae:

$$\left. \begin{aligned} x_1 &= (m_1 + m_2)n/2 + h_1 \\ x_2 &= (m_1 + m_2)n/2 - h_2 \end{aligned} \right\} \quad \dots\dots\dots\dots(11\cdot5)$$

where
$$\left. \begin{aligned} h_1 &= b\sigma^2/(m_1 - m_2) \\ h_2 &= a\sigma^2/(m_1 - m_2) \end{aligned} \right\} \quad \dots\dots\dots\dots(11\cdot51)$$

and n is the number of observations made.

When the cumulative total of the observations is between x_1 and x_2 for the corresponding value of n, a further sample is inspected; but the lot is rejected —assuming that the specified limit is a minimum value—when the cumulative total is less than x_2, or accepted when it is greater than x_1. Alternatively, a graphical procedure may be used in which x_1 and x_2 are plotted against n, giving two parallel straight lines, by reference to which the cumulative total is assessed [see also *Design and Analysis*, Chapter 3].

Example

11·441   The breaking load of a plastic, employing a test piece of defined shape and size, is of the order of 1,350 lb. with a standard deviation of 150 lb. Batches having a mean value as low as 1,150 lb. should not be accepted, and similarly values of 1,350 lb. should not be rejected. The associated risks were fixed at 0·05 and 0·1 respectively. Therefore $m_1 = 1,350$, $m_2 = 1,150$, $a = 0\cdot1$, $\beta = 0\cdot05$ and $\sigma = 150$.

From Expressions *11·4*, the average sample sizes for lots of quality m_1 and m_2 and $\frac{1}{2}(m_1 + m_2)$ are 2·7, 2·2 and 3·7 respectively, sizes which are acceptable. From $(11\cdot5)$:

$$x_1 = 1,250n + 325 \quad \text{and} \quad x_2 = 1,250n - 253$$

and from these a table of acceptance and rejection numbers can be calculated for integral values of n.

In this example interest centres not so much on average sample size as on maximum sample size, since it is convenient to prepare a defined number of test pieces at one and the same time. Although most batches may be sentenced on the results of two or three tests, some may require several more, and a reasonable maximum should be assigned. From the above equations it will be seen that, if the cumulative value of breaking load after five tests lies between 5,997 and 6,575 lb. (i.e. average values of 1,199 and 1,315 lb.)

no decision can be reached to accept or reject the lot. Economic considerations then determine whether (*a*) the lot should be arbitrarily accepted or rejected, employing a relaxation of the risks defined above, or (*b*) five more test pieces should be prepared and tested sequentially.

11·442 The case considered hitherto is that of a specification embodying either a maximum or a minimum limit. Producer's and consumer's risks are then assigned in relationship to this one limit. Many specifications, however, contain both maximum and minimum limits, and values of a, β, m_1 and m_2 will then have to be established with respect to both limits. In practice these will lead to two pairs of parallel lines on the graph relating cumulative value to number of samples. The area will then be divided into five sections, the two outermost indicating rejection, and the central one acceptance; sampling will be continued if the plotted point falls between either pair of parallel lines. Further information on this application of sequential methods is contained in *Design and Analysis*, § **3·25**.

Sequential methods are likely to be of most value when a clear-cut decision is needed and when the physical process of taking samples is easier and cheaper than the measuring operation. In cases where the mean value must be determined with a stipulated precision, a sample of fixed size is likely to be more satisfactory, particularly if the material is not homogeneous. The necessity for taking a truly random sample is as great with sequential as with any other sampling procedure.

Sampling clauses in specifications
11·45 Sampling clauses in specifications should, of course, indicate the quality characteristics which the consumer desires in the product. At the same time, however, they should be related to the level of quality which the producer is able to maintain in his manufacturing process and to the accuracy of testing methods. The inherent variability of batches should also be considered; this is best done by assessing confidence limits, a knowledge of which is very useful in interpreting test results in relation to specification limits. In fact, information obtained over a period in sampling batches of a specified material may well be used in drawing up sampling clauses for specification purposes. Principles may be exemplified by reference to B.S. 771 : 1948, "Synthetic Resin Moulding Materials."

This specification deals with a number of physical properties, such as tensile strength, volume resistivity and water absorption, for which either maximum or minimum limits are indicated. These limits, however, are not specified, but are defined by means of basic values for average and standard deviation; values for these have been agreed at levels which are obtainable with the majority of well-established, acceptable commercial materials.

Furthermore, sample sizes are not specified, but suggestions are brought forward with respect to recommended numbers of test specimens. For each size of sample, if a decrease in the value of a property denotes a worsening of quality, a lower limit is set for the mean such that there is a 0·01 probability that material of basic quality will be rejected. The lower limit is set, in fact, at a value

$$X - \frac{2 \cdot 33\sigma}{\sqrt{n}}$$

where X and σ are the basic values for mean and standard deviation respectively, n is the sample size, and 2·33 is the value of the normal deviate, u, for a 0·01 probability. Similarly, upper limits for sample standard deviation are set by means of a multiplying factor, depending on sample size, and applied to the basic standard deviation.

An important feature of this specification is that it recognises that evidence of conformity can be established by a study of test results obtained on a sequence of batches of material produced during a period not exceeding six months. One batch, assessed purely on its own test results, apparently may be of quite low quality and yet be accepted; but, if a consistently doubtful product is being presented for sampling, the results obtained on a sequence of lots may justify rejection when those on a single lot did not. The producer's risk is taken care of in setting the limit at 0·01 probability level below the basic value, whereas the consumer is protected in the initial setting of the basic value and in the assessment from a sequence of samples, which, by increasing the number of test results, brings the lower limit closer to the basic value. Furthermore, the clauses relating to standard deviation exercise some degree of control on the precision of the testing methods.

This specification on moulding materials makes the inherent assumption that batches are homogeneous, and provides an instructive example of the use of statistical techniques in specifications. When lots are not homogeneous, the physical process of taking a sample should be clearly specified to avoid arguments between producer and consumer. Such materials, however, are likely to be sampled not so much to determine conformity with specification as to ascertain quality for the purpose of fixing price or the process for which the material is fitted.

The need for a realistic approach in drafting specifications must be emphasised. If limits are fixed without adequate consultation, in the hope that the producer will be able to meet them, arguments may well arise on the interpretation of the specification and the testing methods to be used, the only result of which will be to bring the specification into disrepute. A more logical approach is that in which test data are analysed to ascertain levels within which suitable values can be reasonably maintained and to determine the inherent variability of the process and of testing methods. A designed experiment of simple form including a number of lots, and replicate sampling and testing of variables, should be carried out in many instances. If agreement between producer and consumer cannot be reached on the results of such tests, then production methods may have to be altered. The designed experiment should also provide adequate information to enable sample sizes to be specified and to indicate the risks involved in the agreed sampling scheme. Further information may be obtained from *Design and Analysis*, Chapter 3.

Assumptions regarding standard deviation and Normality

11·46 In discussing the sampling of variables several assumptions have been made either implicitly or explicitly. Thus it is assumed that the standard deviation is known and that it maintains a constant value, subject to the usual sampling errors, over a considerable number of batches or lots. Similarly an approximately Normal distribution is assumed. The only way of knowing whether a single batch is likely to be homogeneous is by having a fairly complete knowledge of its previous history, which is not always available. In order to draw up a reasonable sampling plan, therefore, a considerable amount of prior information is required, which can be obtained from an examination of accumulated results. A simple and illuminating method of assessing a series of figures is to plot them on control charts for both means and either standard deviations or ranges [Chapter 10]. Thus, if the standard deviation chart indicates lack of stability, the most likely cause is that the lots are not homogeneous; this could be confirmed by a special investigation employing stratified sampling on a few questionable lots. Similarly the relationship of the mean values to the specified limits provides an indication whether the amount of sampling should be increased or decreased. For instance, reduced sampling could be instituted if it has been established that mean values are statistically stable and the amount of variation is well within that allowed by the specification. Mean values associated with producer's and consumer's risks can be included on the chart, and the plotted points judged with respect to them. It should always be remembered, however, that control charts are only a graphical method for applying statistical tests of significance.

If the value of the standard deviation is required over a number of lots, it can be obtained directly from the control chart. Sampling is rarely carried out with the object of assessing variability rather than mean value, but sequential methods for detecting defined differences in standard deviation are available if required. Cases in which constant variability is assumed are much more common, and these are best dealt with by means of control charts.

The validity of the assumption that mean values are distributed Normally depends on the shape of the parent population and on the number of measurements in the sample. In general, it is inconvenient to take such large samples that tests for Normality can be applied, and the assumption therefore provides an approximation to the true state of affairs. The practical outcome is that probabilities associated with acceptance or rejection of lots may be slightly different from those indicated by theory. For instance, a sampling scheme which theoretically rejects material at a defined level with a probability of 0·05 may in reality operate with a probability of 0·07, a difference which is unlikely to be technically significant.

REFERENCES

[11·1] SHEWHART, W. A. *Economic Control of Quality of Manufactured Product.* Van Nostrand (New York, 1941).

[11·2] DODGE, H. F., and ROMIG, H. G. *Sampling Inspection Tables.* John Wiley (New York, 1944); Chapman and Hall (London).

[11·3] BARNARD, G. A. *Sampling Inspection and Statistical Decisions. J. Royal Stat. Soc.,* B, **16**, 151 (1954).

[11·4] WALD, A. *Statistical Decision Functions.* John Wiley (New York, 1950); Chapman and Hall (London).

[11·5] DUNCAN, A. J. *Quality Control and Industrial Statistics.* Irwin Inc. (Illinois, 1952).

KEY TO MEMORANDA AND TABLES

CONVENTIONS

(i) A clear distinction should always be drawn between parameters and estimates, i.e. between quantities which characterise the Universe, and estimates of these quantities calculated from the observations. To emphasise this distinction it is usual to employ a Greek letter for the parameter and the corresponding Latin letter for its estimate. Thus σ is the standard deviation in the Universe, and s is the estimate of σ. The convention occasionally breaks down owing to lack of perfect parallelism between the two alphabets.

In the binomial distribution, where the observed proportions are usually denoted by p and q, it may be better to avoid the corresponding Greek letters π and χ in order not to clash with the usual meanings of these symbols. In this Handbook Gothic $\mathfrak{p}$ and $\mathfrak{q}$ have therefore been adopted for the parameters of the binomial distribution, although in writing, or where no possibility of confusion arises, π and χ may be, and in fact quite commonly are, employed.

(ii) It is useful to employ a capital letter to denote a total or subtotal of values which are individually denoted by the corresponding small letters. This convention is, however, far from being universally employed; a total of values of x is perhaps more often denoted by $S(x)$ or S_x, or even S.

Notice also that Y is used for the expected or predicted value of y given by a regression equation.

STATISTICAL AND MATHEMATICAL SYMBOLS

Most of the symbols used in this Handbook are those which are in general, if not universal, use. In some cases a symbol is adopted even though it is not the one most commonly used for the purpose. The symbols u and ϕ have however rarely been used by statisticians; but they have been introduced, the former as an alternative to the more common z or t, both of which already have widely accepted meanings, and the latter to avoid confusion with n, denoting the number in a sample.

In reports designed for general reading it is not so necessary to emphasise the distinction between parameters and estimates as it is in a textbook. Thus s and p can be used for standard deviation and proportion irrespective of whether the quantities referred to are parameters or estimates. V may be used for a variance and m for a mean, avoiding the awkward movements of the typewriter carriage needed for the symbols s^2 and $\bar{x}$.

The general order in the following list is that Greek letters precede the corresponding Latin letters, and small letters precede the corresponding capital letters.

a, *b*
The numbers of individuals in two groups into which a sample has been classified, e.g. the numbers defective and effective in a sample drawn for Quality Control. (See also *b*.)

$a_1, a_2, a_3, \ldots$
The numbers of individuals in three or more groups into which a sample has been classified.

β
Coefficient of linear regression on one independent variable.

$\beta_1, \beta_2, \beta_3, \ldots$
Coefficients of linear regression on three or more independent variables. (β_1 and β_2 are also used to denote the parameters of skewness and kurtosis respectively.)

b
Estimate of the coefficient of linear regression, the estimated regression equation being:
$$y - \bar{y} = b(x - \bar{x})$$

$b_1, b_2, b_3, \ldots$
Estimates of the coefficients of linear regression. The estimated regression of y on x_1 and x_2 is, for example:
$$y - \bar{y} = b_1(x_1 - \bar{x}_1) + b_2(x_2 - \bar{x}_2)$$

$\mathrm{cov}(xy)$ or C_{xy}
Covariance of two variables, x and y.

d
A deviation or difference, either with or without sign, according to context.

e
The base of natural logarithms, $e = 2 \cdot 71828 \ldots$

$E(\ldots)$
The expected value of the quantity enclosed in brackets.

$\exp(\ldots)$
The exponential function of the quantity enclosed in brackets.
$$\exp(x) \equiv e^x$$

ϕ
Number of degrees of freedom.

$\phi_1, \phi_2, \phi_3, \ldots$
Numbers of degrees of freedom in different items of the Analysis of Variance.

f
The frequency of observations in any interval of a grouped distribution.

F
(i) The cumulative frequency, i.e. the total frequency of values of a variable less than a given value.

(ii) The variance ratio, defined as the ratio of two independent estimates of variance, the larger estimate always being the numerator:
$$F = s_1^2 / s_2^2$$

k
The number of samples in a batch or group of samples.

μ The mean of a Universe or frequency distribution, especially the mean of a Normal distribution and the parameter of a Poisson distribution.

m (i) Used by many writers as the parameter of the Poisson distribution, although μ is to be preferred.

(ii) May be used for a mean in typewritten documents, to avoid the Greek symbol μ.

(iii) Sometimes used for the mean of a sample. This is correct by the Greek-Latin convention, though the use of the "bar" is more common.

n The number of observations or individuals in a sample.

$n_1, n_2, n_3, \ldots$ The numbers of individuals in subsections of a sample or in a series of samples.

N (i) The number of individuals in a sample which has been subdivided, or the total number of individuals in a group of samples.

(ii) The number of individuals in a finite Universe, from which a sample of n is drawn for examination.

π (i) Ratio of circumference to diameter, $\pi = 3{\cdot}14159 \ldots$

(ii) Can be used for the proportion in the Universe of individuals having a particular attribute.
     (But see $\mathfrak{p}$, $\mathfrak{q}$, and Note (i), *Conventions*.)

$\mathfrak{p}$ The proportion, in the Universe, of individuals having a particular attribute, being the parameter corresponding to an observed proportion p.

p The proportion, in a sample, of individuals having a particular attribute, e.g. the proportion defective in quality control. (Some writers, however, use p for proportion effective.)
$$p = a/n, \quad p_1 = a_1/n, \quad \text{etc.}$$

P Probability, more especially a probability used for measuring significance. Generally the probability that some criterion, such as t or F, will exceed the value tabulated under P.

χ^2 "Chi-squared," the sum of squares of a number of independent Normally distributed variables with mean zero and standard deviation unity.

χ	Can be used for $1 - \pi$, the parameter corresponding to an observed proportion q. (But see $\mathfrak{p}$, $\mathfrak{q}$, and Note (i), *Conventions*.)
$\mathfrak{q}$	The proportion, in the Universe, corresponding to an observed proportion q in the sample, e.g. the true proportion effective in Quality Control. $$\mathfrak{q} = 1 - \mathfrak{p}$$
q	The complement of p, and in particular the proportion effective in a sample drawn for Quality Control: $$q = 1 - p$$
ρ	Coefficient of correlation.
r	Estimate of the coefficient of correlation.
R	Coefficient of multiple correlation or its estimate.
σ	Standard deviation or standard error.
σ_x or $\sigma(x)$	Standard deviation of x. The standard deviation of a mean $\bar{x}$ may, however, be denoted by σ_m to avoid the typographical difficulty of setting $\bar{x}$ as a subscript.
σ^2	Variance.
σ_x^2 or $\sigma^2(x)$	Variance of x. The variance of a mean may be denoted by σ_m^2.
$\Sigma(\ . \ . \ . \ )$	Summation of the values of the quantity enclosed in brackets. The brackets may be omitted in expressions like Σx or Σxy. (See also $S(\ . \ . \ . \ )$.)
s	Estimate of standard deviation. Note that in Quality Control this symbol is commonly used for the so-called "sample standard deviation," which is the usual estimate of standard deviation multiplied by the factor $\sqrt{\{(n - 1)/n\}}$, where n is the number in the sample.
s^2	Estimate of variance. (See also V.)
s_x^2 or $s^2(x)$	Estimate of the variance of x. The estimated variance of a mean $\bar{x}$ may be denoted by s_m^2 to avoid the difficulty of setting $\bar{x}$ as a subscript.
S	A total or subtotal.
S_x	Total of values of x. (See also $S(\ . \ . \ . \ )$.)
$S.D.$	Standard deviation.

S.E.	Standard error.
$S(\ldots)$	Summation, over individuals in a sample, or over samples in a group of samples, of values of the quantity enclosed in brackets. (See also Note (ii), *Conventions*.)
t	"Student's t," the ratio, without sign, of a variate Normally distributed about zero, to an independent estimate of its standard deviation.
u	A Normal variable with mean zero and standard deviation unity. $$u = (x - \mu)/\sigma$$
v	Coefficient of variation $v = \sigma/\mu$ or $(100\sigma/\mu)\%$.
V	Variance or estimate of variance.
$V(\ldots)$	Variance or estimate of variance of the quantity enclosed in brackets. V is a useful alternative to s^2 or σ^2, particularly in typewritten documents.
w	The range in a sample.
x	Any variable quantity, such as an observation or measurement or any quantity calculated from a number of observations or measurements. Used more especially for a continuous variable. For variables which can only take integral values, the symbols a, n, or f are more usual.
$x_1, x_2, x_3, \ldots$	(i) Particular values of the variable denoted by x. (ii) Three or more independent variables in a multiple regression.
$\bar{x}$	The arithmetic mean of values of x: $$\bar{x} = X/n = S(x)/n$$ (Note that $\bar{x}$ is the estimate of μ, the Greek-Latin convention here being ignored.)
X	The total of values of x in a sample or set of data. (See also Note (ii), *Conventions*.)
y	(i) Another variable, more especially one whose expected value is a function of x. (ii) The ordinate of a frequency distribution.
z	"Fisher's z," the difference between the natural logarithms of two independent estimates of standard deviation. $$z \equiv \tfrac{1}{2} \log_e F$$

TABLES OF STATISTICAL FUNCTIONS

A.   Normal Distribution (Single-sided)

B.   Probability Points of the χ^2 Distribution

C.   Probability Points of the t-distribution (Single-sided)

D.   Probability Points of the Variance Ratio (F-distribution)

E.   Values of Correlation Coefficient for Different Levels of Significance

F.   Binomial and Poisson Distributions: Confidence Limits

G.   Control Chart Limits for Average

G.1 and G.2.   Control Chart Limits for Range

H.   Multipliers L_1 and L_2 for the Confidence Limits of the Ratio of Two Standard Deviations

ACKNOWLEDGMENTS

TABLE A. Condensed and adapted from the *Biometrika Tables for Statisticians*, **1**, Table 4, with permission of the Trustees of *Biometrika*.

TABLE B. Condensed and adapted from the *Biometrika Tables for Statisticians*, **1**, Table 8, with permission of the Trustees of *Biometrika*, and from *Statistical Tables for Biological, Agricultural and Medical Research*.

TABLE C. Condensed and adapted from the *Biometrika Tables for Statisticians*, **1**, Table 12, with permission of the Trustees of *Biometrika*, and from *Statistical Tables for Biological, Agricultural and Medical Research*.

TABLE D. Condensed and adapted from the *Biometrika Tables for Statisticians*, **1**, Table 18, with permission of the Trustees of *Biometrika*, and from *Statistical Tables for Biological, Agricultural and Medical Research*.

TABLE E AND TABLE F (*due to W. L. Stevens*). Condensed and adapted from *Statistical Tables for Biological, Agricultural and Medical Research*.

TABLES G, G·1, AND G·2. Reproduced from B.S. 600R (with recensions from *Biometrika* Offprint, **32** (1942), 302–310).

STATISTICAL METHODS

Table A

NORMAL DISTRIBUTION (SINGLE-SIDED)

Proportion (A) of Whole Area lying to Right of Ordinate through

$$u = (x - \mu)/\sigma$$

Deviate (u)	Prefix	0·00 0·01 0·02 0·03 0·04 0·05 0·06 0·07 0·08 0·09	Prefix	Deviate (u)
0·0	0·5	000 960 920 880 840 801 761 721 681 641	0·4	0·0
0·1	0·4	602 562 522 483 443 404 364 325 286 247	0·4	0·1
0·2	0·4	207 168 129 090 052 013 974 936 897 859	0·3	0·2
0·3	0·3	821 783 745 707 669 632 594 557 520 483		0·3
0·4		446 409 372 336 300 264 228 192 156 121	0·3	0·4
0·5	0·3	085 050 015 981 946 912 877 843 810 776	0·2	0·5
0·6	0·2	743 709 676 643 611 578 546 514 483 451		0·6
0·7		420 389 358 327 296 266 236 206 177 148	0·2	0·7
0·8	0·2	119 090 061 033 005 977 949 922 894 867	0·1	0·8
0·9	0·1	841 814 788 762 736 711 685 660 635 611		0·9
1·0		587 562 539 515 492 469 446 423 401 379		1·0
1·1		357 335 314 292 271 251 230 210 190 170	0·1	1·1
1·2	0·1	151 131 112 093 075 056 038 020 003 985	0·0	1·2
1·3	0·0	968 951 934 918 901 885 869 853 838 823		1·3
1·4		808 793 778 764 749 735 721 708 694 681		1·4
1·5		668 655 643 630 618 606 594 582 571 559		1·5
1·6		548 537 526 516 505 495 485 475 465 455		1·6
1·7		446 436 427 418 409 401 392 384 375 367		1·7
1·8		359 351 344 336 329 322 314 307 301 294		1·8
1·9		287 281 274 268 262 256 250 244 239 233		1·9
2·0		228 222 217 212 207 202 197 192 188 183		2·0
2·1		179 174 170 166 162 158 154 150 146 143		2·1
2·2		139 136 132 129 125 122 119 116 113 110	0·0	2·2
2·3	0·0	107 104 102 990 964 939 914 889 866 842	0·00	2·3
2·4	0·00	820 798 776 755 734 714 695 676 657 639		2·4
2·5		621 604 587 570 554 539 523 508 494 480		2·5
2·6		466 453 440 427 415 402 391 379 368 357		2·6
2·7		347 336 326 317 307 298 289 280 272 264		2·7
2·8		256 248 240 233 226 219 212 205 199 193		2·8
2·9	0·00	187 181 175 169 164 159 154 149 144 139	0·00	2·9

Table A (*continued*)

EXTENSION FOR HIGHER VALUES OF THE DEVIATE

Deviate (u)	Proportion of Whole Area (A)	Deviate (u)	Proportion of Whole Area (A)	Deviate (u)	Proportion of Whole Area (A)	Deviate (u)	Proportion of Whole Area (A)
3·0	·00 135	3·5	·000 233	4·0	·0^4 317	4·5	·0^5 340
3·1	·000 968	3·6	·000 159	4·1	·0^4 207	4·6	·0^5 211
3·2	·000 687	3·7	·000 108	4·2	·0^4 133	4·7	·0^5 130
3·3	·000 483	3·8	·0^4 723	4·3	·0^5 854	4·8	·0^6 793
3·4	·000 337	3·9	·0^4 481	4·4	·0^5 541	4·9	·0^6 479
						5·0	·0^6 287

The illustration shows the Normal Curve. The shaded portion is the area (*A*), which is given in the table.

The entries refer to positive values of the argument (*u*). For negative values of *u* write down the complements $(1 - A)$ of the entries.

EXAMPLES

Let u $= + 1·96$. The prefix $= 0·0$ and the entry $= 250$, so that the area to the right $= 0·0250$. Area to left $= 1 - 0·0250 = 0·9750$.

Let u $= - 3·00$. The tabulated value $= 0·00135$. Since *u* is negative, this represents the area to the *left*. Area to right $= 1 - 0·00135 = 0·99865$.

Let u $= + 4·50$. Tabulated value $= 0·00000340$. Area to left $= 0·99999660$.

To find the value of *u* corresponding to a given *A* we use the table in reverse, thus:

Let area to right (i.e. A) $= 0·10$. The two adjacent tabulated values are $A = 0·1003$ for $u = 1·28$, and $A = 0·0985$ for $u = 1·29$. We interpolate linearly to obtain the required value of *u*. Thus $u = 1·28 + (3)(0·01)/18 = 1·2817$.

Table B

PROBABILITY POINTS OF THE χ^2 DISTRIBUTION

ϕ	0·001	0·005	0·01	0·025	0·05	0·10	0·25	0·50	0·75	0·90	0·95	0·975	0·99	0·995
1	10·8	7·88	6·63	5·02	3·84	2·71	1·32	·455	·102	·016	—	—	—	—
2	13·8	10·6	9·21	7·38	5·99	4·61	2·77	1·39	·575	·211	·103	·051	·020	·010
3	16·3	12·8	11·3	9·35	7·81	6·25	4·11	2·37	1·21	·584	·352	·216	·115	·072
4	18·5	14·9	13·3	11·1	9·49	7·78	5·39	3·36	1·92	1·06	·711	·484	·297	·207
5	20·5	16·7	15·1	12·8	11·1	9·24	6·63	4·35	2·67	1·61	1·15	·831	·554	·412
6	22·5	18·5	16·8	14·4	12·6	10·6	7·84	5·35	3·45	2·20	1·64	1·24	·872	·676
7	24·3	20·3	18·5	16·0	14·1	12·0	9·04	6·35	4·25	2·83	2·17	1·69	1·24	·989
8	26·1	22·0	20·1	17·5	15·5	13·4	10·2	7·34	5·07	3·49	2·73	2·18	1·65	1·34
9	27·9	23·6	21·7	19·0	16·9	14·7	11·4	8·34	5·90	4·17	3·33	2·70	2·09	1·73
10	29·6	25·2	23·2	20·5	18·3	16·0	12·5	9·34	6·74	4·87	3·94	3·25	2·56	2·16
11	31·3	26·8	24·7	21·9	19·7	17·3	13·7	10·3	7·58	5·58	4·57	3·82	3·05	2·60
12	32·9	28·3	26·2	23·3	21·0	18·5	14·8	11·3	8·44	6·30	5·23	4·40	3·57	3·07
13	34·5	29·8	27·7	24·7	22·4	19·8	16·0	12·3	9·30	7·04	5·89	5·01	4·11	3·57
14	36·1	31·3	29·1	26·1	23·7	21·1	17·1	13·3	10·2	7·79	6·57	5·63	4·66	4·07
15	37·7	32·8	30·6	27·5	25·0	22·3	18·2	14·3	11·0	8·55	7·26	6·26	5·23	4·60
16	39·3	34·3	32·0	28·8	26·3	23·5	19·4	15·3	11·9	9·31	7·96	6·91	5·81	5·14
17	40·8	35·7	33·4	30·2	27·6	24·8	20·5	16·3	12·8	10·1	8·67	7·56	6·41	5·70
18	42·3	37·2	34·8	31·5	28·9	26·0	21·6	17·3	13·7	10·9	9·39	8·23	7·01	6·26
19	43·8	38·6	36·2	32·9	30·1	27·2	22·7	18·3	14·6	11·7	10·1	8·91	7·63	6·84
20	45·3	40·0	37·6	34·2	31·4	28·4	23·8	19·3	15·5	12·4	10·9	9·59	8·26	7·43
21	46·8	41·4	38·9	35·5	32·7	29·6	24·9	20·3	16·3	13·2	11·6	10·3	8·90	8·03
22	48·3	42·8	40·3	36·8	33·9	30·8	26·0	21·3	17·2	14·0	12·3	11·0	9·54	8·64
23	49·7	44·2	41·6	38·1	35·2	32·0	27·1	22·3	18·1	14·8	13·1	11·7	10·2	9·26
24	51·2	45·6	43·0	39·4	36·4	33·2	28·2	23·3	19·0	15·7	13·8	12·4	10·9	9·89
25	52·6	46·9	44·3	40·6	37·7	34·4	29·3	24·3	19·9	16·5	14·6	13·1	11·5	10·5
26	54·1	48·3	45·6	41·9	38·9	35·6	30·4	25·3	20·8	17·3	15·4	13·8	12·2	11·2
27	55·5	49·6	47·0	43·2	40·1	36·7	31·5	26·3	21·7	18·1	16·2	14·6	12·9	11·8
28	56·9	51·0	48·3	44·5	41·3	37·9	32·6	27·3	22·7	18·9	16·9	15·3	13·6	12·5
29	58·3	52·3	49·6	45·7	42·6	39·1	33·7	28·3	23·6	19·8	17·7	16·0	14·3	13·1
30	59·7	53·7	50·9	47·0	43·8	40·3	34·8	29·3	24·5	20·6	18·5	16·8	15·0	13·8

ϕ is the number of degrees of freedom.

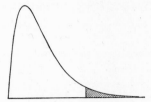

The illustration shows the χ^2 curve for $\phi = 3$. The shaded portion, expressed as a proportion of the total area under the curve, is the columnar heading in the table.

EXAMPLES

Let $\chi^2 = 3.80$, $\phi = 3$. This is between the 0·50 and 0·25 points, and is therefore not significant.

Let $\chi^2 = 20.1$, $\phi = 9$. This is between the 0·025 and 0·01 points, and is therefore significant.

VALUES OF χ^2 FOR $\phi > 30$

For values of $\phi > 30$ the expression $\sqrt{(2\chi^2)} - \sqrt{(2\phi - 1)}$ may be used as a Normal deviate with unit variance, remembering that the probability for χ^2 corresponds to that of a single tail of the Normal Curve.

EXAMPLE

Let $\chi^2 = 124.3$, $\phi = 100$. Then $u = \sqrt{248.6} - \sqrt{199} = 1.66$.
For $u = 1.66$, the value of $P = 0.0485$. χ^2 is therefore just significant.

Table C

PROBABILITY POINTS OF THE *t*-DISTRIBUTION (SINGLE-SIDED)

ϕ	P				
	0·1	0·05	0·025	0·01	0·005
1	3·08	6·31	12·7	31·8	63·7
2	1·89	2·92	4·30	6·96	9·92
3	1·64	2·35	3·18	4·54	5·84
4	1·53	2·13	2·78	3·75	4·60
5	1·48	2·01	2·57	3·36	4·03
6	1·44	1·94	2·45	3·14	3·71
7	1·42	1·89	2·36	3·00	3·50
8	1·40	1·86	2·31	2·90	3·36
9	1·38	1·83	2·26	2·82	3·25
10	1·37	1·81	2·23	2·76	3·17
11	1·36	1·80	2·20	2·72	3·11
12	1·36	1·78	2·18	2·68	3·05
13	1·35	1·77	2·16	2·65	3·01
14	1·34	1·76	2·14	2·62	2·98
15	1·34	1·75	2·13	2·60	2·95
16	1·34	1·75	2·12	2·58	2·92
17	1·33	1·74	2·11	2·57	2·90
18	1·33	1·73	2·10	2·55	2·88
19	1·33	1·73	2·09	2·54	2·86
20	1·32	1·72	2·09	2·53	2·85
21	1·32	1·72	2·08	2·52	2·83
22	1·32	1·72	2·07	2·51	2·82
23	1·32	1·71	2·07	2·50	2·81
24	1·32	1·71	2·06	2·49	2·80
25	1·32	1·71	2·06	2·48	2·79
26	1·32	1·71	2·06	2·48	2·78
27	1·31	1·70	2·05	2·47	2·77
28	1·31	1·70	2·05	2·47	2·76
29	1·31	1·70	2·05	2·46	2·76
30	1·31	1·70	2·04	2·46	2·75
40	1·30	1·68	2·02	2·42	2·70
60	1·30	1·67	2·00	2·39	2·66
120	1·29	1·66	1·98	2·36	2·62
∞	1·28	1·64	1·96	2·33	2·58

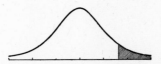

The illustration shows the t-curve for $\phi = 3$. The shaded area corresponds to the columnar headings of the table and the unshaded area to their complements.

EXAMPLE

Single-sided test. For $\phi = 10$ the deviate of the t-curve which cuts off a single tail equivalent to $P = 0.05$ is given by $t = 1.81$. For the Normal Curve the corresponding value of u is 1.64.

TABLE OF THE VARIANCE RATIO (F-DISTRIBUTION)

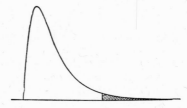

The illustration shows the distribution of the variance ratio for 4 and 16 degrees of freedom. The shaded area, expressed as a proportion of the total area under the curve, is the argument in the first column of Table D.

The variance ratio is always calculated with the *larger* estimate of variance in the *numerator*, and ϕ_1 and ϕ_2 are the numbers of degrees of freedom in the numerator and denominator respectively.

EXAMPLE

Let $F = 4.60$, $\phi_1 = 5$, $\phi_2 = 24$. The 5% and 1% points are 2·62 and 3·90, and the result is significant.

In calculating confidence limits for the variance ratio we require the upper and lower tail areas of the F-distribution. The levels actually tabled refer to the single upper tail area $F_a(\phi_1\phi_2)$.

However, the value $F_{1-a}(\phi_1\phi_2)$ (i.e. the value of F *below which* a proportion a of the whole curve lies) is given by

$$F_{1-a}(\phi_1\phi_2) = \frac{1}{F_a(\phi_2\phi_1)}$$

EXAMPLE

To obtain the 90% confidence limits for the variance ratio we require the values $F_{0.95}(\phi_1\phi_2)$ and $F_{0.05}(\phi_1\phi_2)$.

If $\phi_1 = 4$ and $\phi_2 = 20$, then

$$F_{0.95}(4, 20) = \frac{1}{F_{0.05}(20, 4)} = \frac{1}{5.80} \quad \text{and} \quad F_{0.05}(4, 20) = 2.87$$

The required values are thus 0·172 and 2·87.

PROBABILITY POINTS OF THE VARIANCE RATIO (F-DISTRIBUTION)

ϕ_n (corresponding to greater mean square)

ϕ_a	Probability Point	1	2	3	4	5	6	7	8	9	10	12	15	20	24	30	40	60	120	∞
1	0·100	39·9	49·5	53·6	55·8	57·2	58·2	58·9	59·4	59·9	60·2	60·7	61·2	61·7	62·0	62·3	62·5	62·8	63·1	63·3
	0·050	161	199	216	225	230	234	237	239	241	242	244	246	248	249	250	251	252	253	254
	0·025	648	800	864	900	922	937	948	957	963	969	977	985	993	997	1001	1006	1010	1014	1018
	0·010	4052	4999	5403	5625	5764	5859	5928	5982	6022	6056	6106	6157	6209	6235	6261	6287	6313	6339	6366
2	0·100	8·53	9·00	9·16	9·24	9·29	9·33	9·35	9·37	9·38	9·39	9·41	9·42	9·44	9·45	9·46	9·47	9·47	9·48	9·49
	0·050	18·5	19·0	19·2	19·2	19·3	19·3	19·4	19·4	19·4	19·4	19·4	19·4	19·4	19·5	19·5	19·5	19·5	19·5	19·5
	0·025	38·5	39·0	39·2	39·2	39·3	39·3	39·4	39·4	39·4	39·4	39·4	39·4	39·4	39·5	39·5	39·5	39·5	39·5	39·5
	0·010	98·5	99·0	99·2	99·2	99·3	99·3	99·4	99·4	99·4	99·4	99·4	99·4	99·4	99·5	99·5	99·5	99·5	99·5	99·5
3	0·100	5·54	5·46	5·39	5·34	5·31	5·28	5·27	5·25	5·24	5·23	5·22	5·20	5·18	5·18	5·17	5·16	5·15	5·14	5·13
	0·050	10·1	9·55	9·28	9·12	9·01	8·94	8·89	8·85	8·81	8·79	8·74	8·70	8·66	8·64	8·62	8·59	8·57	8·55	8·53
	0·025	17·4	16·0	15·4	15·1	14·9	14·7	14·6	14·5	14·5	14·4	14·3	14·3	14·2	14·1	14·1	14·0	14·0	13·9	13·9
	0·010	34·1	30·8	29·5	28·7	28·2	27·9	27·7	27·5	27·3	27·2	27·1	26·9	26·7	26·6	26·5	26·4	26·3	26·2	26·1
4	0·100	4·54	4·32	4·19	4·11	4·05	4·01	3·98	3·95	3·94	3·92	3·90	3·87	3·84	3·83	3·82	3·80	3·79	3·78	3·76
	0·050	7·71	6·94	6·59	6·39	6·26	6·16	6·09	6·04	6·00	5·96	5·91	5·86	5·80	5·77	5·75	5·72	5·69	5·66	5·63
	0·025	12·2	10·6	10·0	9·60	9·36	9·20	9·07	8·98	8·90	8·84	8·75	8·66	8·56	8·51	8·46	8·41	8·36	8·31	8·26
	0·010	21·2	18·0	16·7	16·0	15·5	15·2	15·0	14·8	14·7	14·5	14·4	14·2	14·0	13·9	13·8	13·7	13·7	13·6	13·5
5	0·100	4·06	3·78	3·62	3·52	3·45	3·40	3·37	3·34	3·32	3·30	3·27	3·24	3·21	3·19	3·17	3·16	3·14	3·12	3·10
	0·050	6·61	5·79	5·41	5·19	5·05	4·95	4·88	4·82	4·77	4·74	4·68	4·62	4·56	4·53	4·50	4·46	4·43	4·40	4·36
	0·025	10·0	8·43	7·76	7·39	7·15	6·98	6·85	6·76	6·68	6·62	6·52	6·43	6·33	6·28	6·23	6·18	6·12	6·07	6·02
	0·010	16·3	13·3	12·1	11·4	11·0	10·7	10·5	10·3	10·2	10·1	9·89	9·72	9·55	9·47	9·38	9·29	9·20	9·11	9·02
6	0·100	3·78	3·46	3·29	3·18	3·11	3·05	3·01	2·98	2·96	2·94	2·90	2·87	2·84	2·82	2·80	2·78	2·76	2·74	2·72
	0·050	5·99	5·14	4·76	4·53	4·39	4·28	4·21	4·15	4·10	4·06	4·00	3·94	3·87	3·84	3·81	3·77	3·74	3·70	3·67
	0·025	8·81	7·26	6·60	6·23	5·99	5·82	5·70	5·60	5·52	5·46	5·37	5·27	5·17	5·12	5·07	5·01	4·96	4·90	4·85
	0·010	13·7	10·9	9·78	9·15	8·75	8·47	8·26	8·10	7·98	7·87	7·72	7·56	7·40	7·31	7·23	7·14	7·06	6·97	6·88
7	0·100	3·59	3·26	3·07	2·96	2·88	2·83	2·78	2·75	2·72	2·70	2·67	2·63	2·59	2·58	2·56	2·54	2·51	2·49	2·47
	0·050	5·59	4·74	4·35	4·12	3·97	3·87	3·79	3·73	3·68	3·64	3·57	3·51	3·44	3·41	3·38	3·34	3·30	3·27	3·23
	0·025	8·07	6·54	5·89	5·52	5·29	5·12	4·99	4·90	4·82	4·76	4·67	4·57	4·47	4·42	4·36	4·31	4·25	4·20	4·14
	0·010	12·2	9·55	8·45	7·85	7·46	7·19	6·99	6·84	6·72	6·62	6·47	6·31	6·16	6·07	5·99	5·91	5·82	5·74	5·65

For explanation and example see p. 368

B2

Table D (continued)

Proba-bility Point	ϕ_d	ϕ_n (corresponding to greater mean square)																			ϕ_d	Proba-bility Point
		1	2	3	4	5	6	7	8	9	10	12	15	20	24	30	40	60	120	∞		
0·100	8	3·46	3·11	2·92	2·81	2·73	2·67	2·62	2·59	2·56	2·54	2·50	2·46	2·42	2·40	2·38	2·36	2·34	2·32	2·29	8	0·100
0·050		5·32	4·46	4·07	3·84	3·69	3·58	3·50	3·44	3·39	3·35	3·28	3·22	3·15	3·12	3·08	3·04	3·01	2·97	2·93		0·050
0·025		7·57	6·06	5·42	5·05	4·82	4·65	4·53	4·43	4·36	4·30	4·20	4·10	4·00	3·95	3·89	3·84	3·78	3·73	3·67		0·025
0·010		11·3	8·65	7·59	7·01	6·63	6·37	6·18	6·03	5·91	5·81	5·67	5·52	5·36	5·28	5·20	5·12	5·03	4·95	4·86		0·010
0·100	9	3·36	3·01	2·81	2·69	2·61	2·55	2·51	2·47	2·44	2·42	2·38	2·34	2·30	2·28	2·25	2·23	2·21	2·18	2·16	9	0·100
0·050		5·12	4·26	3·86	3·63	3·48	3·37	3·29	3·23	3·18	3·14	3·07	3·01	2·94	2·90	2·86	2·83	2·79	2·75	2·71		0·050
0·025		7·21	5·71	5·08	4·72	4·48	4·32	4·20	4·10	4·03	3·96	3·87	3·77	3·67	3·61	3·56	3·51	3·45	3·39	3·33		0·025
0·010		10·6	8·02	6·99	6·42	6·06	5·80	5·61	5·47	5·35	5·26	5·11	4·96	4·81	4·73	4·65	4·57	4·48	4·40	4·31		0·010
0·100	10	3·28	2·92	2·73	2·61	2·52	2·46	2·41	2·38	2·35	2·32	2·28	2·24	2·20	2·18	2·16	2·13	2·11	2·08	2·06	10	0·100
0·050		4·96	4·10	3·71	3·48	3·33	3·22	3·14	3·07	3·02	2·98	2·91	2·84	2·77	2·74	2·70	2·66	2·62	2·58	2·54		0·050
0·025		6·94	5·46	4·83	4·47	4·24	4·07	3·95	3·83	3·78	3·72	3·62	3·52	3·42	3·37	3·31	3·26	3·20	3·14	3·08		0·025
0·010		10·0	7·56	6·55	5·99	5·64	5·39	5·20	5·06	4·94	4·85	4·71	4·56	4·41	4·33	4·25	4·17	4·08	4·00	3·91		0·010
0·100	12	3·18	2·81	2·61	2·48	2·39	2·33	2·28	2·24	2·21	2·19	2·15	2·10	2·06	2·04	2·01	1·99	1·96	1·93	1·90	12	0·100
0·050		4·75	3·89	3·49	3·26	3·11	3·00	2·91	2·85	2·80	2·75	2·69	2·62	2·54	2·51	2·47	2·43	2·38	2·34	2·30		0·050
0·025		6·55	5·10	4·47	4·12	3·89	3·73	3·61	3·51	3·44	3·37	3·28	3·18	3·07	3·02	2·96	2·91	2·85	2·79	2·72		0·025
0·010		9·33	6·93	5·95	5·41	5·06	4·82	4·64	4·50	4·39	4·30	4·16	4·01	3·86	3·78	3·70	3·62	3·54	3·45	3·36		0·010
0·100	15	3·07	2·70	2·49	2·36	2·27	2·21	2·16	2·12	2·09	2·06	2·02	1·97	1·92	1·90	1·87	1·85	1·82	1·79	1·76	15	0·100
0·050		4·54	3·68	3·29	3·06	2·90	2·79	2·71	2·64	2·59	2·54	2·48	2·40	2·33	2·29	2·25	2·20	2·16	2·11	2·07		0·050
0·025		6·20	4·77	4·15	3·80	3·58	3·41	3·29	3·20	3·12	3·06	2·96	2·86	2·76	2·70	2·64	2·59	2·52	2·46	2·40		0·025
0·010		8·68	6·36	5·42	4·89	4·56	4·32	4·14	4·00	3·89	3·80	3·67	3·52	3·37	3·29	3·21	3·13	3·05	2·96	2·87		0·010
0·100	20	2·97	2·59	2·38	2·25	2·16	2·09	2·04	2·00	1·96	1·94	1·89	1·84	1·79	1·77	1·74	1·71	1·68	1·64	1·61	20	0·100
0·050		4·35	3·49	3·10	2·87	2·71	2·60	2·51	2·45	2·39	2·35	2·28	2·20	2·12	2·08	2·04	1·99	1·95	1·90	1·84		0·050
0·025		5·87	4·46	3·86	3·51	3·29	3·13	3·01	2·91	2·84	2·77	2·68	2·57	2·46	2·41	2·35	2·29	2·22	2·16	2·09		0·025
0·010		8·10	5·85	4·94	4·43	4·10	3·87	3·70	3·56	3·46	3·37	3·23	3·09	2·94	2·86	2·78	2·69	2·61	2·52	2·42		0·010

For explanation and example see p. 368

Table D (*continued*)

ϕ_n (corresponding to greater mean square)

ϕ_d	Probability Point	1	2	3	4	5	6	7	8	9	10	12	15	20	24	30	40	60	120	∞
24	0·100	2·93	2·54	2·33	2·19	2·10	2·04	1·98	1·94	1·91	1·88	1·83	1·78	1·73	1·70	1·67	1·64	1·61	1·57	1·53
	0·050	4·26	3·40	3·01	2·78	2·62	2·51	2·42	2·36	2·30	2·25	2·18	2·11	2·03	1·98	1·94	1·89	1·84	1·79	1·73
	0·025	5·72	4·32	3·72	3·38	3·15	2·99	2·87	2·78	2·70	2·64	2·54	2·44	2·33	2·27	2·21	2·15	2·08	2·01	1·94
	0·010	7·82	5·61	4·72	4·22	3·90	3·67	3·50	3·36	3·26	3·17	3·03	2·89	2·74	2·66	2·58	2·49	2·40	2·31	2·21
30	0·100	2·88	2·49	2·28	2·14	2·05	1·98	1·93	1·88	1·85	1·82	1·77	1·72	1·67	1·64	1·61	1·57	1·54	1·50	1·46
	0·050	4·17	3·32	2·92	2·69	2·53	2·42	2·33	2·27	2·21	2·16	2·09	2·01	1·93	1·89	1·84	1·79	1·74	1·68	1·62
	0·025	5·57	4·18	3·59	3·25	3·03	2·87	2·75	2·65	2·57	2·51	2·41	2·31	2·20	2·14	2·07	2·01	1·94	1·87	1·79
	0·010	7·56	5·39	4·51	4·02	3·70	3·47	3·30	3·17	3·07	2·98	2·84	2·70	2·55	2·47	2·39	2·30	2·21	2·11	2·01
40	0·100	2·84	2·44	2·23	2·09	2·00	1·93	1·87	1·83	1·79	1·76	1·71	1·66	1·61	1·57	1·54	1·51	1·47	1·42	1·38
	0·050	4·08	3·23	2·84	2·61	2·45	2·34	2·25	2·18	2·12	2·08	2·00	1·92	1·84	1·79	1·74	1·69	1·64	1·58	1·51
	0·025	5·42	4·05	3·46	3·13	2·90	2·74	2·62	2·53	2·45	2·39	2·29	2·18	2·07	2·01	1·94	1·88	1·80	1·72	1·64
	0·010	7·31	5·18	4·31	3·83	3·51	3·29	3·12	2·99	2·89	2·80	2·66	2·52	2·37	2·29	2·20	2·11	2·02	1·92	1·80
60	0·100	2·79	2·39	2·18	2·04	1·95	1·87	1·82	1·77	1·74	1·71	1·66	1·60	1·54	1·51	1·48	1·44	1·40	1·35	1·29
	0·050	4·00	3·15	2·76	2·53	2·37	2·25	2·17	2·10	2·04	1·99	1·92	1·84	1·75	1·70	1·65	1·59	1·53	1·47	1·39
	0·025	5·29	3·93	3·34	3·01	2·79	2·63	2·51	2·41	2·33	2·27	2·17	2·06	1·94	1·88	1·82	1·74	1·67	1·58	1·48
	0·010	7·08	4·98	4·13	3·65	3·34	3·12	2·95	2·82	2·72	2·63	2·50	2·35	2·20	2·12	2·03	1·94	1·84	1·73	1·60
120	0·100	2·75	2·35	2·13	1·99	1·90	1·77	1·77	1·72	1·68	1·65	1·60	1·55	1·48	1·45	1·41	1·37	1·32	1·26	1·19
	0·050	3·92	3·07	2·68	2·45	2·29	2·18	2·09	2·02	1·96	1·91	1·83	1·75	1·66	1·61	1·55	1·50	1·43	1·35	1·25
	0·025	5·15	3·80	3·23	2·89	2·67	2·52	2·39	2·30	2·22	2·16	2·05	1·94	1·82	1·76	1·69	1·61	1·53	1·43	1·31
	0·010	6·85	4·79	3·95	3·48	3·17	2·96	2·79	2·66	2·56	2·47	2·34	2·19	2·03	1·95	1·86	1·76	1·66	1·53	1·38
∞	0·100	2·71	2·30	2·08	1·94	1·85	1·77	1·72	1·67	1·63	1·60	1·55	1·49	1·42	1·38	1·34	1·30	1·24	1·17	1·00
	0·050	3·84	3·00	2·60	2·37	2·21	2·10	2·01	1·94	1·88	1·83	1·75	1·67	1·57	1·52	1·46	1·39	1·32	1·22	1·00
	0·025	5·02	3·69	3·12	2·79	2·57	2·41	2·29	2·19	2·11	2·05	1·94	1·83	1·71	1·64	1·57	1·48	1·39	1·27	1·00
	0·010	6·63	4·61	3·78	3·32	3·02	2·80	2·64	2·51	2·41	2·32	2·18	2·04	1·88	1·79	1·70	1·59	1·47	1·32	1·00

For explanation and example see p. 368

Table E

VALUES OF CORRELATION COEFFICIENT FOR DIFFERENT LEVELS OF SIGNIFICANCE

ϕ	P					ϕ	P				
	0·10	0·05	0·02	0·01	0·001		0·10	0·05	0·02	0·01	0·001
1	·988	·997	1·00	1·00	1·00	16	·400	·468	·542	·590	·708
2	·900	·950	·980	·990	·999	17	·389	·455	·528	·575	·693
3	·805	·878	·934	·959	·991	18	·378	·444	·515	·561	·679
4	·729	·811	·882	·917	·974	19	·369	·433	·503	·549	·665
5	·669	·754	·833	·874	·951	20	·360	·423	·492	·537	·652
6	·621	·707	·789	·834	·925	25	·323	·381	·445	·487	·597
7	·582	·666	·750	·798	·898	30	·296	·349	·409	·449	·554
8	·549	·632	·715	·765	·872	35	·275	·325	·381	·418	·519
9	·521	·602	·685	·735	·847	40	·257	·304	·358	·393	·490
10	·497	·576	·658	·708	·823	45	·243	·287	·338	·372	·465
11	·476	·553	·634	·683	·801	50	·231	·273	·322	·354	·443
12	·457	·532	·612	·661	·780	60	·211	·250	·295	·325	·408
13	·441	·514	·592	·641	·760	70	·195	·232	·274	·302	·380
14	·426	·497	·574	·623	·742	80	·183	·217	·256	·283	·357
15	·412	·482	·558	·605	·725	90	·173	·205	·242	·267	·337
						100	·164	·195	·230	·254	·321

ϕ is the number of degrees of freedom.

TABLE OF BINOMIAL AND POISSON DISTRIBUTIONS
(See next page)

To obtain the confidence limits, corresponding to a given probability level P, of an event observed to occur a times out of n, enter the table with a, P and $p = a/n$. Interpolate linearly, if necessary, between values of p. Confidence limits for the Poisson distribution are given directly, taking $p = 0$. For $a > n/2$, enter the table with $b = n - a$ instead of a.

EXAMPLES

A sample of 25 articles is drawn at random from a bulk and 3 of them are found to be defective. What conclusions can we draw about the proportion of defective articles in the bulk?

The value of a is 3 and the value of $p = a/n$ is $3/25 = 0.12$. This value of p is not tabulated and we have to interpolate between the arguments 15 and 30 for n, or 0.2 and 0.1 for p. For $P = 0.025$ the confidence limits are $0.634 + (0.2)(0.016) = 0.637$, and $7.96 - (0.2)(0.75) = 7.81$. Multiplying by 4 to bring these figures to a percentage basis, we assess the percentage defective in the bulk as lying between 2.55% and 31.2%. For $P = 0.10$ the confidence limits are 4.48% and 24.8% (see § **9·152**).

A specification lays down that twelve articles shall be drawn at random and the consignment passed if none of the articles is defective. Discuss the protection given to the consumer.

Take $a = 0$, probability P of a or fewer (i.e. probability that $a = 0$) $= 0.1$, and interpolate at sight between $n = 10$ and $n = 20$, or interpolate with reference to $1/n = 1/12 = 0.08$ . . . between (0.1) and (0.05).

$$2.06 + (0.4)(0.11) = 2.10$$

This is the confidence limit in a sample of 12. The corresponding limit of the percentage defective in the consignment is $(100)(2.10)/12 = 17.5\%$. Hence there is a one-in-ten chance that the consumer would accept a consignment containing as much as 17.5% defective material.

Note that accurate interpolation with respect to p is rarely necessary in practice: it is usually sufficient to make a rough interpolation at sight or even take the nearest value of n tabulated. When a is less than one-twentieth of n, it is usually sufficiently accurate to enter the table with $n = \infty$ ($p = 0$).

Table F
BINOMIAL AND POISSON DISTRIBUTIONS: CONFIDENCE LIMITS

a	n	$p = a/n$	Confidence limits for $\mu = np$ corresponding to probabilities P of					
			0·005	0·025	0·1	0·1	0·025	0·005
			Lower limit			Upper limit		
0	5	(·2)	For a = 0 interpolate			1·84	2·61	3·27
		(·15)	with reference to 1/n			1·95	2·83	3·66
	10	(·1)				2·06	3·09	4·11
	20	(·05)				2·17	3·37	4·65
	∞	0				2·30	3·69	5·30
1	2		·005	·025	·103	1·90	1·97	1·99
	3		·005	·025	·104	2·41	2·72	2·88
	4		·005	·025	·104	2·72	3·22	3·56
	5	·2	·005	·025	·104	2·92	3·58	4·07
		·15	·005	·025	·105	3·14	3·99	4·69
	10	·1	·005	·025	·105	3·37	4·45	5·44
	20	·05	·005	·025	·105	3·62	4·97	6·34
	∞	0	·005	·025	·105	3·89	5·57	7·43
2	4		·118	·270	·570	3·43	3·73	3·88
	5		·114	·264	·561	3·77	4·27	4·59
	6		·112	·260	·556	4·00	4·67	5·14
	7		·111	·257	·552	4·17	4·97	5·54
	8	·25	·110	·255	·549	4·31	5·21	5·94
	10	·2	·108	·252	·545	4·50	5·56	6·48
		·15	·107	·249	·542	4·69	5·94	7·09
	20	·1	·106	·247	·538	4·90	6·34	7·74
	40	·05	·105	·245	·535	5·11	6·77	8·44
	∞	0	·103	·242	·532	5·32	7·22	9·27
3	6		·398	·709	1·21	4·79	5·29	5·60
	7		·387	·693	1·19	5·05	5·71	6·18
	8		·380	·682	1·17	5·24	6·04	6·64
	9		·374	·674	1·17	5·39	6·31	7·03
	10	·3	·370	·667	1·16	5·52	6·52	7·35
	15	·2	·358	·650	1·14	5·89	7·21	8·41
	30	·1	·348	·634	1·12	6·28	7·96	9·61
	∞	0	·338	·619	1·10	6·68	8·77	11·0
4	8	·5	·799	1·26	1·92	6·08	6·74	7·20
	10	·4	·768	1·22	1·88	6·46	7·38	8·09
		·3	·741	1·18	1·84	6·83	8·04	9·06
	20	·2	·716	1·15	1·80	7·21	8·73	10·1
	40	·1	·694	1·12	1·77	7·60	9·47	11·3
	∞	0	·672	1·09	1·74	7·99	10·2	12·6
5	10	·5	1·28	1·87	2·67	7·33	8·13	8·72
		·4	1·23	1·81	2·61	7·72	8·79	9·66
		·3	1·19	1·76	2·56	8·10	9·47	10·7
	25	·2	1·15	1·71	2·52	8·49	10·2	11·7
	50	·1	1·11	1·66	2·47	8·88	10·9	12·9
	∞	0	1·08	1·62	2·43	9·27	11·7	14·1
6	12	·5	1·83	2·53	3·46	8·54	9·47	10·2
	15	·4	1·75	2·45	3·38	8·95	10·2	11·2
	20	·3	1·69	2·38	3·32	9·35	10·9	12·2
	30	·2	1·63	2·31	3·26	9·74	11·6	13·3
	60	·1	1·58	2·26	3·20	10·1	12·3	14·4
	∞	0	1·54	2·20	3·15	10·5	13·1	15·7

For examples see p. 373.

Table F (*continued*)

BINOMIAL AND POISSON DISTRIBUTIONS: CONFIDENCE LIMITS

a	$p = a/n$	Confidence limits for $\mu = np$ corresponding to probabilities P of					
		0·005	0·025	0·1	0·1	0·025	0·005
		Lower limit			Upper limit		
7	·5	2·41	3·23	4·26	9·74	10·8	11·6
	·4	2·32	3·12	4·17	10·1	11·5	12·6
	·3	2·24	3·03	4·09	10·6	12·2	13·7
	·2	2·16	2·95	4·02	11·0	12·9	14·8
	·1	2·10	2·88	3·96	11·4	13·7	15·9
	o	2·04	2·81	3·89	11·8	14·4	17·1
8	·5	3·04	3·94	5·09	10·9	12·1	13·0
	·4	2·92	3·82	4·98	11·3	12·8	14·0
	·3	2·82	3·72	4·89	11·8	13·5	15·1
	·2	2·73	3·62	4·80	12·2	14·3	16·2
	·1	2·65	3·53	4·73	12·6	15·0	17·4
	o	2·57	3·45	4·66	13·0	15·8	18·6
9	·5	3·68	4·68	5·92	12·1	13·3	14·3
	·4	3·55	4·54	5·80	12·5	14·1	15·4
	·3	3·43	4·42	5·70	13·0	14·8	16·5
	·2	3·32	4·31	5·60	13·4	15·6	17·6
	·1	3·22	4·21	5·51	13·8	16·3	18·8
	o	3·13	4·12	5·43	14·2	17·1	20·0
10	·5	4·35	5·44	6·76	13·2	14·6	15·6
	·4	4·20	5·28	6·63	13·7	15·3	16·8
	·3	4·06	5·14	6·51	14·1	16·1	17·9
	·2	3·93	5·02	6·41	14·6	16·9	19·0
	·1	3·82	4·90	6·31	15·0	17·6	20·2
	o	3·72	4·80	6·22	15·4	18·4	21·4
11	·5	5·04	6·21	7·62	14·4	15·8	17·0
	·4	4·87	6·03	7·47	14·8	16·6	18·1
	·3	4·71	5·88	7·34	15·3	17·4	19·2
	·2	4·57	5·74	7·23	15·7	18·1	20·4
	·1	4·44	5·61	7·12	16·2	18·9	21·6
	o	4·32	5·49	7·02	16·6	19·7	22·8
12	·5	5·75	6·99	8·48	15·5	17·0	18·2
	·4	5·55	6·80	8·32	16·0	17·8	19·4
	·3	5·37	6·63	8·18	16·5	18·6	20·6
	·2	5·22	6·47	8·05	16·9	19·4	21·7
	·1	5·07	6·33	7·94	17·3	20·2	22·9
	o	4·94	6·20	7·83	17·8	21·0	24·1
13	·5	6·47	7·78	9·34	16·7	18·2	19·5
	·4	6·25	7·57	9·17	17·1	19·0	20·7
	·3	6·06	7·38	9·02	17·6	19·8	21·9
	·2	5·88	7·22	8·89	18·1	20·6	23·1
	·1	5·72	7·06	8·76	18·5	21·4	24·3
	o	5·58	6·92	8·65	19·0	22·2	25·5
14	·5	7·20	8·58	10·2	17·8	19·4	20·8
	·4	6·96	8·36	10·0	18·3	20·3	22·0
	·3	6·75	8·15	9·87	18·8	21·1	23·2
	·2	6·56	7·97	9·73	19·2	21·9	24·4
	·1	6·39	7·81	9·59	19·7	22·7	25·6
	o	6·23	7·65	9·47	20·1	23·5	26·8

For examples see p. 373.

Table G

CONTROL CHART LIMITS FOR AVERAGE ($\bar{x}$)

To obtain limits $\begin{cases} \text{multiply } \sigma \text{ by the appropriate value of } A_{0 \cdot 025} \text{ and} \\ \quad A_{0 \cdot 001}, \text{ or} \\ \text{multiply } \bar{w} \text{ by the appropriate value of } A'_{0 \cdot 025} \text{ and} \\ \quad A'_{0 \cdot 001} \end{cases}$

then add to and subtract from the average value ($\bar{X}$).

No. in Sample n	For Inner Limits $A_{0 \cdot 025}$	For Outer Limits $A_{0 \cdot 001}$	For Inner Limits $A'_{0 \cdot 025}$	For Outer Limits $A'_{0 \cdot 001}$
2	1·386	2·185	1·229	1·937
3	1·132	1·784	0·668	1·054
4	0·980	1·545	0·476	0·750
5	0·877	1·382	0·377	0·594
6	0·800	1·262	0·316	0·498
7	0·741	1·168	0·274	0·432
8	0·693	1·093	0·244	0·384
9	0·653	1·030	0·220	0·347
10	0·620	0·977	0·202	0·317
11	0·591	0·932	0·186	0·294
12	0·566	0·892	0·174	0·274
13	0·544	0·857		
14	0·524	0·826		
15	0·506	0·798		
16	0·490	0·773	Samples containing more than 12 individuals should not be used when utilising the range of the results.	
17	0·475	0·750		
18	0·462	0·728		
19	0·450	0·709		
20	0·438	0·691		
21	0·428	0·674	These factors should only be used when it is not necessary to calculate s for the samples and when sufficient test data are available to make an accurate estimate of σ from $\bar{w}$.	
22	0·418	0·659		
23	0·409	0·644		
24	0·400	0·631		
25	0·392	0·618		
26	0·384	0·606		
27	0·377	0·595		
28	0·370	0·584		
29	0·364	0·574		
30	0·358	0·564		

Note. For larger values of n use the general formulae:

$$A_{0\cdot025} = 1\cdot96/\sqrt{n}$$

$$A_{0\cdot001} = 3\cdot09/\sqrt{n}$$

EXAMPLE

Let $\bar{X} = 18\cdot0$ min., $\bar{w} = 3\cdot63$ min., and $n = 4$.

Inner Control Limits	$= 18\cdot0 \pm 3\cdot63 \times 0\cdot476$
	$= 19\cdot7$ and $16\cdot3$ min.
Outer Control Limits	$= 18\cdot0 \pm 3\cdot63 \times 0\cdot750$
	$= 20\cdot7$ and $15\cdot3$ min.

or alternatively, since
the estimate of σ $\qquad = \bar{w}/d_n = 3\cdot63/2\cdot059 = 1\cdot76$:

Inner Control Limits	$= 18\cdot0 \pm 1\cdot76 \times 0\cdot980$
	$= 19\cdot7$ and $16\cdot3$ min.
Outer Control Limits	$= 18\cdot0 \pm 1\cdot76 \times 1\cdot545$
	$= 20\cdot7$ and $15\cdot3$ min.

Note. The two sets of figures coincide because the value of σ has been estimated from the value of $\bar{w}$. Had the value of σ been calculated directly the figures would have differed slightly.

Table G·1

CONTROL CHART LIMITS FOR RANGE (w)

(For use when the limits are calculated from the standard deviation)

No. in Sample	For Lower Limits		For Upper Limits		For Average Value of w ($\bar{w}$)
n	Outer $D_{0·001}$	Inner $D_{0·025}$	Inner $D_{0·975}$	Outer $D_{0·999}$	d_n
2	0·00	0·04	3·17	4·65	1·128
3	0·06	0·30	3·68	5·06	1·693
4	0·20	0·59	3·98	5·31	2·059
5	0·37	0·85	4·20	5·48	2·326
6	0·54	1·06	4·36	5·62	2·534
7	0·69	1·25	4·49	5·73	2·704
8	0·83	1·41	4·61	5·82	2·847
9	0·96	1·55	4·70	5·90	2·970
10	1·08	1·67	4·79	5·97	3·078
11	1·20	1·78	4·86	6·04	3·173
12	1·30	1·88	4·92	6·09	3·258

To obtain the limits, multiply σ by the appropriate value of D. To obtain σ, divide $\bar{w}$ (the average value of w) by the appropriate value of d_n.

EXAMPLES

Let $\sigma = 1·76$ min. and $n = 4$.

Inner Control Limits
    Lower: $1·76 \times 0·59 = 1·0$ min.
    Upper: $1·76 \times 3·98 = 7·0$ min.

Outer Control Limits
    Lower: $1·76 \times 0·20 = 0·4$ min.
    Upper: $1·76 \times 5·31 = 9·3$ min.

The constants d_n may be used to obtain an estimate of σ from the mean range ($\bar{w}$) (see § 3.35) from the formula:

$$\text{Estimate of } \sigma = \bar{w}/d_n$$

Mean range, $\bar{w} = 47·9$. Sample size, $n = 5$. From table $d_n = 2·326$.
    ∴ Estimate of $\sigma = 47·9/2·326 = 20·6$

Table G·2

CONTROL CHART LIMITS FOR RANGE (*w*)

(For use when control limits are calculated from average range)

No. in Sample *n*	For Lower Limits		For Upper Limits	
	$D'_{0·001}$	$D'_{0·025}$	$D'_{0·975}$	$D'_{0·999}$
2	0·00	0·04	2·81	4·12
3	0·04	0·18	2·17	2·99
4	0·10	0·29	1·93	2·58
5	0·16	0·37	1·81	2·36
6	0·21	0·42	1·72	2·22
7	0·26	0·46	1·66	2·12
8	0·29	0·50	1·62	2·04
9	0·32	0·52	1·58	1·99
10	0·35	0·54	1·56	1·94
11	0·38	0·56	1·53	1·90
12	0·40	0·58	1·51	1·87

To obtain limits, multiply $\bar{w}$ by the appropriate value of D'.

EXAMPLE

Let $\bar{w} = 3·63$ and $n = 4$.

Inner Control Limits
　　Lower: $3·63 \times 0·29 = 1·1$ min.
　　Upper: $3·63 \times 1·93 = 7·0$ min.

Outer Control Limits
　　Lower: $3·63 \times 0·10 = 0·4$ min.
　　Upper: $3·63 \times 2·58 = 9·4$ min.

Table H
MULTIPLIERS L_1 AND L_2 FOR THE CONFIDENCE LIMITS OF THE RATIO OF TWO STANDARD DEVIATIONS
Probability Level 0·10

ϕ_d \ ϕ_n	1	2	3	4	5	6	7	8	9	10	12	15	20	24	30	40	60	120	∞
1	0·16 / 6·31	0·14 / 2·92	0·14 / 2·35	0·13 / 2·13	0·13 / 2·02	0·13 / 1·94	0·13 / 1·89	0·13 / 1·86	0·13 / 1·83	0·13 / 1·81	0·13 / 1·78	0·13 / 1·75	0·13 / 1·72	0·13 / 1·71	0·13 / 1·70	0·13 / 1·68	0·13 / 1·67	0·13 / 1·66	0·13 / 1·64
2	0·34 / 7·04	0·33 / 3·00	0·33 / 2·34	0·33 / 2·08	0·33 / 1·94	0·33 / 1·86	0·33 / 1·80	0·33 / 1·76	0·33 / 1·73	0·33 / 1·71	0·33 / 1·68	0·33 / 1·64	0·33 / 1·61	0·33 / 1·59	0·33 / 1·58	0·33 / 1·56	0·32 / 1·55	0·32 / 1·53	0·32 / 1·52
3	0·42 / 7·32	0·43 / 3·03	0·43 / 2·32	0·43 / 2·05	0·43 / 1·90	0·44 / 1·81	·044 / 1·75	0·44 / 1·71	0·44 / 1·68	0·44 / 1·65	0·44 / 1·61	0·44 / 1·58	0·44 / 1·54	0·44 / 1·53	0·44 / 1·51	0·44 / 1·49	0·44 / 1·48	0·44 / 1·46	0·44 / 1·44
4	0·47 / 7·47	0·48 / 3·04	0·49 / 2·31	0·49 / 2·03	0·50 / 1·88	0·50 / 1·78	0·50 / 1·72	0·50 / 1·68	0·50 / 1·64	0·51 / 1·61	0·51 / 1·57	0·51 / 1·54	0·51 / 1·50	0·51 / 1·48	0·51 / 1·46	0·51 / 1·45	0·51 / 1·43	0·51 / 1·41	0·52 / 1·39
5	0·50 / 7·57	0·51 / 3·05	0·53 / 2·30	0·53 / 2·01	0·54 / 1·86	0·54 / 1·76	0·54 / 1·70	0·55 / 1·65	0·55 / 1·62	0·55 / 1·59	0·55 / 1·55	·056 / 1·51	0·56 / 1·47	0·56 / 1·45	0·56 / 1·43	0·56 / 1·41	0·56 / 1·39	0·57 / 1·38	0·57 / 1·36
6	0·51 / 7·63	0·54 / 3·05	0·55 / 2·30	0·56 / 2·00	0·57 / 1·85	0·57 / 1·75	0·58 / 1·68	0·58 / 1·63	0·58 / 1·60	0·58 / 1·57	0·59 / 1·53	0·59 / 1·49	0·59 / 1·45	0·60 / 1·43	0·60 / 1·41	0·60 / 1·39	0·60 / 1·37	0·60 / 1·35	0·61 / 1·33
7	0·53 / 7·68	0·55 / 3·06	0·57 / 2·29	0·58 / 1·99	0·59 / 1·84	0·59 / 1·74	0·60 / 1·67	0·60 / 1·62	0·61 / 1·58	0·61 / 1·55	0·61 / 1·51	0·62 / 1·47	0·62 / 1·43	0·62 / 1·41	0·63 / 1·39	0·63 / 1·37	0·63 / 1·35	0·63 / 1·33	0·64 / 1·31
8	0·54 / 7·71	0·57 / 3·06	0·58 / 2·29	0·60 / 1·99	0·61 / 1·83	0·61 / 1·73	0·62 / 1·66	0·62 / 1·61	0·62 / 1·57	0·63 / 1·54	0·63 / 1·50	0·64 / 1·46	0·64 / 1·41	0·64 / 1·39	0·65 / 1·37	0·65 / 1·35	0·65 / 1·33	0·66 / 1·31	0·66 / 1·29
9	0·55 / 7·74	0·58 / 3·06	0·60 / 2·29	0·61 / 1·98	0·62 / 1·82	0·63 / 1·72	0·63 / 1·65	0·64 / 1·60	0·64 / 1·56	0·64 / 1·53	0·65 / 1·49	0·65 / 1·44	0·66 / 1·40	0·66 / 1·38	0·67 / 1·36	0·67 / 1·34	0·67 / 1·32	0·68 / 1·30	0·68 / 1·28
10	0·55 / 7·76	0·58 / 3·06	0·61 / 2·29	0·62 / 1·98	0·63 / 1·82	0·64 / 1·71	0·64 / 1·64	0·65 / 1·59	0·65 / 1·55	0·66 / 1·52	0·66 / 1·48	0·67 / 1·44	0·67 / 1·39	0·68 / 1·37	0·68 / 1·35	0·68 / 1·33	0·69 / 1·31	0·69 / 1·29	0·70 / 1·26

Table H (continued)

$\phi_d \backslash \phi_n$	1	2	3	4	5	6	7	8	9	10	12	15	20	24	30	40	60	120	∞
12	0·56 7·79	0·60 3·07	0·62 2·28	0·63 1·97	0·65 1·81	0·65 1·70	0·66 1·63	0·67 1·58	0·67 1·54	0·68 1·51	0·68 1·47	0·69 1·42	0·70 1·38	0·70 1·35	0·71 1·33	0·71 1·31	0·71 1·29	0·72 1·27	0·72 1·24
15	0·57 7·82	0·61 3·07	0·63 2·28	0·65 1·97	0·66 1·80	0·67 1·69	0·68 1·62	0·69 1·57	0·69 1·53	0·70 1·50	0·70 1·45	0·71 1·40	0·72 1·36	0·73 1·34	0·73 1·31	0·74 1·29	0·74 1·27	0·75 1·24	0·75 1·22
20	0·58 7·86	0·62 3·07	0·65 2·28	0·67 1·96	0·68 1·79	0·69 1·68	0·70 1·61	0·71 1·56	0·71 1·52	0·72 1·48	0·73 1·44	0·74 1·39	0·75 1·34	0·75 1·32	0·76 1·29	0·77 1·27	0·77 1·24	0·78 1·22	0·79 1·19
24	0·58 7·87	0·63 3·07	0·66 2·28	0·67 1·96	0·69 1·79	0·70 1·68	0·71 1·60	0·72 1·55	0·72 1·51	0·73 1·48	0·74 1·43	0·75 1·38	0·76 1·33	0·77 1·30	0·77 1·28	0·78 1·25	0·79 1·23	0·80 1·20	0·81 1·18
30	0·59 7·89	0·63 3·08	0·66 2·27	0·68 1·95	0·70 1·78	0·71 1·67	0·72 1·60	0·73 1·54	0·74 1·50	0·74 1·47	0·75 1·42	0·76 1·37	0·77 1·32	0·78 1·29	0·79 1·27	0·80 1·24	0·81 1·21	0·82 1·19	0·83 1·16
40	0·59 7·91	0·64 3·08	0·67 2·27	0·69 1·95	0·71 1·78	0·72 1·67	0·73 1·59	0·74 1·54	0·75 1·49	0·75 1·46	0·76 1·41	0·78 1·36	0·79 1·31	0·80 1·28	0·81 1·25	0·81 1·23	0·83 1·20	0·84 1·17	0·85 1·14
60	0·60 7·92	0·65 3·08	0·68 2·27	0·70 1·95	0·72 1·77	0·73 1·66	0·74 1·59	0·75 1·53	0·76 1·49	0·77 1·45	0·78 1·40	0·79 1·35	0·81 1·29	0·81 1·27	0·82 1·24	0·83 1·21	0·85 1·18	0·86 1·15	0·88 1·11
120	0·60 7·94	0·65 3·08	0·69 2·27	0·71 1·94	0·73 1·77	0·74 1·66	0·75 1·58	0·76 1·52	0·77 1·48	0·78 1·44	0·79 1·39	0·80 1·34	0·82 1·28	0·83 1·25	0·84 1·22	0·86 1·19	0·87 1·16	0·89 1·12	0·92 1·08
∞	0·61 7·96	0·66 3·08	0·69 2·27	0·72 1·94	0·74 1·76	0·75 1·65	0·76 1·57	0·77 1·51	0·78 1·47	0·79 1·43	0·80 1·38	0·82 1·32	0·84 1·27	0·85 1·24	0·86 1·21	0·88 1·17	0·90 1·14	0·93 1·09	1·00 1·00

L_1 is given by the upper entry in each cell and L_2 by the lower.
ϕ_n represents the degrees of freedom of the standard deviation in the numerator and ϕ_d the degrees of freedom of the standard deviation in the denominator.
The confidence limits for $R = s_1/s_2$ are L_1R and L_2R.
The multipliers for the confidence limits of one standard deviation are given in the row $\phi_d = \infty$.

Table H (*continued*)

MULTIPLIERS L₁ AND L₂ FOR THE CONFIDENCE LIMITS OF THE RATIO OF TWO STANDARD DEVIATIONS

Probability Level 0·05

ϕ_d \\ ϕ_n	1	2	3	4	5	6	7	8	9	10	12	15	20	24	30	40	60	120	∞
1	·079 12·7	·071 4·30	·068 3·18	·067 2·78	·066 2·57	·065 2·45	·065 2·36	·065 2·31	·064 2·26	·064 2·23	·064 2·18	·064 2·13	·063 2·09	·063 2·06	·063 2·04	·063 2·02	·063 2·00	·063 1·98	·063 1·96
2	0·23 14·1	0·23 4·36	0·23 3·09	0·23 2·64	0·23 2·41	0·23 2·27	0·23 2·18	0·23 2·11	0·23 2·06	0·23 2·03	0·23 1·97	0·23 1·92	0·23 1·87	0·23 1·84	0·23 1·82	0·23 1·80	0·23 1·77	0·23 1·75	0·23 1·73
3	0·31 14·7	0·32 4·38	0·33 3·05	0·33 2·57	0·33 2·33	0·33 2·18	0·34 2·08	0·34 2·02	0·34 1·97	0·34 1·93	0·34 1·87	0·34 1·81	0·34 1·76	0·34 1·73	0·34 1·71	0·34 1·68	0·34 1·66	0·34 1·64	0·34 1·61
4	0·36 15·0	0·38 4·39	0·39 3·02	0·40 2·53	0·40 2·28	0·40 2·13	0·41 2·03	0·41 1·96	0·41 1·91	0·41 1·86	0·41 1·81	0·41 1·75	0·42 1·69	0·42 1·67	0·42 1·64	0·42 1·61	0·42 1·59	0·42 1·56	0·42 1·54
5	0·39 15·2	0·42 4·39	0·43 3·00	0·44 2·50	0·44 2·25	0·45 2·09	0·45 1·99	0·46 1·92	0·46 1·87	0·46 1·82	0·46 1·76	0·47 1·70	0·47 1·65	0·47 1·62	0·47 1·59	0·47 1·57	0·48 1·54	0·48 1·51	0·48 1·49
6	0·41 15·3	0·44 4·40	0·46 2·99	0·47 2·48	0·48 2·22	0·48 2·07	0·49 1·97	0·49 1·89	0·49 1·84	0·50 1·79	0·50 1·73	0·50 1·67	0·51 1·61	0·51 1·58	0·51 1·56	0·51 1·53	0·52 1·50	0·52 1·47	0·52 1·45
7	0·42 15·4	0·46 4·40	0·48 2·98	0·49 2·47	0·50 2·21	0·51 2·05	0·51 1·95	0·52 1·87	0·52 1·81	0·52 1·77	0·53 1·71	0·53 1·65	0·54 1·59	0·54 1·56	0·54 1·53	0·55 1·50	0·55 1·47	0·55 1·44	0·56 1·42
8	0·43 15·5	0·47 4·40	0·50 2·97	0·51 2·46	0·52 2·20	0·53 2·04	0·53 1·93	0·54 1·85	0·54 1·80	0·55 1·75	0·55 1·69	0·56 1·63	0·56 1·56	0·57 1·54	0·57 1·51	0·57 1·48	0·58 1·45	0·58 1·42	0·58 1·39
9	0·44 15·5	0·48 4·40	0·51 2·97	0·52 2·45	0·54 2·18	0·54 2·02	0·55 1·92	0·56 1·84	0·56 1·78	0·56 1·74	0·57 1·67	0·58 1·61	0·58 1·55	0·59 1·52	0·59 1·49	0·59 1·46	0·60 1·43	0·60 1·40	0·61 1·37
10	0·45 15·6	0·49 4·40	0·52 2·96	0·54 2·44	0·55 2·18	0·56 2·01	0·56 1·91	0·57 1·83	0·58 1·77	0·58 1·73	0·59 1·66	0·59 1·59	0·60 1·53	0·60 1·50	0·61 1·47	0·61 1·44	0·62 1·41	0·62 1·38	0·63 1·35

Table H (*continued*)

φ_d	1	2	3	4	5	6	7	8	9	10	12	15	20	24	30	40	60	120	∞	φ_n
12	0·46 / 15·6	0·51 / 4·41	0·54 / 2·96	0·55 / 2·43	0·57 / 2·16	0·58 / 2·00	0·59 / 1·89	0·59 / 1·81	0·60 / 1·75	0·60 / 1·71	0·61 / 1·64	0·62 / 1·57	0·63 / 1·51	0·63 / 1·48	0·64 / 1·45	0·64 / 1·42	0·65 / 1·38	0·65 / 1·35	0·66 / 1·32	12
15	0·47 / 15·7	0·52 / 4·41	0·55 / 2·95	0·57 / 2·42	0·59 / 2·15	0·60 / 1·98	0·61 / 1·87	0·62 / 1·79	0·62 / 1·73	0·63 / 1·69	0·64 / 1·62	0·65 / 1·55	0·65 / 1·48	0·66 / 1·45	0·67 / 1·42	0·67 / 1·39	0·68 / 1·36	0·69 / 1·32	0·70 / 1·29	15
20	0·48 / 15·7	0·54 / 4·41	0·57 / 2·94	0·59 / 2·41	0·61 / 2·14	0·62 / 1·97	0·63 / 1·86	0·64 / 1·77	0·65 / 1·71	0·65 / 1·67	0·66 / 1·59	0·67 / 1·53	0·69 / 1·46	0·69 / 1·42	0·70 / 1·39	0·71 / 1·36	0·72 / 1·32	0·73 / 1·29	0·74 / 1·25	20
24	0·48 / 15·8	0·54 / 4·41	0·58 / 2·94	0·60 / 2·40	0·62 / 2·13	0·63 / 1·96	0·64 / 1·85	0·65 / 1·77	0·66 / 1·70	0·67 / 1·65	0·68 / 1·58	0·69 / 1·51	0·70 / 1·44	0·71 / 1·41	0·72 / 1·37	0·73 / 1·34	0·74 / 1·30	0·75 / 1·27	0·76 / 1·23	24
30	0·49 / 15·8	0·55 / 4·41	0·58 / 2·94	0·61 / 2·40	0·63 / 2·12	0·64 / 1·95	0·65 / 1·84	0·66 / 1·75	0·67 / 1·69	0·68 / 1·64	0·69 / 1·57	0·70 / 1·50	0·72 / 1·43	0·73 / 1·39	0·74 / 1·36	0·75 / 1·32	0·76 / 1·28	0·77 / 1·25	0·79 / 1·21	30
40	0·49 / 15·8	0·56 / 4·41	0·59 / 2·93	0·62 / 2·39	0·64 / 2·11	0·65 / 1·94	0·67 / 1·83	0·68 / 1·74	0·69 / 1·68	0·69 / 1·63	0·71 / 1·56	0·72 / 1·48	0·74 / 1·41	0·75 / 1·38	0·76 / 1·34	0·77 / 1·30	0·78 / 1·26	0·80 / 1·22	0·81 / 1·18	40
60	0·50 / 15·9	0·56 / 4·41	0·60 / 2·93	0·63 / 2·38	0·65 / 2·11	0·67 / 1·93	0·68 / 1·82	0·69 / 1·73	0·70 / 1·67	0·71 / 1·62	0·72 / 1·54	0·74 / 1·47	0·76 / 1·40	0·77 / 1·36	0·78 / 1·32	0·79 / 1·28	0·81 / 1·24	0·83 / 1·20	0·85 / 1·15	60
120	0·51 / 15·9	0·57 / 4·41	0·61 / 2·92	0·64 / 2·38	0·66 / 2·10	0·68 / 1·92	0·69 / 1·81	0·70 / 1·72	0·71 / 1·66	0·72 / 1·61	0·74 / 1·53	0·76 / 1·45	0·78 / 1·38	0·79 / 1·34	0·80 / 1·30	0·82 / 1·26	0·84 / 1·21	0·86 / 1·16	0·89 / 1·11	120
∞	**0·51 / 15·9**	**0·58 / 4·42**	**0·62 / 2·92**	**0·65 / 2·37**	**0·67 / 2·09**	**0·69 / 1·92**	**0·71 / 1·80**	**0·72 / 1·71**	**0·73 / 1·65**	**0·74 / 1·59**	**0·76 / 1·52**	**0·77 / 1·44**	**0·80 / 1·36**	**0·81 / 1·32**	**0·83 / 1·27**	**0·85 / 1·23**	**0·87 / 1·18**	**0·90 / 1·12**	**1·00 / 1·00**	∞

L_1 is given by the upper entry in each cell and L_2 by the lower.
ϕ_n represents the degrees of freedom of the standard deviation in the numerator and ϕ_d the degrees of freedom of the standard deviation in the denominator.
The confidence limits for $R = s_1/s_2$ are L_1R and L_2R.
The multipliers for the confidence limits of one standard deviation are given in the row $\phi_d = \infty$.

Table H (continued)

MULTIPLIERS L₁ AND L₂ FOR THE CONFIDENCE LIMITS OF THE RATIO OF TWO STANDARD DEVIATIONS

Probability Level 0·025

ϕ_d \ ϕ_n	1	2	3	4	5	6	7	8	9	10	12	15	20	24	30	40	60	120	∞
1	·039 / 25·5	·035 / 6·20	·034 / 4·18	·033 / 3·50	·033 / 3·16	·033 / 2·97	·032 / 2·84	·032 / 2·75	·032 / 2·69	·032 / 2·63	·032 / 2·56	·032 / 2·49	·032 / 2·42	·032 / 2·39	·032 / 2·36	·032 / 2·33	·031 / 2·30	·031 / 2·27	·031 / 2·24
2	0·16 / 28·3	0·16 / 6·24	0·16 / 4·01	0·16 / 3·26	0·16 / 2·90	0·16 / 2·69	0·16 / 2·56	0·16 / 2·46	0·16 / 2·39	0·16 / 2·34	0·16 / 2·26	0·16 / 2·18	0·16 / 2·11	0·16 / 2·08	0·16 / 2·05	0·16 / 2·01	0·16 / 1·98	0·16 / 1·95	0·16 / 1·92
3	0·24 / 29·5	0·25 / 6·26	0·25 / 3·93	0·26 / 3·16	0·26 / 2·79	0·26 / 2·57	0·26 / 2·43	0·26 / 2·33	0·26 / 2·25	0·26 / 2·20	0·26 / 2·12	0·26 / 2·04	0·27 / 1·96	0·27 / 1·93	0·27 / 1·89	0·27 / 1·86	0·27 / 1·83	0·27 / 1·70	0·27 / 1·77
4	0·29 / 30·0	0·31 / 6·26	0·32 / 3·89	0·32 / 3·10	0·33 / 2·72	0·33 / 2·50	0·33 / 2·35	0·33 / 2·25	0·34 / 2·17	0·34 / 2·11	0·34 / 2·03	0·34 / 1·95	0·34 / 1·87	0·34 / 1·84	0·34 / 1·80	0·34 / 1·77	0·35 / 1·73	0·35 / 1·70	0·35 / 1·67
5	0·32 / 30·4	0·34 / 6·27	0·36 / 3·86	0·37 / 3·06	0·37 / 2·67	0·38 / 2·45	0·38 / 2·30	0·38 / 2·19	0·39 / 2·12	0·39 / 2·06	0·39 / 1·97	0·39 / 1·89	0·40 / 1·81	0·40 / 1·78	0·40 / 1·74	0·40 / 1·70	0·40 / 1·67	0·41 / 1·64	0·41 / 1·60
6	0·34 / 30·6	0·37 / 6·27	0·39 / 3·84	0·40 / 3·03	0·41 / 2·64	0·41 / 2·41	0·42 / 2·26	0·42 / 2·16	0·43 / 2·08	0·43 / 2·02	0·43 / 1·93	0·44 / 1·85	0·44 / 1·77	0·44 / 1·73	0·44 / 1·69	0·45 / 1·66	0·45 / 1·62	0·45 / 1·59	0·45 / 1·55
7	0·35 / 30·8	0·39 / 6·27	0·41 / 3·82	0·43 / 3·01	0·43 / 2·62	0·44 / 2·39	0·45 / 2·23	0·45 / 2·13	0·46 / 2·05	0·46 / 1·99	0·46 / 1·90	0·47 / 1·81	0·47 / 1·73	0·48 / 1·70	0·48 / 1·66	0·48 / 1·62	0·48 / 1·58	0·49 / 1·55	0·49 / 1·51
8	0·36 / 30·9	0·41 / 6·27	0·43 / 3·81	0·44 / 3·01	0·46 / 2·60	0·46 / 2·37	0·47 / 2·21	0·47 / 2·11	0·48 / 2·03	0·48 / 1·96	0·49 / 1·87	0·49 / 1·79	0·50 / 1·71	0·50 / 1·67	0·51 / 1·63	0·51 / 1·59	0·51 / 1·55	0·52 / 1·52	0·52 / 1·48
9	0·37 / 31·0	0·42 / 6·28	0·44 / 3·80	0·46 / 2·98	0·47 / 2·58	0·48 / 2·35	0·49 / 2·20	0·49 / 2·09	0·50 / 2·01	0·50 / 1·94	0·51 / 1·85	0·52 / 1·77	0·52 / 1·68	0·53 / 1·64	0·53 / 1·60	0·53 / 1·57	0·54 / 1·53	0·54 / 1·49	0·55 / 1·45
10	0·38 / 31·1	0·43 / 6·28	0·46 / 3·80	0·47 / 2·97	0·49 / 2·57	0·50 / 2·34	0·50 / 2·18	0·51 / 2·07	0·51 / 1·99	0·52 / 1·93	0·53 / 1·84	0·53 / 1·75	0·54 / 1·67	0·55 / 1·62	0·55 / 1·58	0·55 / 1·55	0·56 / 1·51	0·56 / 1·47	0·57 / 1·43

Table H (*continued*)

ϕ_d \ ϕ_n	1	2	3	4	5	6	7	8	9	10	12	15	20	24	30	40	60	120	∞
12	0·39 / 31·3	0·44 / 6·28	0·47 / 3·79	0·49 / 2·96	0·51 / 2·55	0·52 / 2·32	0·53 / 2·16	0·53 / 2·05	0·54 / 1·97	0·54 / 1·90	0·55 / 1·81	0·56 / 1·72	0·57 / 1·64	0·58 / 1·59	0·58 / 1·55	0·59 / 1·51	0·59 / 1·47	0·60 / 1·43	0·61 / 1·39
15	0·40 / 31·4	0·46 / 6·28	0·49 / 3·78	0·51 / 2·94	0·53 / 2·54	0·54 / 2·30	0·55 / 2·14	0·56 / 2·02	0·57 / 1·94	0·57 / 1·88	0·58 / 1·78	0·59 / 1·69	0·60 / 1·60	0·61 / 1·56	0·62 / 1·52	0·62 / 1·48	0·63 / 1·44	0·64 / 1·39	0·65 / 1·35
20	0·41 / 31·5	0·47 / 6·28	0·51 / 3·76	0·53 / 2·93	0·55 / 2·52	0·57 / 2·27	0·58 / 2·11	0·59 / 2·00	0·59 / 1·91	0·60 / 1·85	0·61 / 1·75	0·62 / 1·66	0·64 / 1·57	0·64 / 1·53	0·65 / 1·48	0·66 / 1·44	0·67 / 1·39	0·68 / 1·35	0·69 / 1·31
24	0·42 / 31·6	0·48 / 6·28	0·52 / 3·76	0·54 / 2·92	0·56 / 2·51	0·58 / 2·26	0·59 / 2·10	0·60 / 1·99	0·61 / 1·90	0·62 / 1·83	0·63 / 1·74	0·64 / 1·64	0·66 / 1·55	0·66 / 1·51	0·67 / 1·46	0·68 / 1·42	0·69 / 1·37	0·71 / 1·33	0·72 / 1·28
30	0·42 / 31·6	0·49 / 6·28	0·53 / 3·75	0·55 / 2·91	0·57 / 2·50	0·59 / 2·25	0·60 / 2·09	0·61 / 1·97	0·62 / 1·89	0·63 / 1·82	0·64 / 1·72	0·66 / 1·63	0·67 / 1·53	0·68 / 1·49	0·69 / 1·44	0·71 / 1·39	0·72 / 1·35	0·73 / 1·30	0·75 / 1·25
40	0·43 / 31·7	0·50 / 6·28	0·54 / 3·75	0·57 / 2·90	0·59 / 2·49	0·60 / 2·24	0·62 / 2·08	0·63 / 1·96	0·64 / 1·87	0·65 / 1·80	0·66 / 1·70	0·68 / 1·61	0·70 / 1·51	0·71 / 1·46	0·72 / 1·42	0·73 / 1·37	0·74 / 1·32	0·76 / 1·27	0·78 / 1·22
60	0·43 / 31·8	0·50 / 6·28	0·55 / 3·74	0·58 / 2·89	0·60 / 2·47	0·62 / 2·23	0·63 / 2·06	0·64 / 1·95	0·65 / 1·86	0·66 / 1·79	0·68 / 1·69	0·70 / 1·59	0·72 / 1·49	0·73 / 1·44	0·74 / 1·39	0·76 / 1·34	0·77 / 1·29	0·80 / 1·24	0·82 / 1·18
120	0·44 / 31·8	0·51 / 6·28	0·56 / 3·73	0·59 / 2·88	0·61 / 2·46	0·63 / 2·21	0·65 / 2·05	0·66 / 1·93	0·67 / 1·84	0·68 / 1·77	0·70 / 1·67	0·72 / 1·57	0·74 / 1·47	0·75 / 1·42	0·77 / 1·37	0·79 / 1·31	0·81 / 1·26	0·84 / 1·20	0·87 / 1·13
∞	0·45 / 31·9	0·52 / 6·28	0·57 / 3·73	0·60 / 2·87	0·62 / 2·45	0·64 / 2·20	0·66 / 2·04	0·68 / 1·92	0·69 / 1·83	0·70 / 1·75	0·72 / 1·65	0·74 / 1·55	0·77 / 1·44	0·78 / 1·39	0·80 / 1·34	0·82 / 1·28	0·85 / 1·22	0·89 / 1·14	1·00 / 1·00

L_1 is given by the upper entry in each cell and L_2 by the lower.
ϕ_n represents the degrees of freedom of the standard deviation in the numerator and ϕ_d the degrees of freedom of the standard deviation in the denominator.
The confidence limits for $R = s_1/s_2$ are L_1R and L_2R.
The multipliers for the confidence limits of one standard deviation are given in the row $\phi_d = \infty$.

C2

Table H (*continued*)

MULTIPLIERS L₁ AND L₂ FOR THE CONFIDENCE LIMITS OF THE RATIO OF TWO STANDARD DEVIATIONS

Probability Level 0·01

ϕ_d \ ϕ_n	1	2	3	4	5	6	7	8	9	10	12	15	20	24	30	40	60	120	∞
1	·016 / 63·7	·014 / 9·92	·014 / 5·84	·013 / 4·60	·013 / 4·03	·013 / 3·71	·013 / 3·50	·013 / 3·36	·013 / 3·25	·013 / 3·17	·013 / 3·05	·013 / 2·95	·013 / 2·85	·013 / 2·80	·013 / 2·75	·013 / 2·70	·013 / 2·66	·013 / 2·62	·013 / 2·58
2	0·10 / 70·7	0·10 / 9·95	0·10 / 5·55	0·10 / 4·24	0·10 / 3·64	0·10 / 3·31	0·10 / 3·09	0·10 / 2·94	0·10 / 2·83	0·10 / 2·75	0·10 / 2·63	0·10 / 2·52	0·10 / 2·42	0·10 / 2·37	0·10 / 2·32	0·10 / 2·28	0·10 / 2·23	0·10 / 2·19	0·10 / 2·15
3	0·17 / 73·5	0·18 / 9·96	0·18 / 5·43	0·19 / 4·09	0·19 / 3·47	0·19 / 3·13	0·19 / 2·91	0·19 / 2·76	0·19 / 2·64	0·19 / 2·56	0·19 / 2·44	0·19 / 2·33	0·19 / 2·22	0·19 / 2·17	0·19 / 2·12	0·19 / 2·08	0·19 / 2·03	0·20 / 1·99	0·20 / 1·94
4	0·22 / 75·0	0·24 / 9·96	0·24 / 5·36	0·25 / 4·00	0·25 / 3·38	0·26 / 3·02	0·26 / 2·80	0·26 / 2·65	0·26 / 2·53	0·26 / 2·45	0·26 / 2·33	0·27 / 2·21	0·27 / 2·10	0·27 / 2·05	0·27 / 2·00	0·27 / 1·96	0·27 / 1·91	0·27 / 1·87	0·27 / 1·82
5	0·25 / 75·9	0·27 / 9·96	0·29 / 5·31	0·30 / 3·94	0·30 / 3·31	0·31 / 2·96	0·31 / 2·73	0·31 / 2·58	0·31 / 2·46	0·32 / 2·37	0·32 / 2·25	0·32 / 2·13	0·32 / 2·03	0·33 / 1·97	0·33 / 1·92	0·33 / 1·87	0·33 / 1·83	0·33 / 1·78	0·33 / 1·74
6	0·27 / 76·5	0·30 / 9·97	0·32 / 5·28	0·33 / 3·90	0·34 / 3·27	0·34 / 2·91	0·35 / 2·68	0·35 / 2·52	0·35 / 2·41	0·36 / 2·32	0·36 / 2·20	0·36 / 2·08	0·37 / 1·97	0·37 / 1·91	0·37 / 1·86	0·37 / 1·81	0·38 / 1·77	0·38 / 1·72	0·38 / 1·67
7	0·29 / 77·0	0·32 / 9·97	0·34 / 5·26	0·36 / 3·87	0·37 / 3·23	0·37 / 2·87	0·38 / 2·64	0·38 / 2·49	0·39 / 2·37	0·39 / 2·28	0·39 / 2·15	0·40 / 2·04	0·40 / 1·92	0·41 / 1·87	0·41 / 1·82	0·41 / 1·77	0·41 / 1·72	0·42 / 1·67	0·42 / 1·62
8	0·30 / 77·3	0·34 / 9·97	0·36 / 5·24	0·38 / 3·85	0·39 / 3·21	0·40 / 2·85	0·40 / 2·62	0·41 / 2·46	0·41 / 2·34	0·41 / 2·25	0·42 / 2·12	0·43 / 2·00	0·43 / 1·89	0·44 / 1·83	0·44 / 1·78	0·44 / 1·73	0·45 / 1·68	0·45 / 1·63	0·45 / 1·58
9	0·31 / 77·6	0·35 / 9·97	0·38 / 5·23	0·39 / 3·83	0·41 / 3·19	0·42 / 2·82	0·42 / 2·59	0·43 / 2·43	0·43 / 2·31	0·44 / 2·22	0·44 / 2·09	0·45 / 1·97	0·46 / 1·86	0·46 / 1·80	0·46 / 1·75	0·47 / 1·70	0·47 / 1·65	0·48 / 1·60	0·48 / 1·55
10	0·32 / 77·8	0·36 / 9·97	0·39 / 5·22	0·41 / 3·81	0·42 / 3·17	0·43 / 2·81	0·44 / 2·57	0·44 / 2·41	0·45 / 2·29	0·45 / 2·20	0·46 / 2·07	0·47 / 1·95	0·48 / 1·84	0·48 / 1·78	0·49 / 1·73	0·49 / 1·67	0·49 / 1·62	0·50 / 1·57	0·51 / 1·52

Table H (continued)

ϕ_d \ ϕ_n	1	2	3	4	5	6	7	8	9	10	12	15	20	24	30	40	60	120	∞
12	0·33	0·38	0·41	0·43	0·44	0·46	0·46	0·47	0·48	0·48	0·49	0·50	0·51	0·51	0·52	0·53	0·53	0·54	0·55
	78·1	9·97	5·20	3·79	3·14	2·78	2·54	2·38	2·26	2·17	2·04	1·91	1·80	1·74	1·69	1·63	1·58	1·53	1·48
15	0·34	0·40	0·43	0·45	0·47	0·48	0·49	0·50	0·51	0·51	0·52	0·53	0·54	0·55	0·56	0·57	0·57	0·58	0·59
	78·5	9·97	5·18	3·77	3·12	2·75	2·51	2·35	2·23	2·14	2·00	1·88	1·76	1·70	1·64	1·59	1·53	1·48	1·43
20	0·35	0·41	0·45	0·48	0·49	0·51	0·52	0·53	0·54	0·54	0·56	0·57	0·58	0·59	0·60	0·61	0·62	0·63	0·64
	78·8	9·97	5·17	3·74	3·09	2·72	2·48	2·32	2·19	2·10	1·96	1·84	1·71	1·65	1·60	1·54	1·48	1·43	1·37
24	0·36	0·42	0·46	0·49	0·51	0·52	0·53	0·55	0·55	0·56	0·57	0·59	0·60	0·61	0·62	0·63	0·65	0·66	0·67
	79·0	9·97	5·16	3·73	3·08	2·70	2·46	2·30	2·17	2·08	1·94	1·81	1·69	1·63	1·57	1·51	1·45	1·40	1·34
30	0·36	0·43	0·47	0·50	0·52	0·54	0·55	0·56	0·57	0·58	0·59	0·61	0·63	0·64	0·65	0·66	0·67	0·69	0·71
	79·1	9·97	5·15	3·72	3·06	2·69	2·45	2·28	2·16	2·06	1·92	1·79	1·67	1·61	1·54	1·48	1·42	1·36	1·30
40	0·37	0·44	0·48	0·51	0·53	0·55	0·57	0·58	0·59	0·60	0·61	0·63	0·65	0·66	0·67	0·69	0·70	0·72	0·74
	79·3	9·97	5·14	3·71	3·05	2·67	2·43	2·26	2·14	2·04	1·90	1·77	1·64	1·58	1·52	1·45	1·39	1·33	1·26
60	0·38	0·45	0·49	0·52	0·55	0·57	0·58	0·60	0·61	0·62	0·63	0·65	0·67	0·69	0·70	0·72	0·74	0·76	0·79
	79·5	9·97	5·13	3·69	3·03	2·66	2·41	2·24	2·12	2·02	1·88	1·75	1·61	1·55	1·49	1·42	1·36	1·29	1·21
120	0·38	0·46	0·50	0·54	0·56	0·58	0·60	0·61	0·63	0·64	0·65	0·68	0·70	0·72	0·73	0·75	0·78	0·81	0·85
	79·6	9·97	5·12	3·68	3·02	2·64	2·40	2·22	2·10	2·00	1·86	1·72	1·59	1·52	1·45	1·38	1·31	1·24	1·15
∞	0·39	0·47	0·51	0·55	0·58	0·60	0·62	0·63	0·64	0·66	0·68	0·70	0·73	0·75	0·77	0·79	0·82	0·87	1·00
	79·8	9·98	5·11	3·67	3·00	2·62	2·38	2·20	2·08	1·98	1·83	1·69	1·56	1·49	1·42	1·34	1·27	1·17	1·00

L_1 is given by the upper entry in each cell and L_2 by the lower.

ϕ_n represents the degrees of freedom of the standard deviation in the numerator and ϕ_d the degrees of freedom of the standard deviation in the denominator.

The confidence limits for $R = s_1/s_2$ are L_1R and L_2R.

The multipliers for the confidence limits of one standard deviation are given in the row $\phi_d = \infty$.

C2*

NOMOGRAM FOR INTERPOLATING STATISTICAL TABLES FOR OTHER PROBABILITY LEVELS

Modern tables of statistical criteria, t, χ^2, F, etc., usually show the values corresponding to a series of levels of significance. The chosen levels commonly belong to the following sequence, though the sequence is often incomplete and levels not belonging to the sequence are also encountered:

$$P = 25 \quad 10 \quad 5 \quad 2\cdot5 \quad 1 \quad 0\cdot5 \quad 0\cdot25 \quad 0\cdot1 \ldots \%$$

For most practical purposes it is sufficient to quote the significance of the result within limits, e.g. using the table of F given in this book, one can always state that P is greater than 10%, between 10 and 5% or 5 and 1%, or less than 1%.

Some people, however, prefer to make a rough interpolation between the two tabular entries in order to quote the actual significance of the result. Direct linear interpolation is unreliable, particularly when the two values of P are widely spaced. Linear interpolation is more accurate when performed against a transformed scale of P, such as log P or $u(P)$, i.e. the Normal deviate corresponding to P.

The nomogram opposite provides a rapid method for interpolating linearly with reference to $u(P)$, which although not necessarily the best method for any given criterion, is probably the best general method to be applied to all of them. The nomogram gives, in principle, an exact interpolation for any criterion with a Normal distribution, and for other criteria it is at least likely to be considerably more reliable than simple linear interpolation with reference to P.

It is occasionally desirable to interpolate between values in standard tables with greater accuracy than can be attained using the nomogram. For this purpose reference should be made to [T5].

Similarly, for interpolation between degrees of freedom, linear interpolation is usually sufficiently accurate. When more accurate results are desired, reference should be made to [T6].

To use the nomogram proceed as follows: Obtain from the tables values of the function at two standard probabilities, one higher and the other lower than the value to be examined. Find the differences between this value and each of the standard values. These differences can be multiplied or divided by any common factor to bring them to a convenient size. On the nomogram find the horizontal line corresponding to one of the standard probabilities and measure that difference along it from the central line. Repeat this for the other difference on the corresponding probability level, measuring the two differences in opposite directions. A straight line through the two points so obtained intersects the central line at the required probability.

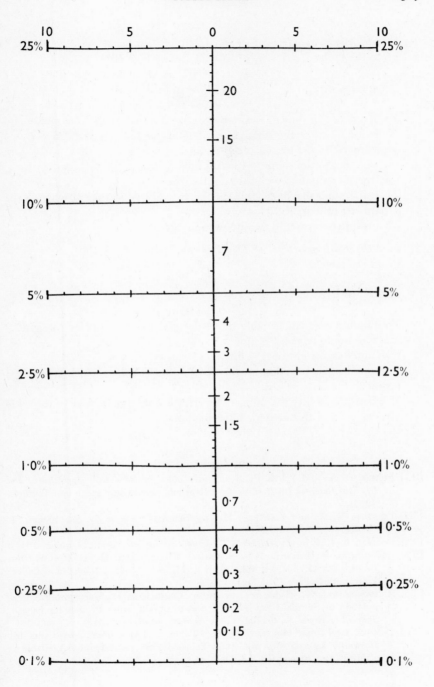

EXAMPLES

1. *Find the significance level of* $\chi^2 = 14 \cdot 240$ *for* $\phi = 8$.

   From the tables for $\phi = 8$, $\chi^2 = 13 \cdot 362 \qquad P = 10\%$

   $\qquad\qquad\qquad\qquad\qquad \chi^2 = 15 \cdot 507 \qquad P = 5\%$

   Differences are $\qquad\qquad\quad + 0 \cdot 878$ from $P = 10\%$

   $\qquad\qquad\qquad\qquad\qquad - 1 \cdot 267$ from $P = 5\%$

   To obtain a convenient scale move the decimal point one place and divide by 2, giving differences of $+ 4 \cdot 4$ and $- 6 \cdot 3$ respectively.

   Measure $4 \cdot 4$ to the left on the 10% line

   $\qquad$ and $6 \cdot 3$ to the right on the 5% line.

   Join these two points with a straight-edge.

   Then the point of intersection on the central line is $7 \cdot 60\%$, which is the required probability.

   This result is correct to two decimal places.

2. *Find the significance level of* $F = 3 \cdot 20$ *for* $\phi_1 = 8$, $\phi_2 = 15$.

   From the tables $\qquad\qquad\quad F = 2 \cdot 64 \qquad P = 5\%$

   $\qquad\qquad\qquad\qquad\qquad F = 4 \cdot 00 \qquad P = 1\%$

   Differences are $\qquad\qquad\quad + 0 \cdot 56$ from $P = 5\%$

   $\qquad\qquad\qquad\qquad\qquad - 0 \cdot 80$ from $P = 1\%$

   To obtain a convenient scale move decimal point one place to right.

   Measure $5 \cdot 6$ to left on 5% line

   $\qquad$ and $8 \cdot 0$ to right on 1% line.

   The point of intersection on the central line is $2 \cdot 7\%$, which is required probability.

   The true probability is $2 \cdot 50\%$. The error is not large in view of the wide range used in this case for interpolation.

REFERENCES

[T1] FISHER, R. A., and YATES, F. *Statistical Tables for Biological, Agricultural and Medical Research* (fifth edition). Oliver and Boyd (Edinburgh and London, 1957).

[T2] PEARSON, E. S., and HARTLEY, H. O. *Biometrika Tables for Statisticians*, 1. Cambridge University Press.

[T3] COMRIE, L. J. (Editor). *Barlow's Tables of Squares, etc.* Spon (London, 1941).

[T4] PEARSON, E. S. (Editor). New Statistical Tables. Available as offprints from *Biometrika*, **32**, 151–91; **32**, 300–10; **33**, pp. 73–99. *Biometrika* Office, University College (London).

[T5] RICHARDSON, J. T. Table of Lagrangian Coefficients for Logarithmic Interpolation of Standard Statistical Tables to obtain Other Probability Levels. *Journal of Royal Statistical Society Supplement*, **8** (2), (1946).

[T6] COMRIE, L. J., and HARTLEY, H. O. Table of Lagrangian Coefficients for Harmonic Interpolation in Certain Tables of Percentage Points. Available as offprint from *Biometrika*, **32**, October 1941.

GENERAL INDEX

INDEX OF PROPER NAMES